The Bloody Fields of Waterloo
Medical Support at Wellington's Greatest Battle

M.K.H. Crumplin
MB BS FRCS (Eng and Ed) FINS

KEN TROTMAN PUBLISHING

Published in 2013 by Ken Trotman Publishing.
Booksellers & Publishers
P.O. Box 505
Godmanchester
Huntingdon PE29 2XW
England
Tel: 01480 454292
Fax: 01480 384651
www.kentrotman.com

Design and Index by Dr. Stephen Summerfield

ISBN 978-1-907417-41-2

Contents

Foreword by Peter Snow

It is only 200 years since the horrific sufferings of the casualties of Waterloo and the unimaginably primitive remedies applied by the surgeons of the time. And yet amid all the blood and blundering the beginnings of a serious study of the nature of wounds and the science of surgery can be discerned. This book is a comprehensive account of the way medicine was practised at the Battle of Waterloo by a distinguished medical historian, a surgeon himself. It's an electrifying story of how countless wounds were inflicted and treated. And it's a gripping human story of the victims and the medical men who struggled to heal them. The tragedy, as Michael Crumplin demonstrates, is that after all the brave efforts of these pioneers, so little was learned from them by the time of the Crimean War forty years later, when British military medicine was a shameful disgrace.

The author meticulously lists and describes the doctors in Wellington's army from the Director General, the matchless Sir James McGrigor, down to the humblest hospital assistants. He examines in detail the nature of medicine at the time and concentrates particularly on the researches of Professor John Thomson, who made an exhaustive, although poorly annotated, study of the Waterloo wounded. The contrasts he reveals with modern medicine are striking: the medical pipes - catheters - that unfortunate sufferers of damaged bladders had to use, were made of silver, pewter or gum elastic, unlike today's flexible tubes. One of Thomson's most telling findings was that amputations carried out speedily after a wounding were twice as likely to be successful than ones delayed by a day or more.

But for me the most arresting parts of this book are chapters 5-10, where the author recounts the stories of scores of officers and men who were severely and sometimes fatally wounded at Waterloo. Most of them showed the most extraordinary courage at a time when there was no effective anaesthetic. The Earl of Uxbridge appears to have retained a steady pulse rate throughout the amputation of his leg. The redoubtable Thomas Picton kept the painful wound he suffered at Quatre Bras secret as he was determined to fight in the decisive battle of Waterloo that followed two days later. Not all were so brave. The author describes one trooper of the Royal Dragoons stoically enduring having his arm amputated but having to put up with the lusty bellowing of another patient, a Frenchman. Once the trooper's arm was off he beat the Frenchman on the chest with it, telling him to shut up.

This is a fine book, fully documented and colourfully but rigorously written. It is a rare glimpse in detail of the state of medical science just two centuries ago.

Acknowledgements

I must firstly acknowledge the significant and enthusiastic support of Gareth Glover, an inveterate researcher author and military historian of these times. He graciously declined to take joint authorship of this publication, but has been inordinately generous with his assistance.

There are many people to whom I remain deeply grateful for their personal help. Firstly to Peter Snow, who not only has been most supportive of the Waterloo200 project, but also has kindly written a foreword to this work. His recent publication, *'To War with Wellington'* has rekindled much interest in the wars of 1793-1815. To the President and Council and Staff of the Royal Colleges of England and Edinburgh, go out my thanks for allowing both images and data to be reproduced here.

I wish also to acknowledge my sincere gratitude to Dr Stephen Summerfield who has worked tirelessly to design the layout of this book. Also Mr Neil MacKinnon FRCS, who has been of considerable assistance with this publication.

Alan Harrison and Gary Barnshaw have kindly allowed me to use images of Captain Noel Harris's coat and an item belonging to Surgeon Samuel Good, respectively. David Hunter likewise has permitted me to use the images of Surgeon Hunter's coat and bicorn hat, worn at Waterloo. Mr John Franklin, another meticulous researcher, has helped with aspects of medical support for the defence of Hougoumont Farm. Mr Stewart Mellor loaned me the image of Sergeant Ewart in later years for this publication. Mrs Jane Leaper co-operated with Mrs Watkin's tale. Carole Divall and Dr Anne-Marie Liethen have been of great assistance with data concerning the King's German Legion. I thank Mr Clifford Mansfield, who has kindly helped with the image of Major Thornhill, whose family I also thank. He also has provided the image of Purefoy Lockwood. Mr Peter Steele and Mrs L Pashley – also Mrs Margaret Humphries – have been kind enough to loan data and grant permission for images of their ancestors to appear in the text. I am also indebted to Mr David Milner for information on Dr Henry Emery. Dr JM Cruickshank is always willing to help with data, especially relating to Scottish medical officers - to him also, thanks.

Captain Peter Starling and the Army Medical Services Museum granted usage of the paintings by Sir Charles Bell. Other institutions I must thank for allowing me to reproduce images; Stratfield Saye Trust, Abbotsford House Trust, Musée Wellington in Waterloo village, the Gordon Museum, Guy's and St. Thomas's Hospital, the Thackray Museum of Leeds, both Mold and Abergele parish churches and Osprey Publishing.

Preface

Despite a few anecdotes, little enough is known about the medical staff present and the challenges they faced at the Battle of Waterloo on 18 June 1815. I have first given a brief overview of the principal battle of the 1815 campaign, with medical commentary, where appropriate. After this, the next two chapters give a short outline of the ranking and types of medical staff are given with their responsibilities. There was one notable visitor to Brussels after Waterloo, Britain's only (Regius) Professor of Military Surgery in Edinburgh, John Thomson,[1] who toured the Belgium hospitals after the battle and wrote a valuable report on his findings among the wounded.[2] The fourth chapter concerns Thomson's visit and is annotated. This is followed by chapters containing a collection of (largely British Army) medical anecdotes relating to wounded officers and men, some better known than others.

These precede an epilogue and a comprehensive list of members of the Army Medical Department who served in the battle, or who arrived later to assist with the large number of casualties in the Low Countries.

A force, commanded by the Duke of Wellington consisting of two army corps of the British Army and its Allies, was hastily assembled to meet the threat of Napoleon Bonaparte's Armée du Nord, of around 125,000 men, heading rapidly northwards to cross the River Sambre into Belgium. A titanic struggle, consisting of four main actions, was contested with the Prussian Army and the polyglot force under Wellington, pitched against an experienced and devoted French army, between the 15 and the 18 June 1815.

Sir James McGrigor, the doyen of the Army Medical Department in the Peninsular War and other notable campaigns, had been appointed Director General of the Department on the 13 June 1815 - just five days before the battle. This was to allow him little time to assemble and direct all the best and most experienced of his medical staff in time to make ready for the ensuing campaigns. Many of his underlings were exhausted, worn out during the long Peninsular Campaigns, and had become unavailable for service, but a proportion of veteran surgeons came back on their half pay. Of 43 medical staff (senior non-regimental medical men) and 170 battalion or ordnance regimental surgeons, present at Waterloo, only 49% had had Peninsular War service. Almost two thirds of the senior staff (27 of 43) had been with the Duke in Iberia, whilst only 45% of regimental surgeons had such experience. Of 16 cavalry regiments, six had no medical staff with such experience and of 25 infantry battalions/units, six had surgeons with no Peninsula service and nine had just one of two or three battalion surgeons who had served in Spain or Portugal.

Many were taken by surprise at the speed of their recall, so swift was Bonaparte's movement and thus the Medical Department had little enough notice to prepare an

---

[1] Kaufman (2003).
[2] Thomson (1816).

adequate and cohesive service, thus, to some degree, it did not have the mettle of Wellington's Peninsular Medical Department.

There is some modern, well-illustrated material on the medical aspects of the wars against Republican and Napoleonic France. The books, listed below, were written by a surgeon (the author of this book) and a physician, Dr Martin Howard. They give particular account of the training and practice of contemporary surgeons and physicians, also the damage done to men in combat and on campaign. They remind the reader of an often overlooked but highly relevant aspect of conflict:

> '*Men of Steel*' describes the training of surgeons and gives much detail of wounding and surgical practice. '*A Surgical artist at War*' contains all the paintings of victims of injury from the actions at Corunna and Waterloo - important and almost unique visual images - executed by Sir Charles Bell, who was an anatomist, surgeon and artist. '*Guthrie's War*' tells the story of Surgeon Guthrie, a major British medical figure in the Peninsular War.

> '*Wellington's Doctors*', written by Dr Martin Howard, contains a broad overview of medical practice during these wars. The book includes detail of hospitals, transport and disease, likewise '*Napoleon's Doctors*' contains unusual and much useful knowledge of military medical practice in the French Army at these times. These and other relevant books are listed in the bibliography.

Chapter 1:
Medical Aspects of the Campaigns
15-18 June 1815

Whilst the Army Medical Department matured during the long Peninsular War (1808-14), the lightning campaigns of 1815 took Britain and the rest of Europe by surprise and thus the preparedness of the department had been inevitably limited. James McGrigor's appointment as Director General preceded the Waterloo campaigns by less than a week and relevant regiments were dispersed in various parts of the British Isles, Ireland and North America.

The Allied Army was hastily assembled to respond to Bonaparte's rapid and yet unknown objectives with his large Armée du Nord. At the top, Sir James McGrigor had a monumental task on his hands. Just a year or so previously hundreds of worn out or sick medical staff had finished their long tours of arduous duty in Portugal and Spain. Climate, disease, intermittent poor diet and absence from family had taken their toll. Many had thought the war was over. Medical men released from service wished to set up in civilian practice and remained on half-pay - these were duty bound to return to the colours. For some action in Belgium was to be a new adventure.

The Farm of Mont St Jean where around 6,000 casualties were treated.
(Author's collection)

Inspector James Robert Grant, the British Principle Medical Officer (see below) had seen to the opening or freeing up of general hospitals at Ostend, Bruges, Ghent, Antwerp and Brussels.

In this he was ably assisted by Professor S Brugmans, Inspector General of the Medical Services of the Army of the Low Countries. Medical Officer First Class J Kluyskens was a surgeon from Ghent, who was also to play a pivotal role after the battle. He had been recently promoted Surgeon-in-Chief to the Southern Provinces of the Low Countries. Brussels was the main general receiving station and Antwerp remained an overflow and decanting medical base.[3]

The terrain on which Wellington and the Allies had to confront Bonaparte's force, somewhat depleted by the separation of the French IIIrd and IVth Corps, was undulating, with shrubs, copses and spinneys and more woodland than there appears today. Behind Wellington was the dense forest of Soignies, which could provide cover for a retiring army. Farm dwellings and huts dotted the landscape and it would be these, with the three defended farms of Hougoumont, La Haye Sainte and Papelotte, which provided refuge for the injured. As for the rest of the open Brabant countryside there was little cover for regimental aid posts and during lulls in the fighting men would often have to be carried or have struggled alone over to the main dressing stations, where there was shelter, water and surgical support. For the Allies, this was the Ferme de Mont St Jean, a kilometre or so behind the crossing of the roads from Brussels to Charleroi and Braine l'Alleud. More than 5,000 casualties accumulated here and many of the camp followers were bivouacked behind these buildings. They would help to care for the wounded during and after the battle.

Casualties wounded in the vicinity of these three fortified farms were given surgical aid in those buildings. Not infrequently, it was too risky or inconvenient to move field casualties away during the fighting on account of artillery fire, cavalry advances and infantry assaults. The same issues would apply to infantry squares. A junior battalion surgeon would treat the injured within the square, the dead men being placed outside the square. Here water was given, dressings were applied, wounds explored and sutured and occasionally amputations carried out.

The weather in the night preceding the Battle of Waterloo had been horrendous - rain had poured down in torrents, making sleep and cooking well nigh impossible for most. Thus many units had had little to eat. This was hardly the way to start a bloody contest on the 18 June.

The battle commenced around 1130hrs, with a bombardment from at least four batteries of artillery on Bonaparte's left flank. This was a preliminary to a strong infantry assault by General Reille's II Corps on the farm of Hougoumont and the chestnut woods in front of the buildings. The farm projected well out in front of the Duke's ridge and was latterly held by light companies of the Coldstream and 3rd Foot Guards and companies from Nassau, Field Jaeger Corps, Lüneburg and

---

[3] Evrard (no date) pp. 426 and 430-431

Grübenhagen regiments. For the first hour of the conflict around the wood, including its loss along with part of the great orchard, the Guards companies occupied gardens to the west of the buildings.

Inspector Robert Grant,
Principal Medical Officer at Waterloo.
(Author's collection)

As the harsh combat for the farm progressed, there were frequent infantry assaults through the woods and into the 'killing zone', between the woods and the south garden wall of the farm. Here, wounded Frenchmen were isolated and would have been dragged back into the woods to a field dressing station in the rear. Allied casualties were taken into the farm for treatment, during the ebb and flow of the conflict. The walls of the farm gardens were high and clambering up them was a huge physical effort for the French assailants, encumbered with their equipment - only to be shot from below or clubbed as their heads and shoulders appeared above the top of the wall. There were some fire steps and holes punched out of the walls, from which fire could be poured into the French.

Many of the French 6e and 9e Divisions would be shot at close quarters as they heaved themselves up the wall or were shot down milling around below the walls. At most, around 2,600 men defended Hougoumont and roughly 847 (33%) became casualties. Of the attacking forces, it is said that between four and five thousand casualties accrued on the 18 June.[4]

Six hundred of these French and Allied corpses were known to have been burnt, and then interred, near the south gate by local peasant labour.

There is some uncertainty about the provision of surgical care in the chateau during the day. Surgeon Good, of the 3rd Foot Guards was known to have been at Mont St Jean dressing station during the battle. It is just inconceivable that there would have been no surgeon present at the chateau all day, since there were hundreds of casualties to manage and there was cover in which a surgeon could work. Thus, inside the buildings, it was probably Surgeon William Whymper (Coldstreams) who provided medical support. With or without an assistant, he would have had to treat around 3-400 wounded. Whether assistants Smith and Hunter of the Coldstreams and Good's assistant surgeons (unlikely since John Warde was in Brussels and thus Francis Hanrott would be required to stay on the ridge with his battalion) were there is conjectural - possibly one or two of his assistants joined later as more help was required. They would have worked initially in the main chateau, amputating, exploring and dressing wounds and burns.

When a haystack, then the main building caught fire, the Duke had messaged the occupants to evacuate the house. The casualties were then moved into the outhouses of the farm. Such foresight illustrates the Commander's attention to detail and care of his soldiers.

---

[4] Adkin (2001) pp. 342-343.

Interior of main barn at Mont St Jean Farm.
The photograph was taken in 1963. The interior appears as an operating theatre,
more or less as it might have done in 1815. (Author's collection)

Local peasants building a funeral pyre for corpses of both armies
outside the south gate of Chateau Hougoumont.
(Author's collection)

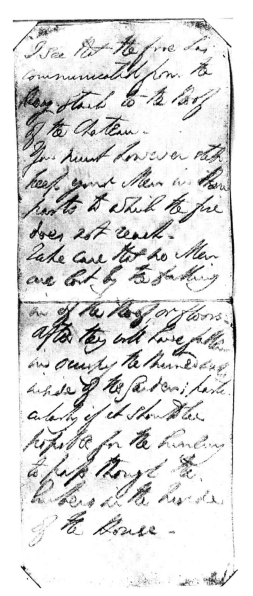

Surgeon Good was commended by his battalion for his lifetime service and his efforts at the battle. He was presented with a battalion King's Colour. This and the surgeon's memorial were in the cathedral at Worcester until the tattered colour was removed for destruction. Of the original 134 men making up two companies of Coldstreams, only thirteen mustered at the end of the day

While this deadly mayhem continued, at around 1pm fire from Bonaparte's grand battery roared out from a ridge, facing north and thus to the left of the Allied defence line. Around 2,000 sweating French gunners served 80 pieces of ordnance (18 x 12-pdrs, 42 x 6-pdrs, and 20 howitzers) and kept up fire for around 30 minutes (1300 to

1330hrs). Most guns discharged solid round shot. Mark Adkin in his 'Waterloo Companion' calculates that 22,300 rounds of round/shell and case were available to the grand battery, whose target area was around 1,200m wide and 375m deep, between 700m and 1000m away. The front line of the target was made up of artillery pieces and sharpshooters, the back line of 21 infantry battalions (ten British and King's German Legion) and three companies of 1/95th Rifles. Thus around 15,000 men were exposed to about 3,500 rounds. Adkin reckons that because of wet ground, overshoot, target areas that were hard to distinguish and also relatively small number of shots in widely dispersed target area, only 500 Allied soldiers were killed or maimed.[5] Injuries were thus somewhat scattered and were caused by large lumps of iron smashing into soldiers, decapitating, destroying body cavities and tearing off limbs. There were also many wounds caused by exploding shells, throwing out portions of iron casing from ground or airbursts, or from those projectiles that thumped into the wet ground. Little or no canister rounds would have been used until the British Household and Union Cavalry Brigades advanced to counter the next French assault. Not an easy proposition for the gunners, particularly with their own retiring infantry and cavalry milling about.

A model of Surgeon William Whymper, Coldstream Guards about to amputate a limb of a wounded guardsman at Chateau Hougoumont.
(Author's collection)

[5] Adkin (2001) pp. 296-301.

Following this softening up exercise, Bonaparte deployed Count Drouet d'Erlon's I Corps of more than 17,000 bayonets and flanking cavalry. Passing in file through the guns of the grand battery, they trudged down the muddy slope towards the Allied lines, 500-700m away. The French artillery barrage transiently resumed whilst the French columns dipped down in the muddy valley, but then had to fall silent as Quiot's, Donzelot's, Marcognet's and Durutte's men, preceded by hundreds of voltigeurs, panted up the slope towards the centre and left of the Allied line. The four Allied batteries, with a further three or so on the flanks, faced these dense columns and had been playing on them as they came on. Initially round shot were used to cut great swathes in the dark blue columns. But as the masses came nearer gunners were ordered to change to light or heavy canister (tins packed with either 85 x 1.5 oz or 41 x 3.5 oz iron balls). These were used to maximum effect at around 150 to 300m and were especially destructive when double-shotted. The front few ranks were particularly hard hit and the mass of writhing wounded and dead slowed up the men behind. Few would have survived such injuries to head or trunk. As the last 200m between the lines closed, increasing musketry fire took its toll as infantrymen stood up and discharged their volleys into the blue columns. As the Allied ridge was reached and the line wavered under the massive French assault, Henry Paget, Lord Uxbridge, gave the order for a heavy cavalry advance - Somerset's Household Brigade on the right, ploughing into Dubois's 800 strong cuirassiers, around and through La Haye Sainte farm, full of Light companies of the King's German Legion. On the left facing Quiot, were the 1st Dragoons (the Royals), in the centre of the Union Brigade, facing Donzelot's men, were the 6th (Inniskilling) Dragoons and on the left, in reserve were the 2nd Royal North British Dragoons (Scots Greys).

Scattered out a fair bit, these two brigades of heavy cavalry weaved between retiring Allied guns and infantry formations and fast trotted into the shattered front enemy formations. The cavalry probably could have been checked by a very determined resistance (some French squares were formed), but confusion and panic resulted in d'Erlon's Corps now retiring to its start line. Injuries here were now caused by falls from mounts, horse kicks and sabre cuts especially around the head, necks and arms of infantry and cavalry. The three men killed by Sergeant Ewart of the Greys, when he seized the Eagle of the 45e Ligne, were all fatally wounded in the face or cranium. Apart from two Eagles captured, around 2,000 live or wounded prisoners were taken by Pack and Kempt's men and also by Belgian infantry. The remains of the Household and Union Brigade now breathlessly fired up by the French rout, pushed on their winded and blown mounts to the Grand Battery, where they were decimated by 2,500 fresh lancers and cuirassiers. Sir William Ponsonby was fatally lanced and the seven regiments of the two brigades sustained 40-50% casualties during the charge.

During this great French infantry assault, Kempt and Pack's battalions had their assistant surgeons with them to treat the wounded. The battalion surgeons were arranged in front of, or near to, Mont St Jean Farm, around 400-600m away to the north and rear. What is hard to research is the position of the British cavalry surgeons. It is most likely that the most senior assistant of two, (there were eleven assistant surgeons in the two heavy cavalry brigades) or the only assistant would ride with the senior officer and the regimental surgeons would remain behind. One of the problems with treating mounted casualties was finding and retrieving them. There were many examples of badly hurt horsemen lying out unattended on the field, at the risk of combat movement and plunderers. Assistant Surgeon Gibney of the 15th Hussars was (as were many other surgeons) forced to shift his aid post on account of the cannon fire and take his casualties back to Mont St Jean Farm.[6]

Mrs Elizabeth Watkins, in later life.
Wearing about her neck a cloth sac, which she used to dunk in her tea - perhaps reflecting on memories of squeezing water into the mouths of casualties, after the Battle of Waterloo. She was the longest living survivor of the Battle, dying in 1904.
(Courtesy Mrs Jane Leaper)

This action by the French and counter attack by the Allies lasted from approximately 1330hrs until about 1500hrs. Between 1500hrs and 1600hrs, assaults on Hougoumont and La Haye Sainte continued, with Wellington bolstering up his line and the two farms. During these times casualties were taken to safe places, principally field

---

[6] Gibney (1896) pp. 190-191.

hospitals at Mont St Jean farm, Hougoumont, Papelotte for the Allies and the ground around Belle Alliance, Rossome and Le Caillou for the French. Here groups of battalion and staff surgeons worked furiously to cope with the deluge. Mont St Jean had at one stage around 6,000 casualties within and about its buildings moved there from all over the battlefield during the day. Many camp followers were spread around this area and helped the toiling doctors. One of these was the longest living person to have witnessed the Battle of Waterloo - Elizabeth Watkins (née Gale - daughter of Daniel Gale of the 95th Rifles). She and her mother scraped lint and gave water to wounded men on the field after the action.

Around 1530hrs Marshal Michel Ney was concerned at the attempts to take the vital central position at La Haye Sainte. At 1600hrs, he had come forward, frustrated by the repeated failed assaults on the farm. He perceived the shuffling movement on the Allied ridge, noticed retrograde direction of troops sheltering from the sporadic French battery fire and the carriage of wounded and prisoners to the north. He had mistaken this for Allied disorder and a possible retreat. He next precipitated one of the most sanguinary and wasteful displays of equine valour ever witnessed, competing with our own charge by the Light Brigade in the North Valley at Balaclava in 1854. Should the Allies have been wavering and in the early stages of retirement, the massed charges by the French cavalry would have been a formidable danger to the fleeing infantry as they passed north into the Forest of Soignies or packed onto the already cluttered chausées. The Allies were clearly aware of the movements of the enemy horse. Had Ney been a little more careful with his scouting and intelligence, he would have realised that our forces were not moving away. In fact they were to form the deadliest defence against thousands of the best horsemen in Europe.

After a preliminary bombardment by a dozen or so batteries, Ney chose to send his first wave of magnificent cavalry, not round the flanks, but straight up the damp slopes into the mouths of the dozen or so Allied batteries placed in front of the two dozen or so infantry squares - a mighty challenge indeed. Eight regiments of cuirassiers and two regiments of light cavalry of the Imperial Guard fast walked or trotted up to the Allied lines, around 4,500-5,000 cavalry in all. These units were forced to advance between the farms of Hougoumont and La Haye Sainte, which was a compressed 1,000-metre front. As these vast hordes of horsemen passed in front of dozens of cannon (more than 70 pieces) discharging round shot and heavy case (to bring down the horses) and through the intervals between the squares, they faced harassment by Allied light cavalry and infantry volleys. The plate body armour of the cuirassiers and carabiniers proved of little use against direct round and case shot strikes, but afforded some protection against tangentially inflicted blows or missiles.

There were several other hazards and retarding issues for the horsemen - mud, the ground littered with carcasses, and horses wounded or hard to control. The mounts were the prime targets for the artillery and muskets. This was borne out by there being well over 2,000 killed and injured horses noted after the battle.

Although some of the formations may have doubled back in disorder, many passed through the squares and peeled off right or left to return to their start lines. The fact that no Allied guns were spiked or removed shows how little opportunity there was for these gallant men to do anything but circuit the squares or retire. On retirement, some Allied units wheeled out of square into line to deliver more firepower at the retiring cavalry. Eventually residual French cavalry units had to go back and regroup. This would have meant a circuit of at least 3-4,000m. They were mostly all beyond reach of their surgeons. Those wounded or dismounted would have been taken prisoner or perished, for it was a long way back to the start line.

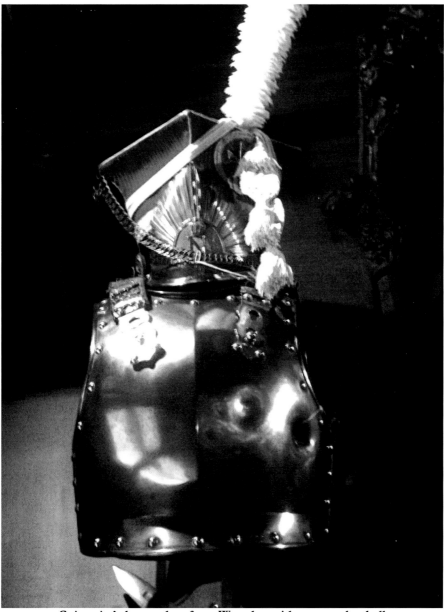

Cuirassier's breastplate from Waterloo with two musket ball strikes - one penetrating, the other a spent ball.
(Courtesy Abbotsford House Trust)

A second major assault by the hard-pressed French cavalry was launched around an hour later, with roughly the same number of sabres. Although these two major attacks were seen as set pieces, once the squadrons were milling, around the regimental and squadron commanders chose to move in the best direction they could, retiring and re-advancing as ordered. Overall, there may have been as many as a dozen or more advances, the mounts struggling in the muddy crops. When the ground was transiently clear of their horsemen, French horse artillery batteries caused considerable damage to the squares. The toll on the French cavalry was heavy - Adkin quotes a casualty rate of 74% amongst the French generals leading their men to the 'charge'.[7] The majority of the wounded French troopers were significantly isolated from medical rescue.

So effective was the Allied defence at this stage that possibly only one square formation was transiently disrupted by artillery or horse assault (that formed by the 33rd and the 69th Regiments). Between 13 and 27 Allied squares (forming according to threat) were steady forms of protection against even the most determined horse-borne assault, each side being three or four lines deep. With each file nearly shoulder to shoulder there was nervous stability only occasionally shattered by French ordnance, which opened up as the French horse retired. There was thus a feeling of relief when the steel-plated horsemen and Imperial Guard cavalry reappeared. There were some examples of exasperated anger from injured and dismounted horsemen (even suicide) witnessed by the troops in square. Few Allied soldiers were damaged by the frustrated French cavalry sabres, pistols and carbines, as the troopers lapped around the jeering Allied squares. Not many Frenchman would have reached within 5-10m of the glistening rows of bayonets and muskets without becoming casualties. One thought does strike the reader and that is, despite the chequered position of the squares, would there not have been many friendly fire accidents? Of course there would.

As to medical support in the squares, the senior assistant surgeon or surgeon was in the square, which acted as a forward battalion dressing station. Allied dead were thrown out of the squares and the files closed up to make good the gaps. Inside the square, wounds were inspected, probed and dressed - even an occasional amputation was carried out. Captain Rees Gronow of the 1st Foot Guards described the squares:

> *'During the battle, our squares presented a shocking sight. Inside we nearly suffocated by the smoke and smell of burnt cartridges. It was impossible to move a yard without treading on a wounded comrade or upon the bodies of the dead; and the loud groans of the wounded and dying were most appalling. At four o'clock our square was a perfect hospital, being full of dead, dying and mutilated soldiers. The charges of the cavalry were in appearance very formidable, but in reality a great relief, as the artillery could no longer fire on us; ……..'*

It was most likely that during the action at Quatre Bras, assistant surgeon Frederick Gilder (1st Foot Guards) had the task of amputating Captain Adair's leg in the square. Gilder's knife was blunt and Adair ironically commented, "Take your time Mr Carver", as the knife took over many sweeps to divide the soft tissues of the leg.

---

[7] Adkin (2001), p. 359.

Sadly Adair did not survive to reach home. He died on the 23 June in Brussels.[8] During this phase of the battle, which lasted around two hours, there were the occasional lulls in the cavalry assaults that allowed a risky transfer of men to Mont St Jean farm - the 1st Corps dressing station about 300-1,000m distant. This stage of the Battle of Waterloo took place roughly between 1600 and 1800hrs.

Files of men forming square (2/30th and 2/73rd) receiving cavalry - June 18, afternoon.
(Author's collection)

While all this was going on, of course Bonaparte was being challenged on a second front as between 1630 and 1700hrs, Count Bülow's Prussian 4th Corps surged towards, then into Plançenoit. Bitter street clashes, with house-to-house fighting, resulted in many injuries, the casualties cared for or sheltered in the houses of local folks. There were accounts of no quarter, merciless shootings and murder of the wounded in these dwellings as the French and Prussians surged around. Many years ago, I was visiting a house bordering the village green in Plançenoit. The owners of the house explained, showing me the damage inflicted by musket balls, how French soldiers had shot several wounded Prussians in one of their rooms and in their cellar. The to and fro movements of French and Prussians made life very tricky for the battalion medical staff. More and more French and Prussians became engaged, sapping Bonaparte's ability to continue pressure on the Allied front. General Ziethen's 1st Corps was not to link up with Wellington's left flank until around 1930hrs, more or less at the time that the Imperial Guard commenced its assault up the ridge on Wellington's right flank, the last phase of the battle. The desperate struggle for Plançenoit ebbed and flowed for four hours, from 1630 to 2030hrs. Of the 7,000 Prussian casualties, many were caused during this titanic struggle for the village.

---

[8] Robinson (2009), p. 376.

Determined artillery, infantry and cavalry assaults had failed to open any large gaps in the Duke's line. Failing at Hougoumont and to punch a gap in the lines left Bonaparte with his next option - to capture the defended farm of La Haye Sainte and mount a severe assault on the Duke's centre.

La Haye Sainte Farm had been intermittently assaulted from 1330hrs until it finally fell into French hands at around 1830hrs. The buildings, courtyard, orchard, gardens and environs of the farm were stoutly defended by German light troops commanded by Major George Baring and included 2nd Light Battalion KGL (around 350-400 men), 5th Line Battalion KGL and some men from the 2nd Nassau Regiment. Like Hougoumont, the farm projected forward from the Duke's ridge position and was prone to isolation. During D'Erlon's grand assault described previously, dozens of casualties were treated in the farmhouse and stables. Although uncertain, we can suppose that at least one of the two battalion surgeons from the 2nd Light Battalion (for there were two full surgeons serving in this unit - George Christian Heisse, who drew up the casualty list for the whole Legion 1803-16 and Ernst Nieter) and at least one of their two assistants (Henry Gehse and Frederick Müller), would have been present. They would have had much to do. All but Heisse had served in the Peninsula. During the massed cavalry attacks, fire was directed at the hordes of cuirassiers passing the farm, many of who would perish through lack of evacuation and care. Later in the afternoon the French pressed home their attacks on the defenders, whose ammunition supply for their rifles had run short. Some of the farm door fixtures were missing and casualties were mounting. Several fires were started on the barn roof, which were extinguished by a chain of men passing company camp kettles from well to rooftop. There must have been several burns for the surgeons to treat, but as the evening wore on, masses of French light and line troops burst into the courtyard and Baring had no option but to leave. Ensign Franks was one of the casualties and was being treated in one of the farmhouse upstairs bedrooms. As the French pushed into the house, two less able wounded men were bayoneted to death, but Franks hid in the room and managed to escape with his life. At about 1830hrs, the farm fell into French hands with clumps of survivors running back to the safety of their own lines. The farm was surrounded and filled with Frenchmen. This was now a significant threat to Wellington's centre.

Around half the Germans (originally a maximum of around 800 men)[9] had become casualties and there must have been at least 200 wounded to be cared for in the buildings. Some would die at the hands of the French, some would struggle back to their lines and others would be taken prisoner. We know that all four of the surgeons of the 2nd Light Battalion survived.

What was Bonaparte's situation? Dusk was drawing in, he was severely threatened on his right flank, he had as yet failed to break through Wellington's line and Hougoumont still held out. If he were to have a miniscule chance of success, he would have to commit his final reserves to try and crash through the depleted right of Wellington's line and roll up the Allies in so doing. He now had to commit some of

---

[9] Adkin (2001), p. 377.

his loyal and undefeated Imperial Guard, consisting of the Old, Middle and Young Guards. The Young Guard and some Old Guard had been detached to hold the Prussians at Plançenoit. Five battalions of the Middle Guard and three of the Old Guard were ordered to prepare for the final assault, around 4,500 of Bonaparte's finest infantry. Around 1930hrs, the Emperor himself led his 'Immortals' down the slope and up towards La Haye Sainte, where he was deterred from moving on. Marshal Ney took command of the last phase. Backed up by other artillery, cavalry and infantry remnants, Bonaparte's last manoeuvre commenced. Lead by Ney (later dismounted for the fifth time) and General Friant (wounded), eight squares of Guards plodded up the slope, flanked by units of Guard artillery, which caused continued damage to those on the ridge. On the French right, two battalions of Grenadiers came under fire from Halkett's brigade and artillery. On the left the three battalions of chasseurs were confronted by 1,500 of Maitland's hidden Guards, flanked by Adam's Brigade, which had wheeled to pour fire into the veterans' sides. Heaps of French dead and wounded impeded forward movement of the Guard. Incidents of individual combat were recorded. In one a six-foot-seven inches Welshman, named Hughes, was noted to have clubbed or bayoneted around 12 opponents. Despite several moments of Allied confusion and temporary retirement, formations reassembled. Lieutenant Colonel Sir John Colborne of the veteran 52nd led a decisive wheeling movement, despite losing nearly 200 men, and became responsible (despite some controversy) for the final rout of the Chasseurs of the Guard. South West of La Haye Sainte, further units of the Old Guard gave token resistance yet refused to surrender, whilst the 1st and 2nd Battalions of the 1e Grenadiers of the Guard finally drew off towards Charleroi.

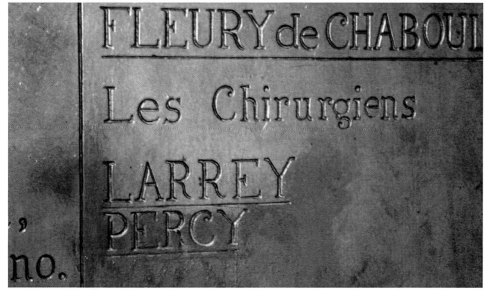

French memorial plaque in Bonaparte's headquarters at Le Caillou Farm, indicating that both Larrey and Percy rested (and worked) there before and during the battle.
(Courtesy Musée Le Caillou)

During the whole battle - and most must have been lost on that last slope - of the 4,127 men of the Middle and Old Imperial Guard, 82% were casualties. Overall casualties in the Imperial Guard were 13,112 of 20,692 (63%).[10] Of course some of the missing Guard may have re-joined later, but the Middle and Young Guard at Plançenoit had been decimated.

The farm of Le Caillou, Bonaparte's headquarters the night before the battle, had been the main rear French field hospital and was packed with wounded Frenchmen. The senior French surgeons worked here as casualties poured in. Surgeon of the Guard Jean Dominique Larrey operated here, as did Baron François Percy.

A small brick-encased ossuary in the garden remains as a sad memorial to the fallen in that area.

Mortality figures in all conflicts reflect a race between advances in destructive weaponry and constructive surgical and anaesthetic technology on or near the battlefield. Overall British soldier mortality in the French Wars is difficult to be accurate about. However, we lost around 250,000 soldiers and the army was - at its largest - around this size. The Royal Navy had lost around 100,000 sailors and marines. Adkin quotes American mortality rates of 8% for WWI (UK less, around 4%), 4% for WWII, 3% for the Korean conflict, 1.5% for the Vietnam War and, amongst British Army personnel in the Falklands, less than 1%. However with the intensely destructive nearby explosives of modern IEDs, in Afghanistan we had lost 108 service personnel in 2009 (of around 8,000 serving), which is 1.4% mortality. Modern military surgical success in Afghanistan is shown in the impressive survival of those with severe injuries. Of all wounded men retrieved and arriving in hospital alive, over 95% will survive. Few of these would have stood a chance in 1815. Although there was only 9% in-hospital mortality in the Brussels hospitals, hundreds more men would have been 'salvaged' today. In fact, in June 1815, to get to hospital at all was a reasonable predictor of survival.

We can never be completely certain over the various casualty rates quoted, since men who were 'lost, presumed dead' later re-appeared; men who were reported killed, survived, and many men who were discharged 'well' died sooner or later, as a consequence of infection or contagion. Desertion also made estimates tricky. Thus losses of the various forces engaged during the several actions of the Waterloo campaign are bound to be questionable, in particular with regard to the category of 'missing' combatants.

By the standards of this drawn out war, Waterloo was not the most sanguinary - after the Battle of Borodino (Moskova) in September 1812, Russian peasants were said to have interred around 65,000 human remains. At the conflict around Leipzig in October 1813, there had been combined losses of around 125,000 soldiers of both armies (including missing). During all the actions of the Waterloo campaigns (Gilly/Charleroi, Ligny, St Amand, Fleurus, Sombreffe, Wavre, Quatre Bras,

---

[10] Bowden (1983), p. 337.

Genappe and the Battle of, and retreat from, Waterloo), there were around 21-22,000 Anglo-Allied, 36-37,000 Prussian and 55-65,000 French casualties (all figures include 'missing').

I reckon that around 55,000 casualties occurred during the Battle of Waterloo itself - in the Anglo-Allied-Prussian forces around 21,000 (Prussians about 7,000) and the French Army around 30,000 (that is, to say, killed and wounded, not including significant numbers of missing personnel).

Re-enactment of French surgeons and stretcher-bearers - brancardiers, some of who were at Waterloo (this unit were filmed near Boulogne).

Considering the totality of casualties on Waterloo fields, of around 14,000 Anglo-Allied, there were 3,500 killed and 10,200 wounded.[11] In the British and KGL ranks, there were 1,781 deaths and 5,734 wounded, with a further 810 missing, possibly dead.[12] These data give a fairly low kill to wound ratio of 1:3. When compared with modern combat and the destructive effects of high explosive devices (e.g. in Afghanistan), but much enhanced surgical support, the kill to wound ratio is similar, at 1:4.6.[13]

Another estimate of French killed and wounded at Waterloo would be between 25,000 and 30,000 of about 40-45,000 killed, wounded and missing (accepting a

[11] Adkin (2001), p. 73.
[12] Fletcher (2001), pp. 171-172.
[13] Anon (2012) "Fatality and casualty data to 31 May 2011," Website of the *Defence Analytical Services Agency*.

guesstimate of say 15,000 'missing'), which represents an inevitably higher loss than the Allies, as a consequence of the French retreat, wide dispersal and desertion.[14] Thus the French casualty rate according to muster roles a short time later (including the missing, AWOL etc) was around 55-60%.

Thus of the 55,000-odd Anglo-Allied-Prussian and French casualties at Waterloo itself, about 15,000 were dead, leaving approximately 35,000 men wounded and if we included, say almost 4,500 casualties from Quatre Bras (although many wounded men died before reaching medical aid), this enormous load of around 40,000 patients landed mainly on the Allied hospital medical staff and the Belgian surgeons, particularly as many Anglo-Allied battalion surgeons soon moved on towards Paris. It is no wonder we see so many additional surgeons arriving late to the campaign!

Despite the significant superiority of the number of general officers in the Armée du Nord, compared with the Anglo-Dutch-Belgic Force (90:28 respectively) at Waterloo, the proportional losses to each force were similar and high (42%:46% respectively). During the day, the overall attrition rate amongst the officers of both armies was also high: in the British/Allied force, it was 950 of 3,300 (29%); in the Armée du Nord 1,677 of 3,200 (52%) officers were killed, injured or taken prisoner, almost twice that of the Allied army. Losses amongst the other ranks and NCOs of the Anglo-Allied force, by comparison, were proportionally less than those of their officers, at 16,200 of 69,700 (23%). Casualty rates amongst the non-officer ranks in the French force are less easy to be certain of.

The reader has to appreciate that being wounded at these times often meant the patient expired before he had any access to medical aid. This would skew data towards improved results if casualties were counted at the hospital base. After all, if the victim was fit enough to make it to a dressing station or hospital, he had a chance of living. So survival after devastating modern wounds reflect efficient collection rates ('scoop and run'), resuscitation and results of surgery overall. So, if the soldier could expect a 1 in 4/5 chance of being hurt or killed at Waterloo, what chances did he have with retrieval and hospital treatment, primitive as it was? If we accept Cantlie's figures, around 9%,[15] possibly more, of those admitted to hospital wounded, would die (856 of 9,528 soldiers, who made it off the field) after Waterloo and Quatre Bras.[16] Of 373 of the 92nd wounded in the battle, only thirteen died (5%). One series of mortality rates in a large general hospital at Toulouse in 1814, revealed a hospital mortality rate of 11%. These are still remarkable results, occurring well before the advent of better field surgery, anaesthesia, antisepsis and modern physiological surgical support.

[14] Bowden (1983), p. 327.
[15] Cantlie (1974), Volume 1, p. 391.
[16] Crumplin (2007), Men of Steel, p. 78.

Burying comrades - soldiers collect their dead companions after Waterloo.
(Author's collection)

Carriage and burial of the dead near La Haye Sainte Farm.
(Author's collection)

One of the biggest problems in this battle was the lack of stretcher-bearers. This essentially meant that hundreds or maybe thousands of men perished for lack of timely evacuation to hospital. In 1813, the French Service de Santé had created a cadre of brancardiers whose sole task was to evacuate the casualties. Inevitably there were not enough of these to go round.

Overall hospital mortality (i.e. deaths from sickness and wounds) in the Peninsular War ranged between 4% and 7%, rather less than the Waterloo figure of 9%. In Iberia, wound mortality figures became diluted by the lower death rates associated with admissions for disease, rather than battle injury. Numerically, while a greater number of men died of disease rather than combat injury in these wars, the chance of dying of a wound was higher.

Immediately after trauma, most men were exhausted and many a casualty would die from the lack of triage, transport and sufficient medical staff, bleeding quietly to death on the field or in hovels and courtyards, awaiting succour. Thirst was also a huge problem. For those left injured on the field, isolation, further injury or murder awaited many, at the hands of marauding and unscrupulous soldiers.

Many of these latter, as at other contemporary conflicts, knocked out quality teeth from the dead young men. These treasures were sold at home for the manufacture of dentures. Few local inhabitants would risk their lives on the battlefield at this immediate time on the nights of the 18 and 19 June. Their time for plunder, clothes and relics would come later. Prisoners, local labourers and combatants were overseen burying the dead – mostly in mass graves near Hougoumont, La Haye Sainte and Plançenoit – around the place.

Meanwhile, as the injured progressed or died locally, the roads were choked with wounded men, walking, on horseback or taken in commandeered carts, the eleven-odd miles to Brussels. There was help here, at last, but it was not until the morning of the 19 June that the 48 lumbering spring wagons began to evacuate the severely wounded to Brussels. These convoys took four days to bring the broken soldiers in.

Sergeant Ned Costello of the 95th arrived in Brussels on the 19 June. He recounts a story of the compassionate care given to the wounded, which contrasts with the accounts of pillage and removal of teeth on the battlefield;

In the morning [19 June], the scene surpassed all imagination. It baffles description for there were upwards of 40,000 wounded French, Belgians, Prussian and English [British] intermingled with carts, wagons, and every other vehicle attainable, which continued to arrive heaped with unfortunate sufferers. The wounded were laid on straw, with avenues between them, in every part of the city, with no discrimination between friends and foes. They were nearly destitute of surgical attendance, but the humane and indefatigable exertions of the fair ladies of Brussels, greatly made up for this deficiency. Numbers were busily employed strapping and bandaging wounds; others were serving out tea, coffee, soups, and other nourishments, many occupied themselves dressing them in clean shirts, and other habiliments. Careless of fashionable scruples, the fairest and wealthiest of the ladies of the city venture to assert their pre-eminence on the occasion. That their companions were in need called forth the sympathies that bind the sexes in mutual dependence.'

A soldier of the 42ⁿᵈ Foot and a Brunswick hussar being tended in a Brussels home. Note the stretcher case being given water and the cart-load of wounded outside the house.
(Courtesy Musée Wellington, Waterloo)

Costello noted one poignant case,

> *'One lady I noticed particularly. She was attended by a servant bearing on his shoulder a kind of pannier, containing warm and cold refreshments. She was about eighteen, and the peculiarity of the moment made her appear beyond the common order of humanity. As she hurried along, her eyes glancing about for those whom she thought most in need of her assistance, a tall highlander drew her attention with a deep groan, which arose from the anguish of a severe wound in the thick part of the thigh. In a twinkling she knelt at his side. The soldier looked at her with surprise. Gently she moved aside his blood-stained kilt, and commenced washing the wounded part. The Scotsman seemed uneasy at her importunity, but with the sweetest voice imaginable, she addressed him in broken English: "I will not hurt*

you" The wounded man, before he could recover his rough serenity, found his wound bandaged, and at ease, under the operations of his fair attendant. Such acts as these must ever draw forth our admiration.'[17]

In Thomson's account of the state of the hospitals in Belgium, he was mightily impressed by the efforts made by the citizens of Brussels and he comments with great admiration on the efforts of the populace to take in officers and privates into private homes for care.

Dr Seutin (1793-1862).
He performed 32 amputations after the action
at Quatre Bras. He was 18 years old.
(Courtesy Musée Wellington, Waterloo)

---

[17] Hathaway (1997), 285.

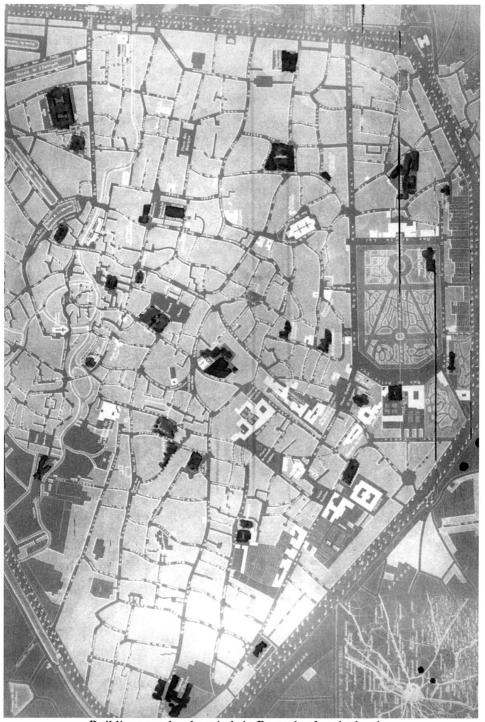

Buildings used as hospitals in Brussels after the battle.
(Author's collection)

~ 33 ~

Some medical order had now to be brought to the vast numbers of casualties. Buildings had to be found that were roomy, ventilated and well lit. As the deluge of casualties arrived from Quatre Bras, extra hospitals were prepared (e.g. the Hospital St Jean and St Pierre) and barracks emptied. By 1100hrs a young Belgian surgeon, M. Seutin, had already performed 32 amputations on Quatre Bras casualties.[18]

Many buildings in the city were used as hospitals - but six principally.

There had been around 11,000 men serving in the British Army, who had been injured at Quatre Bras and Waterloo. By the end of June 1815, there were still 5,000 wounded lying in Brussels hospitals, but by April 1816, just under one year later, of 6,831 wounded convalescing in Britain or Belgium, 5,235 (77%) had rejoined the force - 167 to veteran battalions. Of the remainder, 506 had been discharged from the service, 236 patients had been amputated, their dispersal was unknown, and 854 men were still in hospital. The work had been intense and the speed of the campaigns, relative lack of experienced Peninsular surgeons and delay in casualty retrieval at several levels, had mitigated against best outcomes.

After the battle, prize money was awarded according to rank - full battalion surgeons received £90-7 shillings 3¾ pence (that is, around £90.45p i.e. c. £6,280 today) and assistant surgeons had £34-14 shillings 9½ pence (that is around £34.74p i.e. c. £2,412 today).

Well before listing members of the medical staff who were in attendance during or shortly after the Waterloo campaigns, the following chapter sets out to explain details of the ranking of medical staff and the responsibilities of each grade.

---

[18] Laudy (1921), pp. 25-26.

**Colonel William Johnston, author of the 'Roll of Commissioned
Officers in the Medical Service of the British Army, etc.'**
(Author's collection)

Chapter 2:
Medical Staff of the
Regular Army 1661-1815

Management & Governance of the Army Medical Services

The nomenclature and variety of medical staff is somewhat confusing and changed over the course of time. Much of the data explained below is sifted from the seminal publication, *Roll of Commissioned Officers in the Medical Service of the British Army, who served on full pay within the period between the accession of George II and the formation of the Royal Army Medical Corps - 20 June 1727 to June 1898, with an introduction showing the evolution of the Corps.*[19] This tome was compiled and written by Colonel William Johnston CB MA LLD and MD of the Army Medical Staff and published in 1917 by the University Press, Aberdeen. He was heir presumptive to the baronetcy of Johnston of Caskieben. He served in the Zulu, Sekukuni and Boer campaigns and predeceased the above publication, dying in 1914. Credit must go to him for his sterling efforts.

On the restoration of Charles II to the throne, the Parliamentary Army was received into the new sovereign's service. By 1661, the regular army consisted of just 5,000 men - two cavalry regiments and six regiments of foot, incorporating the Life Guards and Horse Guards, several regiments of Foot Guards and the Royal Scots (1st Foot). At first each regiment of foot and horse had a surgeon, but the Life Guards had a surgeon for each troop. Chirurgeon's mates were added to regiments in 1673. By 1684, each regiment had a surgeon and a mate, the former commissioned, the latter warranted.[20] Apothecaries and hospital mates were also appointed only by warrant.

On campaign and in garrisons, it had become obvious that a greater number of senior medical men would be required for service. The earliest garrisons on the Restoration were Berwick, Hull, Portsmouth, Plymouth, the Tower of London, the Irish Establishment and Dunkirk. A governing body then consisted of a Surgeon, Physician and Apothecary General. The medical establishment between 1664 and the 1680s expanded with newer garrisons and the need to establish general hospitals, particularly in times of conflict. These hospitals were managed by military directors (or governors) and staffed by more experienced medical staff (designated master surgeons in the 1690s) and their mates. Other types of hospital also required staffing. These were the more temporary hospital stations, known as 'field', 'flying' or 'marching' hospitals. Such units would be served by experienced clinicians and also have some transport capability, nurses and servants/orderlies. When Marlborough's wars were over, these transient types of hospital disappeared until the nineteenth century.

---

[19] Johnston W. (1917)
[20] Walton (1894), p. 753.

Physicians for the Army were recommended by the Royal College of Physicians and the Physician General. Although the Company of Barber Surgeons was similarly requested to provide surgeons for the army, impressments of surgeons (by the 'Serjeant Chiruirgen' [sic]) had apparently taken place on occasion, e.g. in 1680, for the Tangiers expedition.[21] Mates' qualifications and training left much to be desired and there were significant shortages of junior surgeons in times of war - there being no universal conscription. In fairness, there was little appropriate training available to prepare an aspirant surgeon for the battlefield.

John Hunter
The father of scientific surgery in Great Britain, also Surgeon General 1790-3.
(Courtesy the Royal College of Surgeons of England)

---

[21] Walton (1894), p. 486

Surgeons to regiments were originally appointed by the commanding officer of that battalion or they could obtain their commission by purchase. Interestingly, although John Hunter, when serving as Surgeon General (1790-3), had exerted the proper influence of senior military medical staff on the appointment of regimental medical officers, this was not a new edict. As early as 5 July 1666, all commissions at home or abroad had not only to be signed by the Secretary of State for War or the Commander in Chief of the Army or Station respectively, but also required approval by the Surgeon General.[22] Such approval did not always prevent nepotism.

Early control of the Army Medical Services was with the Physician and Surgeon General. The former officer was responsible for putting forward names of suitable physicians for commissions, examining men for the posts of hospital mates and exerting some control over the apothecaries and the inspection of their medications. They also became involved in various medical duties concerning the running of larger hospitals.

The Surgeon General had considerable influence in the medical services, recommending surgeons and mates for appointment to regiments and hospital staff, no doubt often resisting inappropriate patronage by senior military men. Replacement of medical officers on Foreign Service or the appointment of new staff overseas was sometimes seen as inappropriate to local needs. His views would also sometimes conflict with those medical officers serving on that station, who had clear understanding about local and acclimatised doctors, working in that theatre, who had already proved their mettle.

Until 1756, just three years before Canada fell to the British, there was little change in the system, but then, by command of the Duke of Cumberland and the Secretary of State for War, Lord Barrington, a proper organisation was introduced. A board was created, which consisted of physicians of the hospitals, the Surgeon General and the principal surgeons and purveyors to the hospitals. These officers were given the responsibility for studying hospital management and for stores and the care of the sick.[23] This board seemed to be of little moment and influence seemed to have slid back to the Physician and Surgeon General.

In 1790, John Hunter, the great doyen and founder of scientific surgery, was appointed Surgeon General and Inspector of Regimental Infirmaries. He also fulfilled the role of Physician General, since the frail Sir Clifton Wintringham - well into his seventies - was unable to cope with his responsibilities. Thus Hunter pretty well ran the whole of the department. His term included eight months of war, which had broken out against Republican France in February 1793. Wrestling with internal politics at St George's Hospital, including an argument with John Gunning, who became the subsequent Surgeon General, Hunter died of myocardial ischaemia on 16 October of that same year. What is generally little realised, were his strident efforts, not only to provide for ten overseas expeditions, but also to bring quality to the

---

[22] Calender of State Papers (1864), p. 502.
[23] Clode (1869), p 463.

appointment of medical staff and to organise an appropriate and structured training format. After Hunter died, his position was taken over by Mr John Gunning. The now separate post of Inspector of Regimental Hospitals was given to John Keate, a Guards medical officer. This post assumed responsibility for hospital supplies, equipment, inspections and appointments.

After Wintringham's demise, also in 1793, Sir Lucas Pepys was appointed Physician General in January 1794. Pepys, although a highly qualified doctor, President of the Royal College of Physicians and having royal patronage (after caring for George III as Physician-in-Ordinary during the late 1780s) was a significantly inexperienced military clinician. He proved inadequate for his post in many ways. So, at the beginning of the long war, the Army Medical Board consisted of a triumvirate of men, Gunning, Pepys and Keate. From 1794 to 1798, all army medical appointments were made by this board.

The requisite and evolving responsibilities of these three Board members will now be described. The Physician General recommended physicians for service at home or overseas and, with the Surgeon General, was responsible for the inspection and checking of bills of purchase by the Apothecary General (not a member of the Board). He was also President of Medical Boards on Officers, to deal with their various medical problems, was one senior member of the examinations group (Court of Examiners) to preside over the testing of candidates for regimental or staff commissions, and for the examination of physicians to the army.

The Surgeon General also put forward men for and appointed men to, regimental or staff surgeon's posts (and their assistants) and appointed staff surgeons to general hospitals, camps and districts. He also directed the Inspector of Regimental Hospitals to appoint apothecaries, mates and other relevant staff to general hospitals for which he was responsible. He had to keep up communication with hospitals on foreign stations. He gave counsel on surgical matters affecting medical officers and presided over the examination of hospital mates. The selection of appropriate surgical instruments for the armed services was reviewed annually by an elected trio of senior examiners from the Company (later College) of Surgeons of London. Advice for such matters and also the provision and inspection of surgical equipment were also responsibilities for the Surgeon General.

The third member of the Board was the Inspector of Regimental Hospitals. He recommended and appointed Inspectors of Hospitals, hospital mates, apothecaries, purveyors and their assistants and any other staff at the formation of any new establishment e.g. larger or temporary infirmary. As his title conveys, he was also responsible for the efficient upkeep and running of regimental hospitals. He acted as an assistant to support the Surgeon General in deciding on surgical matters affecting medical staff and also in the examination of hospital mates. He was medically responsible to the staff of the Commander-in-Chief, was Controller of Army (medical) Accounts and provided medication for the Guards regiments. To add to the mishmash of responsibilities, he was responsible for the training of medical cadets, who were aspiring to the appointment of Hospital Mate.[24] A cadre of army medical cadets existed for a short time and were salaried unattached hospital mates, who wandered the London hospitals, learning the craft of surgery under supervision of designated staff surgeons.[25] The name of the rank of Inspector of Regimental Hospitals was changed in 1801 to Inspector General of Army Hospitals, a name which remained unaltered until 1 March 1873.

The table below indicates the Board members in place at the dates referred to, until radical changes were made to the Board's structure, on 27 February 1810:

Table 1. Composition of the Army Medical Board from 1793 until 1809.

	Surgeon General	Physician General	Inspector of Regimental Hospitals
1793	Mr John Hunter	Sir Clifton Wintingham	Mr Thomas Keate
1794	Mr John Gunning	Sir Lucas Pepys	Mr Thomas Keate
1798	Mr Thomas Keate	Sir Lucas Pepys	Mr John Rush
1801-09	Mr Thomas Keate	Sir Lucas Pepys	Mr Francis Knight (IGAH)[26]

There were also other appointments to assist the three principal Board members, the Apothecary General, who was responsible for the purchase and provision of drugs, instruments and dressings. The senior purveyor and the Commissariat controlled the supply of food, drink and clothing and other necessities for hospital use. All such items were purchased from contractors, after due tenders had been submitted.

As to the running of the establishment of the Army Medical Department, it seemed that before the formation of the Board in the mid 18th century, there was no formal office or administrative provision. After foundation of the Board, support for this important group was limited - merely £100 a year for the Inspector of Regimental Hospitals to cover office costs, such as rent, staff salaries, postage and stationery.

For whatever reason, possibly the cumbersome running of the board, it was dissolved by Royal Warrant of 12 March 1798, which instead gave each of the three members their own answerable responsibilities, recommendations and actions. The 'Board' was nevertheless still referred to in transactions and documents and was so named when reshuffled twelve years later. After the restructuring of the Board, the office establishment consisted merely of one clerk (who took on secretarial duties) and two junior clerks. Total annual expenses then were £556-5s (today's value - £47,300).[27]

---

[24] Chaplin (1919), p. 80.
[25] The Fifth Report of the Commissioners of Military Enquiry (26 Jan 1808) Volume II, p. 7.
[26] Change of nomenclature to Inspector General of Army Hospitals. Knight was also appointed Comptroller of Hospital Accounts and Surgeon to the Staff of the Commander-in-Chief.
[27] The Fifth Report of the Commissioners of Military Enquiry (26 Jan 1808) Volume II, p. 8.

In 1803, the office of the Board was located at 4 Berkeley Street, Piccadilly (later purchased by the renowned military surgeon George Guthrie), but by 1808, the office had moved to Upper Brook Street. By 1806, the staffing had slightly improved - now comprising three assistants (Deputy Inspectors on full pay); two to the Surgeon General (one paid as a purveyor) and one to the Inspector General. There was also a secretary acting as a chief clerk, a clerk to the Surgeon General, an accountant and five junior clerks. Thus by 1806, the annual running costs of the Board, met by the government had leapt to £2,423-3s-3¾d (today's value - £162,110). The total expenditure on salaries for the Army Medical Department, including pay for the board members and office contingencies, was in 1799, £3,415-11s-3d and by 1806 it had more than doubled, to £7,448-3s-3¾d. During this year, the three assistants were promoted to the rank of full Inspector. The salary of the Surgeon General was 40 shillings each day (£192 in today's money, i.e. £70,080 per annum). When Sir Lucas Pepys was appointed Physician General in 1794, his pay was ten shillings (later raised to 40 shillings). The Inspector of Regimental Hospitals was paid 20 shillings per diem. The Surgeon General and Inspector of Hospitals had the temerity to complain that their military responsibilities had, 'very much interfered with the [lucrative private] practice which they [had] heretofore enjoyed.'[28]

In addition to the sparse administrative provision, the civilian, military and private medical practices of these men were onerous. John Gunning, for example, was consulting surgeon to St George's Hospital, ran his private practice and was Master of the Company of Surgeons in London, until his death in 1798. All this must have severely curtailed the commitment and time devoted to their Board responsibilities.

At and after the turn of the century it became evident, even to the public, that there was increasing inefficiency, ineptitude and quarrelling among the board members. This was inevitable with over committed, competitive and militarily inexperienced 'managers' who, while relishing their generous salaries, felt they were there merely to be directed by government, rather than to personally implement innovative and efficient running of the army medical services at home and abroad. Lack of cohesion often led to friction. Whilst two members of the Board (the Physician and Surgeon General) might recommend medical personnel, it was often another (e.g. the Inspector of Regimental Hospitals), who had to select them for a particular service and be responsible for their conduct. In mitigation, with delays in transport and communications and lack of understanding of local problems abroad on active service, command and control in the medical department was not simple. For example, there was often resentment amongst Board members of the actions taken by senior doctors on Foreign Service. Official hours of work for Board members were few, being midday until 1400hrs. Members who were supposed to convene on a monthly basis rarely met. There were personality clashes, problems over selection and promotion of medical officers and arguments over the types and merits of larger or smaller infirmaries.

---

[28] The Fifth Report of the Commissioners of Military Enquiry (26 Jan 1808) Volume II, p. 7.

On 26 January 1808, a Fifth Report was published by the Commission of Military Enquiry (there was a series of nineteen such enquiries, published between 1806-12). This gave a detailed account of the Army Medical Department. A snap shot of total expenditure on the Department, taken for the year 1806, was £254,339 (in today's values, £18.25 million). Recommendations of the commission were firmly made to the government to re-organise the hierarchy of the department, revise supplies of medications and instruments, tidy up the financial governance and redirect the appointment of various grades of military medical staff. The new senior hierarchy of the Board was consisted of a new Director and two Principal Inspectors. It was emphasised that these men, unlike their forebears, were required to be acquainted with the details of military service, i.e. they must have served in a regimental and hospital capacity.

Eventually the controversial and disastrous management of the old Board led to escalating public and government concern, particularly with regard to the failures of many individuals, inefficiency, nepotism and bickering. Finally, the catastrophic summer campaign of 1809 at Walcheren, was the final justification for the radical re-organisation of the board, previously planned.

On 27 February 1810, an announcement was seen in the *London Gazette*:

> *'His Majesty has been pleased to approve of the following officers being appointed and formed into a Board for superintending and conducting the whole medical business of the Army, viz.*
>
> *John Weir, Esq. To be Director General,*
> *Theodore Gordon, M.D.,*
> *Charles Kerr, M.D., to be Principal Inspectors'*

This was the new regime that was in place at the time of Waterloo. On 25 December 1815, six months after the Battle, the number of Principal Inspectors was reduced from two to one. This reconstituted Board was an improvement on the old regime, since these newly appointed senior men had experience of field medicine, but nevertheless the new hierarchy was no sinecure.

As to the formation of proper military transport and hospital organisation, little was to emerge until the turn of the 19th century. In 1796, in the West Indies there had been a temporary Hospital Corps, designated the Royal Hospital Corps. After this, in 1811, Dr James Frank had proposed the formation of a Hospital Corps, although that never materialised. Following the long French wars, an experienced surgeon, J G van Millingen, in his *Army Medical Officer's Manual*, rightly proposed many sensible suggestions for the care of wounded soldiers - some based on French innovations - but through parsimony, complacency or non-progressive planning, nothing transpired. The Hospital Conveyance Corps (1854) and Medical Staff Corps (1855) employed in the Crimean campaigns were considered failures and a new Army Hospital Corps was created in 1857, introducing a wide range of staff and duties. Re-organisations were effected in the Corps in 1873, 1881 and 1882. By 1884, a further re-organisation saw the Staff Corps divided into Medical Staff (doctors and quartermasters) and the Medical Staff Corps (warrant officers, NCOs and privates)

Eventually, on June 23 1898, 83 years after the Battle of Waterloo, a Royal Warrant was issued to found the present Royal Army Medical Corps, with more authority, better pay, some improved conditions of service and appropriate designation of ranks.

The workings of the evolving Medical Department of the Army will be explained by description of its three principal divisions, namely, the senior superintending staff, the hospital staff (surgeons, physicians, apothecaries and purveyors) and the regimental surgeons. As emphasised, nomenclature is sometimes confusing and often changed. Many senior and junior ranks and personnel were created to serve the exigencies of wartime, especially staff surgeons and mates.

Senior Superintending Medical Staff
Superintendent General
A title given to some very senior medical officers appointed to 'superior' positions, e.g. Superintendent General of Hospitals for the British Forces in North America, one John Mervin Nooth, appointed in 1779. The post of Superintendent General was discontinued on issue of a Royal Warrant of 22 May 1804.

Inspector General
A few officers held this post at the end of the eighteenth and beginning of the nineteenth centuries but the post disappeared with the Warrant of 1804. One officer did retain this title after the above warrant had been issued - Mr Francis Knight, later PMO in the Peninsula until Dr James McGrigor's arrival - appointed to the Army Medical Board at that rank in December 1801. When Inspector James Robert Grant (Principal Medical Officer at Waterloo and afterwards in occupied France) was knighted by the Prince Regent in Carlton House in 1819, he was erroneously titled as Inspector General of Hospitals. His title was that of Inspector of Hospitals. As with Deputy Inspectors General, this rank was restored by Royal Warrant in 1830.

Deputy Inspector General
Few in numbers by the end of the 18th century, this rank, as with the rank of Inspector General, was abolished by the Royal Warrant of 1804, but was restored in a further Royal Warrant of July 1830.

Resident Military Officers/Commandants
In 1797, the secretary to the Commander-in-Chief, Colonel Brownrigg, issued an order that Resident Military Officers (i.e. Commandants) were to be appointed to the general hospitals at Deal, Gosport and Plymouth. A certain Colonel Sontag was to recommend these men to their posts and they would rank as captain for pay and receive an additional five shillings per diem. Sontag was not a medical officer, but was appointed Lieutenant Colonel, Military Superintendent of Hospitals in South Britain on October 20 1797. He was attached to the York Hospital, Chelsea and reviewed captains holding similar posts at the hospitals at Deal, Gosport and Plymouth. His

duties, as with the other superintendents, were to ensure military discipline, inspect stores and have control over expenditure in those infirmaries. Also, he was to occasionally visit the other general hospitals mentioned and see that monthly returns were submitted to the Commander-in-Chief and Secretary at War.[29] During 1807, many of the south coast hospitals were closed and only the York Hospital and the depot hospital on the Isle of Wight were up and running. Interestingly, the risk of such closures must have been perceived with this parsimony, since the staff medical men that had been appointed to those recently closed hospitals, were directed to be kept on 'stand by'.[30]

The Hospital Staff (including Recruiting Surgeons)

Directors and Inspectors (including Assistant Directors) of Hospitals

The rank of Director of Hospitals (or sometimes, Chief Director of Hospitals or Director General of Hospitals) was brought in to denote a senior officer, not necessarily a medical man, who had overall administrative command of a permanent general hospital, later of more than one. The last director to be appointed was Sir John McNamara Hayes, who was appointed 'Director of Hospitals under the Earl of Moira' on 20 November 1793.

On the outbreak of war with Republican France in 1793 and the inevitable need for more senior posts, the rank of Assistant Director was introduced. Between 1795 and 1804, around 24 such appointments were made.

During the American war of Independence, around 1777, another medical rank was created - Inspector of Hospitals of the Army. Roughly at the same time, the rank of Inspectors of Regimental Infirmaries appeared (and by 1782, this title was changed to Inspector of Regimental Hospitals). In 1795, the title of Inspector General of Hospitals was introduced, its first incumbent being John Weir, appointed on September 16. There were only three such appointments in the dying days of the 19th century and they all served abroad. This rank was not to be confused with Inspector of Regimental Hospitals, mentioned above, which was an appointment serving alongside the Surgeon and Physician General as one of the triumvirate, which made up the Army Medical Board. When Mr John Rush, Inspector of Regimental Hospitals died in 1800, Mr Francis Knight took over, but to confuse matters further, was re-titled Inspector General of Army Hospitals!

---

[29] The Fifth Report of the Commissioners of Military Enquiry (26 Jan 1808) Volume II, p. 19.
[30] The Fifth Report of the Commissioners of Military Enquiry (26 Jan 1808) Volume II, p. 25.

A Deputy Inspector of Hospitals c. 1805.
(Author's collection)

Inspectors of Hospitals

This rank of senior medical officer did not exist before 1798 (the same applies to Deputy Inspectors). Inspectors were appointed on the recommendation of the Inspector General (until 1804) and taken from regimental and staff surgeons. By 1807, there were eight Inspectors, two acted as assistants in London, one was in charge of the depot hospital in the Isle of Wight and the remaining five were employed as chiefs of the medical staff on expeditions or at foreign stations. They were first employed in an inspectorial role, overseeing the performance of duties within regimental hospitals. Their salary was 40 shillings a day, with an additional one guinea per week lodging money and £40 per year for forage to feed four horses.[31] The creation of this rank clearly gave a diversity of skills and administrative duties to men who might not have been so highly qualified as physicians.

Both Inspectors and Deputy Inspectors could be appointed as temporary ranks, when on Foreign Service.

Deputy (Assistant) Inspectors of Hospitals

In the early part of the 19th century, yet another change of nomenclature was brought in, that of Deputy Inspector of Hospitals, so replacing, by Royal Warrant of May 1804, the previous nomenclature of Assistant Inspector of Hospitals.

By mid 1807, there were 18 of these posts occupied, five directing medical issues in home districts, and 13 in charge of medical issues on expeditions abroad or on foreign stations. The five 'Home' deputy inspectors had certain districts allotted to them and they were responsible for regimental hospitals in those areas and the regimental medical officers. About this time (1807) their pay was 15 shillings per day.

The rank of Assistant Inspector was reintroduced in 1830, at which time the post of 'Physician to the Forces' had been altered to Assistant Inspector of Hospitals.

Principal Medical Officers and Inspectors of Field Hospitals

Towards the end of the 18th century, the post of Directors of Hospitals (vide supra) disappeared, the medical control of a large hospital being under direct control of a senior medical officer - usually a physician. In 1798, the Army Medical Board issued an edict that any hospital officer (even a hospital mate) could be appointed Principal Medical Officer; a temporary rank only applied locally to a man who would command a general hospital. The post was abolished after the Commission of Military Inquiry of 1808.

Inspector of Field Hospitals (or Field Inspector) was a designation given only in wartime and to a few officers on foreign field service alone. Introduced at either the end of the 18th or beginning of the 19th century, it ranked below Deputy Inspector of Hospitals and was no longer in use after May 1804.

---

[31] The Fifth Report of the Commissioners of Military Enquiry (26 Jan 1808) Volume II, pp. 12-13.

Physicians

These men were considered the élite of the military medical fraternity but were restricted to the prevention and management of disease and the practice of internal medicine. Such physicians as Sir John Pringle, author of 'Observations on Diseases of the British Army' (1752), Dr Richard Brocklesby, author of 'Oeconomical and Medical Observations tending to the Improvement of Military Hospitals' (1764) and Dr Donald Monro, who in 1780 wrote 'Observations on the Means of Preserving Health of Soldiers' had made enormous contributions to the potential benefits to be gained by fresh water supply, sensible camp siting, cleanliness, suitable clothing and the general welfare of soldiers. Often, however, during the prosecution of larger and mobile campaigns it proved nigh impossible to implement such sensible measures and this would often fuel conflict between the necessity of the military situation and medical requirements. Such challenges often limited the physicians' jurisdiction.

Physicians were recommended for appointment to the Army Medical Board by the Physician General (until 1810) and the candidates for the post usually came from civil practice or sometimes from the ranks of apothecaries or staff surgeons. They were relatively highly qualified men, but usually with little military experience. When John Hunter was Surgeon General to the Army Medical department, the Physician General (Sir Clifton Wintringham) was infirm and Hunter rightly made it plain that no medical man would be eligible for the post of physician unless he had served as a staff surgeon, regimental surgeon or apothecary. Following Hunter's death, Sir Lucas Pepys, the next Physician General, rescinded this ruling (in 1793/4) and excluded surgeons, on educational grounds, from being advanced to the rank of Physician. Lucas had rather damned surgical candidates and stated, 'the Army Surgeons are not so fit for the appointment, because their education does not lead them to the knowledge of principles'.[32] By the Royal Warrant of March 1798, it had been clearly dictated that, although a degree from Oxford or Cambridge or being a licentiate or fellow of the Royal College of Physicians of London was desirable, it was also feasible to gain the rank of Physician if one had obtained a degree from another British or Irish university and after an examination by the Physician General and two army physicians.

The Commander-in-Chief would have a physician with his staff in the field. This post was held by Dr John Robert Hume for many years of the French Wars, and he served as personal physician to the Duke of Wellington at Waterloo. He had been an army surgeon for nine years and surprisingly, did not obtain his MD (St Andrew's) or his FRCP (Edinburgh) until 1816. Hume must have had an exceptional reputation as a physician. When working in a large hospital, the physician would have the appointed apothecary, who acted as his clerical assistant, under his direction.

Physicians were few in number, which is somewhat ironic when we consider that disease, deprivation and climate - not battle injury - killed most soldiers. The year before the Peninsular campaigns were launched, there were merely 17 army

---

[32] The Fifth Report of the Commissioners of Military Enquiry (26 Jan 1808) Volume II, p. 16.

physicians, two of whom were on home service at the York Hospital and the Depot Hospital on the Isle of Wight, and the rest were on foreign service.

Staff Surgeons

There had to be medical staff apart from those who served their regiment. For these purpose surgeons, physicians, apothecaries and purveyors were required. The last three classes of medical men were never employed in line units, but surgeons could progress on from their battalions, with growing skill and experience and become staff surgeons. This surgical rank had originally been created by Surgeon General John Hunter.

Staff surgeons were promoted from hospital mates, apothecaries or experienced regimental surgeons. Able civilian surgeons could be granted commissions to serve on the staff. Those less physically able could be employed with the fencibles or militia, at home. In peacetime most staff surgeons remained on half pay, the rest worked in garrison hospitals or foreign stations. So, for example in 1787, there were eight garrison surgeons at home and 11 abroad. Confusingly, the extra rank of Surgeon Major existed, not only in the Foot Guards (see below), but also occasionally in the Indian Medical Service. It was sometimes applied, in the 18th century, to a few senior hospital staff surgeons or to senior men in the field or garrison in India.[33] It was not until 1859 that the rank of Surgeon Major was applied to officers who had completed 20 years service.

Up until the creation of a Director General of the AMD (1810), staff surgeons were appointed by the Surgeon General and most worked in hospitals other than the smaller regimental hospitals, much like consultant surgeons do today. They also could be appointed as divisional surgeons, to assist at brigade or divisional level, accompany divisional staff and, if necessary, tend senior battle casualties. In war, lines of communication and fields of combat required temporary infirmaries, where freshly sick or injured patients could be cared for, en route, during or after action. Staff surgeons would be posted at these if necessary or assist with overwhelming numbers of trauma cases after combat.

Around 1790, in the London Gazette, staff appointments appeared as Physician or Surgeon to the Forces. The nomenclature changed in 1793, at the outset of war, to Staff or Hospital Staff. In 1802, a variant of staff surgeon was created, that of District Surgeon or Surgeons to a Recruiting District, who worked in diverse areas of Britain. By 1808, there were 26 of these officers, but by 1810, these appointments had been re-designated staff surgeons.

Clearly then, the rank of staff surgeon was largely a wartime expedient, such that in 1807, of 60 staff surgeons extant, seven served at home (Hilsea, Maidstone, Isle of Wight, the Military College at Marlow, two at Chelsea and, finally, one superintending the education of the Medical Cadets in London), but 53 were serving abroad. During this year, just before the Iberian campaigns, 18 served on the West Indies stations, 12

---

[33] Crawford (1914), p. 330.

in the Mediterranean and Gibraltar, 7 in North America, 6 under orders for the continent, 3 in South America, 3 with foreign expeditions, 2 at the Cape of Good Hope and Africa and 1 each for Guernsey and Jersey. In 1813, nearing the end of the Peninsular War, of 343 staff appointments, which included all types of hospital staff, 293 were serving under Wellington. Working at and after the Battle of Toulouse, there were ten staff surgeons of 69 hospital staff in the general hospitals. At Waterloo, there were ten (including the King's German Legion) present on the day and 23 later arrivals to assist after the debacle. Assistant Staff Surgeon was a subsidiary rank to Staff Surgeon.

Staff surgeons required decent tools for their craft yet they, as well as their line brethren, had to purchase their own capital and pocket instrument sets. At some depots, garrisons and general hospitals however, there were instruments in store, under the care of the apothecary, which were supplied by government for hospital or depot use. In the autumn of 1807, there were 604 such sets of capital (larger sets) and pocket instruments in use around the globe. Also, by dint of fear of invasion, there were 794 sets in storage. Yet, by 1807, it was still deemed fair by government for staff surgeons to buy their own sets (for around £15 - £25, that is £1,075 - £1,800 in today's money) or they might be purchased from government stores at a discount rate of 2/3 the cost had they been purchased from the instrument maker.

Fifteen years after Waterloo staff surgeons were divided into two classes - 1st and 2nd class. Regimental surgeons then were ranked with staff surgeons, i.e. 2nd class.

Recruiting District Surgeons

These medical officers, implicitly involved in the inspection of men entering the army, were appointed by the Surgeon General. In the Fifth Report of the Commissioners, there were noted to be 26 'District Surgeons', who were responsible for the examination of recruits in Great Britain and Ireland, prior to their enlistment. Should there be no District Surgeon available, a resident civil practitioner in that area could be empowered to examine recruits.[34]

Garrison Surgeons

These officers formerly (prior to 1807) were appointed to serve at 'our islands and stations abroad'. This designation and the fact that they were in no respect under the direct control of the Army Medical Board, but regulated by the garrison commander, caused them to be renamed Surgeons to the Forces, which would make their appointments and disposition more flexible. The term 'Garrison Surgeon' was still used to describe those medical officers on home establishment e.g., the Tower of London. Some of these doctors received pay for very small responsibilities and the Fifth Report of the Commissioners suggests they fulfilled little use.

---

[34] The Fifth Report of the Commissioners of Military Enquiry (26 Jan 1808) Volume II, p. 14 and p. 17.

Hospital Mates (Assistants), Mates in General Hospitals or Hospital Assistants to the Forces

These were the junior hospital medical men who performed all the day-to-day chores, under the direction of the orderly surgeon of the day. They were warranted men only and were appointed before 1756 by the Physician General for general medical duties, i.e. dispensing, bleeding and assessing patients, and by the Surgeon General for mainly surgical tasks, such as assisting at dissections (post-mortems) and operations. After 1756, when a Medical Board had been set up, it made the appointments. After 1798, the Surgeon General dictated the number of mates required. Candidates were examined by examiners chosen by the Company (College) of Surgeons, in the presence of two members of the Army Medical Board, usually the Surgeon General and the Inspector of Hospitals. If successful (and standards are difficult to ascertain), the Inspector of Hospitals appointed them to their posts.

By Royal Warrant of 22 May 1804, mates were separated into two groups, those with a commission, denominated 'Hospital Mates for General Service' and those designated 'Warranted Hospital Mates' (or 'Hospital Mates for Temporary Service' or 'Hospital Mates for Local Service'). The warrant actually pre-dated May 1804, taking effect from 20 April 1803. Presumably, commissions could be purchased or granted without purchase - depending on merit and need. The names of the first 23 commissioned mates did not appear in the London Gazette until 1809. By 1807 there were 126 Hospital Mates and only ten were working on home stations. Not until 1813 were these junior hospital doctors renamed Hospital Assistants. We frequently get the impression of these young men being unqualified, inexperienced, heartless and pretty slipshod - surely many were, but campaigns in Iberia, the Low Countries and the West Indies must have sharpened many a medical wit and it is hard to believe that the experience gained by most of these fellows did not benefit them and their charges considerably.

On 8 June 1813, the designation of these men changed yet again, the two ranks being nominated 'Hospital Assistant to the Forces' for commissioned men and the warranted appointments keeping their rank of 'Hospital Mate'. It was the latter junior surgeons who often had minimal and inappropriate training, some being promoted from orderlies, who had shown aptitude. The examination of these men (for example to gain a commission) could be undertaken on Foreign Service by senior medical staff - a deputy inspector, a physician and a staff surgeon.[35]

The rank of Hospital Assistant to the Forces was replaced by Assistant Staff Surgeon by a Royal Warrant of 29 July 1830.

---

[35] Anon. (1813) *Instructions for the Regulation of Military Hospitals and the Sick with Divisions of the Army in the Peninsula*, pp. 30-31.

Regimental cavalry surgeon c.1798.
(Courtesy Army Medical Services Museum, Ash Vale)

Apothecaries and Apothecaries' Mates

Three Master Apothecaries (the senior apothecary in the field or in a large hospital) and three Apothecaries' Mates were first appointed to hospitals during the reign of William III. The last Master Apothecary was appointed in 1778.

Commonly promoted from junior surgical ranks (usually assistant surgeons or hospital mates, directed by a Royal Warrant of 1798), or dispensers of medicines, apothecaries were appointed by the Inspector General (or Physician General). Many were men of decent qualification and thus were sometimes promoted to the senior rank of physician. The Apothecary General (in 1807, a gentleman called Mr Garnier, who employed two assistants) ran a so-called Army Elaboratory in Bury Street, St James's in London. This was a place where the assembly, packaging and storing of medications and equipment took place. Despite this building and its contents being liable to inspection by the Physician General, there seemed to be little quality control of the supplies distributed to the various stations, whose requirements varied widely according to the prevalence of local diseases.[36] The supply of drugs, comforts and surgical instruments permitted considerable profit to be gleaned by the Apothecary General. This post was abolished in 1810.

The rank of Apothecary to the Forces, a senior dispenser in a theatre of war, e.g. at a larger base hospital, was abolished in 1830. Interestingly, this post was resurrected by Sydney Herbert by a Warrant of October 1854, in anticipation of the conflict in the Crimean Peninsula. It was only during these latter times that they achieved an equivalent rank of lieutenant for the first 15 years of service, after which these dispensers could be elevated to captaincy.

Purveyors and Deputy Purveyors

These medical staff members were also first encountered during William III's reign, *'to perform the duty of butler for distributing the provisions to the sick and wounded.'*[37] These were appointments of designated men who acted as the suppliers of food, drink and other medical comforts to hospital patients and who were responsible for appropriate purchases from government and local merchants. They were totally accountable to the senior medical officer and commandant of the hospital. Deputy Purveyors did not appear until later than purveyors and both ranks were well paid, so these posts were much coveted. They were promoted until 1798 by the Surgeon General, from medical men (or later from men 'able with financial matters', e.g. purveyor's clerks) and by a Royal Warrant of 1798, they were to be selected from more senior staff and regimental officers and paid 10-12 shillings a day (in today's money £50-60). After 1798, their appointments were made by the Inspector of Hospitals. By 1807, however, just before the Peninsular campaigns, there were only eight purveyors and 14 deputies and all but one were in service overseas. These men were sometimes prone to peculation and could pocket significant profit in their dealings. In 1793, Mr Keate stated that, when he first came into office as Inspector of Regimental Hospitals, he had observed that being appointed Purveyor was a step in promotion.

---

[36] The Fifth Report of the Commissioners of Military Enquiry (26 Jan 1808) Volume II, p. 42.
[37] The Fifth Report of the Commissioners of Military Enquiry (26 Jan 1808) Volume II, p. 17.

This he had regarded as an 'inconvenience' and recommended that, in future such appointments should be made from men who were, 'versed in accounts'.[38] These posts were virtually abolished in 1830.

Regimental Medical Staff

The Regimental Surgeons

Regimental surgeons, who possessed a varying degree of operative skills, acted as general practitioners for their battalion. These surgeons were the most frequent of all the medical staff. Sir Neil Cantlie, in Volume 1 of his *History of the Army Medical Department*, states that in 1814, regimental medical staff numbered 886 (of whom 313 were full battalion surgeons) and 354 hospital medical staff. Regimental surgeons were usually promoted from hospital or regimental assistants (mates). Battalion appointments were often made by the commanding officer, after perusal of their merits by the Army Medical Department. Although not allowed to exercise it in a military sense, the surgeon had an equivalent rank as a captain (the assistant surgeon as a lieutenant - see below). This came about by a Royal Warrant of 30 November 1796, which also gave an improvement in pay (after 150 years!), the cessation of an allowance for medicines and hospital expenses, these items being paid by other means, in addition there was an improvement in allowances for the allocation of quarters. After 20 years of services they were entitled to a pension of five shillings a day. A similar warrant was issued in Ireland on 1 June 1797. These warrants assisted in boosting numbers of men joining the army, such that by 1799, most positions were filled.

Line battalion surgeons and hospital staff received an increase of pay in 1804, in order to attract more men into the army, after the end of the transient Peace of Amiens. Line surgeons and their assistants had a further increase in salary and half-pay by Royal Warrants of 22 May 1814 and 3 August 1814. There were further pay enhancements in 1830 and 1840.

Table 2. Daily pay scales for army surgeons through the ages (with no allowances or increases for longer service).

£1 = 20s (shillings) = 240d (old pennies); 1 mark = 2/3s of a pound sterling

Year	Royal, Senior or Staff Surgeon	Surgeon or Regimental Surgeon	Assistant Surgeon or 'Servant'
13th-14th century	2 s	1 s	6 d
1415	0.8 mark		6 d
16th century	2 s	1s/3d	6 d
17th century	6s/8d – 10s	4 s	2s/6d
18th century	6s/8d – 10s	4 s	2s/6d
1795	6s/8d – 10s	4 s	2s/6d - 5 s
1797	12 s	10 s	3s/6d - 7s/6d
1804	15 s	11s/4d	7s/6d

---

[38] State Papers for Ireland - King's Letter Book 1, p. 110.

By comparison, nurse pay ranged from six pence per diem, for a junior nurse to two shillings and six pence for a matron per diem.

In the three regiments of Foot Guards, the three most senior surgeons (known as surgeons major, a rank introduced in 1804) were paid 15 shillings a day. They ranked as captains of companies - i.e. lieutenant colonels, thus taking precedence over captains in line regiments and being senior to the surgeons of the Foot Guard regiments. There were also, in the Guards, one battalion surgeon and three assistants ranking as captains and ensigns respectively. Both had similar precedence over line regimental medical staff, but were themselves subordinate to the surgeons major. In the cavalry, the surgeon to the regiment was ranked as the most junior captain and the assistant surgeon as the most junior subaltern.

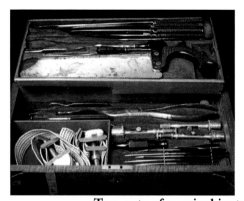 

Two sets of surgical instruments used at Waterloo
Left – A comprehensive British general surgical case;
Right – A French Imperial Guard set, retrieved from the battlefield.
(Courtesy; left, Royal College of Surgeons, England;
right, Musée Hôspital Notre Dame à la Rose, Lessines, Belgium)

Regimental surgeons had always to purchase their own instruments and until 1796, some battalion medications as well. By 1815, a common method of entry of a full battalion surgeon into the service was by his promotion from assistant surgeon or a warranted mate and for this an examination was required. An alternative method of entry at battalion surgeon's level was by purchase of a commission or direct appointment of a suitable candidate from civilian practice (after appropriate training, experience and examination by a licensing corporation, i.e. one of the Royal Colleges), and then by further assessment by the Army Medical Board in Berkeley Street. These regimental men had varied abilities, as a result of diverse training opportunities, some being more able on the surgical front, and others better at physic, diagnosis and medical management. Day-to-day they would work in their regimental hospitals, which varied between a marquee, requisitioned dwelling or, occasionally at home, a purpose-built infirmary (regimental hospitals ceased to exist after 1873).

A Regimental Infantry Surgeon c.1815.
(Courtesy Osprey Publishing)

In combat, which took up very little of their service time, they could be isolated and presented with overwhelming challenges. They sometimes worked together in field hospitals, often being supervised by staff surgeons, who were appointed at divisional level. In 1798, when patients were admitted to regimental hospitals their pay was stopped, to the tune of nine pence per day to provide them with '*reasonable comforts and indulgences*'.[39] In 1799, the stoppages were reduced to four shillings each week. Weekly expenditure returns were made and the surgeon sent these on to the Inspector General. In 1802, stoppages were raised to ten pence per day.

Peacetime promotion opportunities were few, despite a burgeoning empire, but in wartime there was a greater chance of moving on. Many battalion and hospital surgeons retired on half pay after the conflict was over, so flooding the civilian medical market.

John Hunter had felt that many experienced regimental surgeons were better qualified to serve as physicians rather than hospital operating surgeons, since they had had to deal with a broad variety and a large number of diseases on diverse campaigns.

The Regimental Assistant Surgeons (mates)

The lowly status and military appointment by warrant only, of the (hospital) mates has already been alluded to. In the Royal Warrant of 1796, regimental mates' pay was improved and their new designation was to be as Assistant Surgeons to the regiment, thus achieving improved nomenclature before their junior hospital equivalents. Up until late 1803 only one assistant surgeon or mate was permitted, even in larger regiments. In September 1803, however, a second regimental mate was allowed in battalions of more than 500 bayonets. This was a war-time expedient and considered unnecessary for the militia.[40] These men were designated to the equivalent rank of lieutenant, for pay and promotional purposes, but, as with their senior regimental colleagues, had no disciplinary powers in the military sense. Assistant surgeons were first commissioned to the Royal Horse Guards and the three regiments of Foot Guards in 1796, but were not appointed to the 1st and 2nd Life Guards until 1804.

Interestingly, in 1826, three assistant surgeons were allowed for regiments of 500 or more, on account of the amount of sickness in the regiments and also in the medical staff. Sometime between 1790 and 1793, John Hunter had wisely recommended promoting regimental mates into hospital mates, few having seen hospital practice at this time. This was to gain experience of disease, contagion and some major trauma, prior to serving with a regiment. But by 1806, the latter situation had been reversed and it was directed that battalion assistants were to be selected from hospital mates. This ensured that battalion junior staff had been exposed to some degree of hospital medicine and surgery, rather like newly qualified doctors today. So, by 1815, we can see that most battalion assistant surgeons had already served in a hospital setting. Before joining their battalion therefore, the young military trainee would serve at Plymouth, Deal, Chatham, Carisbrooke or the York hospitals.

---

[39] The Fifth Report of the Commissioners of Military Enquiry (26 Jan 1808), Volume II, p. 29.
[40] The Fifth Report of the Commissioners of Military Enquiry (26 Jan 1808), Volume II, p. 31.

Chapter 3:
The Medical Department
of the Ordnance

Until the reform of the British Army following the Crimean War, supplying the army was complicated with the Board of Ordnance and the Commissariat being completely separate from the Army. Co-ordination was only possible at Cabinet level where the Army was represented by the Secretary of War, the treasury by Chancellor of Exchequer and the Board of Ordnance by the Master General of Ordnance.[41]

Woolwich Hospital - later, the Royal Herbert Hospital. The central main (paler) part of the complex was the original Georgian building.
(Courtesy Captain P. Starling, Army Medical Services Museum, Aldershot)

The Board of Ordnance function, size and power increased considerably from 1683 including barracks, the Land Survey (known today as the Ordnance Survey), fortifications, contracts and the control of armament factories. It provided the weapons (swords, muskets, bayonets, cannon etc...), ammunition and greatcoats to

---

[41] Summerfield (2012) "The Board of Ordnance and Army Supply in 1815," *Smoothbore Ordnance Journal,* Issue 5, pp. 14-16.

both the British Army and the Royal Navy. The Master General of the Ordnance controlled the Royal Artillery, Royal Engineers and Ordnance Field Train. By the Napoleonic Wars, The Board of Ordnance was the second largest Department of State, next only to the Treasury, and the Master General had a seat in the Cabinet.[42] In addition, it supplied all the needs of the Board of Ordnance troops including the Royal Artillery, Royal Engineers and even had its own Ordnance Medical Department that was separate to the British Army.[43] The Commissariat supplied the food and fodder for the army.

Before long it became essential to maintain a peacetime depot of artillery, both in mainland Britain, at Woolwich and in Ireland. In the later part of the 18th and early 19th centuries, the ordnance surgeons and their mates were merely appointed by warrant, on recommendation of the Inspector General of that Department.[44]. These warrants were signed and issued by the Master General of the Ordnance, whose office was a direct Crown appointment. Promotion in this department was made solely on seniority. Thus in 1804, all ordnance medical staff officers were Crown appointments, excepting supernumerary, extra and temporary assistant surgeons.

This led to a medical department quite separate from the Army Medical Department and remained so until February 1853. Interestingly the Ordnance Medical department never had a physician in its corps and only once a Physician General, Dr Richard Brockelsby (1794-7), author of the *Oeconomical and Medical Observations tending to the Improvement of Military Hospitals'* (1764).

The medical department and staff serving both the Royal Regiment of Artillery and the Brigade of Horse Artillery were, by a Royal Warrant of 1 September 1801, formed into a new organisation, now named 'Medical Establishment for the Military Department of the Ordnance'. In 1814, the Army List contained a separate listing for the medical members under, 'Ordnance Medical Staff' but, by yet another Royal Warrant of 12 December 1814, the department was renamed, in rather a cumbersome way (except in the Army Lists), 'Medical Establishment for the Military and Civil Departments of the Ordnance'.

During the period preceding the French Wars and until 1822, the following changes that affected the various ranks of medical officers of the Ordnance came about by Royal Warrants (given in brackets) and are shown below:

---

[42] Dupin (1820, rp2011), *Military Force of Great Britain during the Napoleonic Wars,* Ken Trotman Publishing, Volume 1.
[43] Calendar of Treasury Papers (1868), Volume XXVII, p. 346.
[44] The Fifth Report of the Commissioners of Military Enquiry (26 Jan 1808), Volume II, p. 35.

Table 3: Designated ranks in the Ordnance Medical Department (1801-13)

1 Sept 1801	27 June 1804	7 May 1806	21 Feb 1812	1 Aug 1813
-	-	Inspector General of Ordnance Hospitals	Inspector-General	Director-General
Surgeon General	Surgeon General (& Inspector)	Surgeon General (& Inspector)	Surgeon General (& Inspector)	Surgeon General (& Inspector)
-	Assistant Surgeon General (*Deputy Inspector*)	Assistant Surgeon General (*Deputy Inspector*)	Assistant Surgeon General (*Deputy Inspector*)	Assistant Surgeon General (*Deputy Inspector*)
Senior Surgeon	-	-	Resident Surgeon	Resident Surgeon
Surgeon	Surgeon	Surgeon	Surgeon	Surgeon
-	-	-	Apothecary	Apothecary
*Senior Assistant	-	-	-	-
*Assistant Surgeon	Assistant Surgeon	Assistant Surgeon	Assistant Surgeon	Assistant Surgeon
*Supernumerary Assistant Surgeon	Supernumerary Assistant Surgeon	Supernumerary Assistant Surgeon	Second Assistant Surgeon	Second Assistant Surgeon

Same grade - varied pay

The Inspector General was generally in residence in London and would regularly visit Woolwich Hospital and all other ordnance hospitals in the UK. He received weekly returns on the state of the sick in hospitals.

Before any ordnance medical officer was allowed on Foreign Service, he had to attend duties at Woolwich, an extremely well appointed and designed depot hospital. Although there was no ordnance medical officer serving on the Court of Examiners at the London College of Surgeons, most ordnance officers held a diploma from London, Dublin or Edinburgh. No difficulty was found in appointing medical men to this arm of the service, since it was so efficiently managed.

On St Valentine's Day 1853, the governance of the Ordnance Medical Establishment fell under the control of the Superintendent of the Army Medical Department, Inspector General Andrew Smith, who then became Director General of both the Army and Ordnance Medical Departments from 25 February 1853. The following day, the two departments merged. In 1855, the command of the Ordnance was handed over to the Commander-in-Chief and the Board of Ordnance was abolished.

Chapter 4:
Aftermath of Victory

After the Brabant campaigns in the summer of 1815, 2,512 British had been hurt at Quatre Bras and the retreat therefrom and 6,500 - 7,000 from the action at Waterloo. There were also 3,046 sick in hospital. Thus over 12,000 beds had to be found in the Belgian cities and towns for British Army casualties alone. Interestingly, Wellington, in his dispatch, mentions that 1,875 men were missing during and after the battle. Many of these were probably (against orders) taking injured comrades to medical care.

For thousands of families there was grief. For thousands of men the aftermath of victory would be a bitter pill, with often premature death, preceded by prolonged suffering, amputation or a lifetime of pain or disability.

For some of these men, a full recovery meant a rare and respected place in their community, a medal and two years added service towards their pension, (with a 'W' or 'Waterloo Man' after their name) also a small amount of prize money, which was dispensed in 1817. For privates, drummers, corporals and chosen men - £2 11s 4d (£168 in today's money), for sergeants - £19 4s 4d, for subalterns - £34 14s 9d, for captains - £90 7s 4d, for officers of field rank (majors, Lieutenant colonels and colonels) - £433 2s 5d, for generals - £1,275 10s 11d and for the Commander-in-Chief, no less than £61,000 (just over £4 million in today's money!)

What about the men hospitalised after Waterloo? To Professor John Thomson, Sir Charles Bell and Inspector George James Guthrie credit must be given for procuring data on the progress of casualties, either using illustration, surgical case histories or descriptions of dissection (post mortem) findings. These fascinating vignettes give a rare insight into the nature of wounds, the behaviour of the victims and contemporary surgical management. Whilst there is little account of triage or prioritisation, there must be little doubt, as a general rule, that senior officers and Allied casualties, would have been recovered before the French wounded. Many hundreds of men perished from delayed intervention, particularly the French as they sequestered themselves in local dwellings, many hoping to evade capture. There is some evidence that 'mercy killings' took place after the battle[45] and that corpses were robbed and teeth removed for sale back home for the manufacture of dentures.[46]

---

[45] Crumplin M. (2007), *Men of Steel*, pp. 90-1.
[46] Crumplin M. (2007), *Men of Steel*, p. 90.

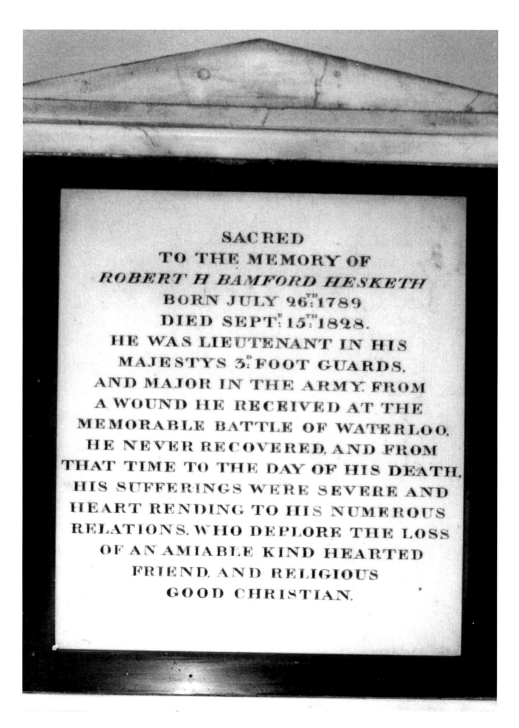

Poignant memorial at Abergele Church, reminding us of the chronic suffering after Waterloo by so many - this poor soul was Lieutenant Hesketh of the 3rd Foot Guards.
(Author's collection)

Detailed accounts of the wounded at Waterloo by Charles Bell and George Guthrie are described in previous publications (see bibliography). It has to be admitted that when Guthrie, of extraordinary experience in the Peninsula, observed the work carried out on the victims of the Waterloo campaigns, he was not impressed,

> '*I found the assistant surgeons doing everything they should not have done…. Nothing could recall ….the irretrievable mischief insufficient care had occasioned in the first few days.*'[47]

One just feels that lessons are soon forgotten, particularly if there is no rigorous set training schedule, as today.

Let us now follow John Thomson's journey through the wards and 'dead rooms' of the Belgian hospitals. He set out from Edinburgh, with Dr Somerville, a senior physician, Deputy Inspector and Chief Medical Officer for Scotland, after obtaining permission from Sir James McGrigor, Director General of the Army Medical Department in London. They set out from London on the 4 July and reached Brussels on the 8th - just 20 days after Waterloo. They met up with Mr Gunning (PMO 1st Corps) and Dr McNeil, a senior physician and DIH, who had arrived after the battle. Gunning and McNeil made the visitors welcome and gave them free rein to study and help with the patients. They were impressed with the zeal and dedication of the medical staff, but ruefully and accurately recalled the limitations of their approbation,

> '*But the duties of the medical man, to whom the charge of the wounded in battle is committed, though less brilliant in the eyes of the world, are often not less dangerous to himself than the exertions of the warrior, no less deserving of public esteem and reward. The fatigue, anxiety and disappointments to which he is subjected, can be conceived only by those who have experienced them. The gratitude of his patients is the fruit of his success, and sometimes the reward of his labours; but in meeting with neglect or ignorant censure, how often is this useful servant of the public obliged to be satisfied with the silent approbation of his own heart, as his only recompense for the utmost endeavours of his skill and humanity.*'[48]

Thomson commented that the battle was contested around a month or so before the 'sickly period' in Belgium, where the autumnal onset of fevers and dysentery could have taken a greater toll on the combatant. Thomson found increasing efforts in the hospitals to preserve good ventilation and personal cleanliness.

All those casualties who could not be accommodated in the Belgian capital, were shipped by canal (no doubt more comfortably than by road) to Antwerp and some to Termonde. The medical staff worked intensively for several days and nights. There were allocated one NCO and three battalion men to work as orderlies, for every 100 casualties.[49] With an interesting insight into the effect such labours must have had on medical morale, Thomson recorded,

---

[47] Cantlie N. (1974), Volume 1, pp. 390-1
[48] Thomson J., (1816) *Report of Observations made in the British Military Hospitals in Belgium after the Battle of Waterloo with some remarks on amputations*, pp. 3-4.
[49] Cantlie N., (1974), Volume 1, p. 390.

'Several of these officers confessed to me, that the sight of so much misery as presented itself after the Battle of Waterloo, rendered them indifferent to life; and that, in the state of intense excitement in which they were for some days, they lost all recollection of, and regard for, themselves.'[50]

Thomson reckons around 2,500 wounded (probably more) were collected into six Brussels hospitals - the Jesuits, Elizabeth, Annonciate, Orpheline, Notre Dame and the Gens d'Armerie. The former five holding Allied patients and being situated on higher ground were considered to have been in a healthier situation than the Gens d'Armerie, which housed the Frenchmen (c.300 patients). The latter seemed to be in a more parlous state, possibly from the delay in retrieval. In the first week after the battle a great many men had succumbed from 'bilious remittent or continued fevers' before Thomson and Somerville had arrived. Much of this mortality, I suspect, was from wound sepsis rather than contagion. The two visiting doctors spent 12 days in Brussels and then, on the way to Antwerp, called in on the 250 or so French patients in Termonde, a considerable number of whom were in the throes of intermittent fever or benign tertian malaria. Dr Perkins[51] in charge of the French wounded had reckoned that Dr Fowler's solution (containing dilute arsenic) had proved of more value than bark (containing quinine).

The pair travelled on to Antwerp, where they were greeted by Mr Summers Higgins of Talavera renown, the PMO there. He had charge of around 2,500 patients, collected into five hospitals: the Mînimes, Façon, Augustines, Hotel du Nord and the Corderie. The last was a converted rope-works on the right bank of the River Scheldt. It was a quarter of a mile long and housed the French patients. Interestingly, it was the civilian medical profession of this town (some having reasonable French), under a Dr Vranken, who, under the general direction of and help from the British, looked after these men. After noting some cases progressing towards sepsis and some patients with possibly infective hepatitis, the two medical gentlemen returned to Brussels on the 29 July. They found some cases who had developed febrile illnesses 24 hours or so after surgery, which they mistook for intermittent or bilious fevers. They noted infected wounds and sores and they commented on some cases of dysentery. They returned to Antwerp on 7 August and made the observation, perfectly correctly, that the septic state of the wounds must reflect, 'an infectious [and contagious] nature' - without of course, recognising the culprit of the transmission.[52] Most of the British convalescents (c.800 patients) were now recuperating in the Façon lazarette and the 1,400-odd French wounded were in the Corderie. The general management of the febrile illnesses consisted of blood-letting, purgatives and diaphoretics. Later in the disease, Peruvian bark, stimulants and a nourishing diet were given. As to the management of infected sores and wounds at Antwerp, caustic agents, such as mineral acids, corrosive sublimate (mercuric chloride) and a solution of arsenic were applied. The milder cases in Brussels were managed with vegetable poultices (e.g. carrot or bread).

---

[50] Thomson J., (1816) pp. 8-9.
[51] A 'British medical officer' that the author has been unable to trace - possibly a senior physician visitor.
[52] Thomson J., (1816) p.16.

The hospital rooms were clean and plenty of fresh bedding was available - also food, especially fruit, was cheap and abundant at that time of year. What was interesting was the fairly logical step, noted by our two visitors, of trying to convalesce men with similar types of injuries together. This must have made it much easier for surgical management.

When reporting on wounds, Thomson recognised the common classification of wounds - incised, punctured, lacerated and gunshot injuries, with further comments on haemorrhage. He then went on to deal with regional injuries. One of the most frustrating issues with the multiple anecdotal accounts that Thomson related was that he did not produce manageable statistics. He clearly kept notes[53] and enumerated some conditions, but what a plethora of data could have been better used if his notes had been more detailed and subjected to analysis, in the same way as Surgeon Guthrie used to keep his records. Thomson's accounts also lacked details of outcome, but they remain the only cohesive collection of Waterloo casualties.

Incised wounds were inflicted by sabres and were frequently found on the head, neck, shoulders and back. What is fascinating is the different management of these injuries, the French surgeons pushing lint into the cut and the British trying to drag the wound edges together with adhesive straps. On the whole Thomson considered that primary closure with just a few straps was best (to allow exudates and purulent material to escape). Whilst stitching such incisions was rarely in use, he nevertheless regarded this practice to have been perfectly reasonable.

Punctured wounds were inflicted by lance and a few by bayonet, the latter appeared to heal less well than the former. A few cases of mild tetanus resulted from these wounds and Thomson relates the favourite French remedy for tetanus at the time - the application of the hot cautery into the wound. Baron Larrey (the notable French military surgeon) had made claims of success with this technique, but his views were treated by Thomson with a healthy degree of scepticism.[54]

Contused or lacerated wounds were usually caused by round shot, case shot and chunks of iron released by fragmentation of the common shell or shrapnel. Clearly there was a vast range of the types of damage inflicted, which varied with the shape, speed and weight of the missile. The type of wound ranged from simple bruising to severe maceration of soft tissues and bone, and avulsion of limbs. The problem was that there was often a great deal of crushed tissue and this was a veritable feast for aerobic and anaerobic (those bacteria which thrived in an atmosphere of no oxygen) bacteria. Since débridement (literally unbridling or releasing of tissue tension, but latterly inferring thorough cleansing and excision of dead or dying tissue) was not routinely practised, severe infection was almost inevitable.

---

[53] Thomson J., (1816) p.136.
[54] Thomson J., (1816) p. 30.

Lacerations around the head, neck and chin, caused by a cavalry sabre.
(Courtesy Captain P. Starling, the Army Medical Services Museum)

Several phenomena interested Thomson. Firstly the so-called 'wind of the ball' - he considered that damage to tissues from the close passage of a ball to be erroneous. Where there was a close shaving injury to the trunk, with minimal or no external mark of injury, organs in body cavities could be contused or even ruptured. Equally men who had clothing or small body parts (e.g. the nose) carried off by round shot were often in no way otherwise harmed. Secondly, he noted that there was often little bleeding when a limb was torn away, because the tearing nature of the wound allowed biochemical substances to be released locally and these would act to narrow down the injured artery, whilst a clean and partial cut into the vessel usually did not allow such advantage. He was in agreement with Surgeon Guthrie in that when a missile passed very close to an artery, the internal structure of the artery could be so deranged as to obstruct the further flow of blood down that vessel.

Underpinning the fact that most combatants were damaged by small arms fire another observation made by Thomson on Waterloo casualties, was that, *'By far the greater number of wounds, which we saw, had been produced by musket-balls,….'*[55]

These wounds had small openings and there was a tract of damaged soft tissues, which would not allow adequate drainage of contaminated blood, serous fluid or pus. Since the missile was of low velocity (i.e. was frequently a 'spent' missile), and its surface spherical, filthy pieces of clothing were pushed into the wound, thus increasing the chance of deep infection. Balls could be deflected by bone or hard objects or they might travel round the edge of a rib or the muscles of the abdominal wall, i.e., take the easiest course available. These issues meant that balls were often difficult to find.[56] Thomson rightly reminded the students that lead balls were not infrequently split into two by bony prominences (for example the knee-cap, the shoulder blade or, more often, the cranial bones). As to the need for dilating gunshot wounds (make a larger opening of the entrance wound with a scalpel or bistoury), it was clearly necessary to understand that this practice was rarely required - usually in cases of uncontrolled bleeding to gain access to a blood vessel, or to facilitate the extraction of buried missiles or debris. Professor Thomson rightly pointed out that extraction of a ball or debris is best undertaken as soon as possible after injury, when the pain, bruising and sepsis have yet to develop more. He also emphasised that a lead ball if left in the body rarely, in itself, causes much harm.

Next Thomson makes some observations on haemorrhage, commenting that most casualties on the battlefield died from bleeding. He discussed the various ways that the surgeon might control haemorrhage, by ligature, tourniquet, but preferably by accurate pressure from a pad or finger placed over the blood vessel, upstream of the wounded part. He alludes to primary (i.e. continued uncontrolled bleeding, occurring immediately) and secondary bleeding (i.e. bleeding occurring after sepsis has damaged blood vessel integrity, which commonly set in from five to twelve days after wounding or surgery). He described a later form (between three and four weeks after

---

[55] Thomson J., (1816) p. 36.
[56] Crumplin M., (2007) p. 226.

surgery), which seemed to be a widespread oozing from granulating (healing) surfaces and may well have reflected a general clotting disorder.

Of secondary bleeding, Thomson noted 50 cases in his visits - most of which were a result of hospital gangrene, induced by, so our surgeon reflected, '...*too liberal an allowance of wine and animal food*' - a commonly held view at the time.[57]

Interestingly, Thomson makes no reference to reactionary haemorrhage, another pattern of bleeding, whereby a patient who was shocked, with a low blood pressure, begins to recover and, as the pressure comes up, bleeding restarts. Such a complication probably spelt the end for poor Colonel Gordon (see below).

A miscellany of regional injuries suffered at Waterloo was described by Thomson during his visits.

Head, neck and face wounds

Most of these were caused by sabre or musket balls and in general healed well, the region having a rich blood supply. Thomson observed surprisingly few wound infections in these cases. Sabre cuts frequently sliced off a portion of the skull, and the protective membrane covering the brain - the dura mater, so exposing brain. He describes a French casualty with a portion of the cerebellum (i.e. the portion of brain below the main cerebral hemispheres) quite exposed and which was observed to pulsate in the depth of the wound for eight weeks. The patient had a great feebleness and some weakness in the legs. Another Frenchman was nursed with 20 sabre cuts over his body, one into the elbow joint became infected with a fatal result. When a post mortem was performed (many of these, referred to as 'dissections' were performed as a teaching exercise), no less than thirteen cuts were found in the top of the skull, none of which had penetrated the full thickness of the cranium. These strangely superficial injuries remain unexplained - probably inflicted when the patient was fallen.

The specimen of this skull was taken back to Britain and remains in the (Balingall) collection of the Royal College of Surgeons of Edinburgh.

Two interesting observations were made by the Professor; firstly that (because the nerve tracts from the brain cross over) left sided penetrating head wounds produced right sided paralysis and vice versa and, secondly, when a depressed fracture of the skull occurred from a musket ball wound, widespread contusion (i.e. multiple haemorrhages) were commonly found in the brain. Both these phenomena are today fundamental to the understanding of head injury. He also observed speech defects, when the appropriate area of the brain was injured, and changes in the pupils, pulse and respiration with those men suffering from raised intracranial pressure. All these clinical observations were of great value when surgeons had to decide when to intervene surgically i.e. perform trepanation.

---

[57] Thomson J., (1816) p. 48.

Diffuse inflammation of the coverings of the brain (meningitis) was noted, as were the unhealthy protrusions of swollen infected brain (cerebral herniation) that often pushed through the bony wound or trepan defect in the skull. Some survived with adequate protection and dressings. Thomson observed, on occasion, that these herniations of infected brain were managed by the application of escharotics (e.g. silver nitrate) or paring with a scalpel. Frequently gentle pressure by circular bandage was applied to coax the portion of infected brain back into the skull.

Stupor, paralysis and convulsions (epileptic fits) were frequently observed and Thomson quotes 'several' cases where the application of the trepan improved these symptoms and the patients recovered.[58]

Facial injuries ultimately healed fairly well, but often disfigurement and functional disorders arose. Thomson comments that wounds of the face were 'numerous'.[59] Sabre cuts were mostly treated by the application of adhesive straps.[60] When lead balls entered the face, the missile often flattened or was split into pieces. The passage of the missiles sometimes caused fistulous openings of the various facial sinuses onto the skin. There were numerous cases of damage to the eyes and when the optic nerves were divided blindness resulted (sometimes called 'gutta serena'). Worse were the initial swelling and subsequent deformities resulting from canister ball wounds. Noses, tongues, the fore part of the face, jaws and teeth were torn away. Some cases were noted where a spent ball had entered the mouth and been spat out! The problems with these cases were pain, swelling, difficulty in eating and swallowing. When the parotid salivary gland or its duct was divided, saliva would leak out onto the face, a distressing problem without a cure.

There were remarkable instances of missiles passing through the neck, missing vital nerves and blood vessels in their course. Most cases of haemorrhage from the neck were controlled by compresses, but in two examples, the carotid artery had been tied off. Although Thomson did not come across a case of oesophageal injury, he did observe three patients, whose pharynx had been damaged, necessitating assistance with swallowing. When the throat was so hit, not only swallowing but speech defects and troublesome coughing resulted from structural or nerve injury. Those men whose jaw had been shot away, remained in a parlous state, with saliva flowing out uncontrollably and their feeding was sometimes assisted by passing a tube or using a funnel. A French casualty at Antwerp with such an injury was noted to be greatly emaciated by this injury and had survived two months. Although there was no mention of numbers, several instances of injury to the brachial plexus, following neck wounds caused by missile or lance were noted. This left the soldier with a flaccid and useless arm.

---

[58] Thomson J., (1816) p. 59.
[59] Thomson J., (1816) p. 63.
[60] Crumplin M., (2007) p. 244.

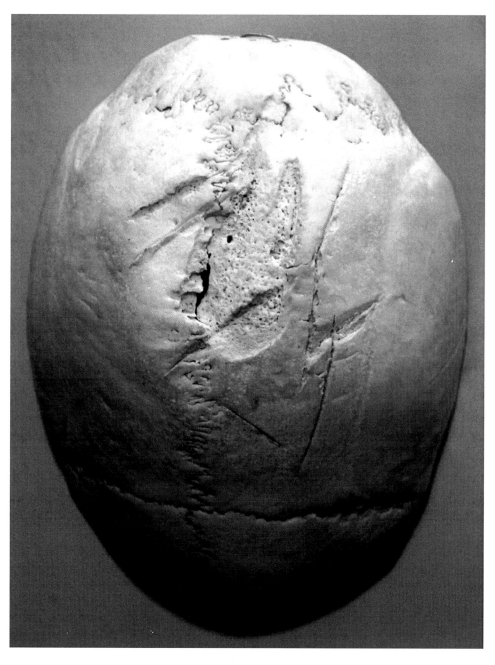

Cranium of a French fatality with multiple cuts inflicted by a sabre.
(Courtesy of the Royal College of Surgeons of Edinburgh)

Chest wounds

Thomson relates inexactly, that the numbers of wounds of the chest that he saw were 'very considerable'. Most thoracic trauma was caused by small arms fire, only a small proportion by lance or bayonet.

He observed that one soldier, whilst kneeling received a spent ball onto his sternum (breastbone) the ball tracked right down to the man's scrotum. He noted other examples of superficial tracking by spent missiles, the balls passing around, but not entering the chest. Most of these wounds were survived, but even without wadding or a piece of clothing going in with the ball, an abscess could form along the tract, as bacteria were dragged into the soft tissues. One unusual case struck him. A ball had passed above the clavicle (collar bone), apparently without traversing the cavity of the chest, yet pleurisy set in and an empyema (one cavity of the chest full of pus) formed. This was drained. Clearly the missile had damaged the apex of the chest cavity. Fearsome haemorrhage could take place from the injuries to the chest wall externally - from damage to the blood vessels lying along the ribs (intercostal vessels), or internally - blood escaping into the bronchial tubes, threatening to suffocate the patient - this latter was more likely to occur following lance wounds than musket ball penetration. With external bleeding from the thoracic cage, external compression with a tight pad was all that was required for one soldier, who had been lanced in the chest. Other such victims might require a stitch passed on a large curved needle round a rib, to compress the intercostal blood vessels hard against the bone.

Thomson clearly acquiesced to the time-honoured, but illogical, practice of vigorous venesection or the application of leeches to chest injuries. This was thought to reduce bleeding in the chest and also discourage inflammation. In one case of a lance wound of the chest with repeated haemorrhage by mouth, the patient suffered the removal of 250ozs (7.5 litres), blood over 18 days!! This must have worked by:
   a)   Natural cessation of bleeding
   b)   Low blood pressure induced by haemorrhage and 'therapeutic' blood loss.

More than a dozen cases of balls tracking right through the chest and being retained in the cavity, or exiting completely, were observed. One man had air and pus exuding from his wound, whilst others passed small fragments of infected shoulder-blade or ribs through their entry wounds. Two soldiers survived a ball passing right through both sides of the chest. Surgical emphysema was described (air escaping into the chest wall, following injury to the lungs) in a few cases.

Urgent closure of open chest wounds was not discussed or noted by Thomson, rather surprisingly, in view of the teachings of Guthrie in the Peninsula,[61] but several cases of empyema occurred in such cases. One persistently refused surgery,

> 'We saw one man, a Frenchman, die of empyema in great agony, who obstinately resisted every proposal made to relieve him by operation.'[62]

---

[61] Crumplin M. (2007), p. 266
[62] Thomson J. (1816) p. 91-2.

To drain off the pus, an incision would have been made in a dependent part of the chest, by incising the skin and muscle, between two ribs, low down in the side of the chest. The opening could have been kept open with a lint plug or 'tent'. Thomson noted that, occasionally, there was a protrusion of part of the lung seen in the wound - a lung hernia.

He noted only one unusual and interesting case at post mortem, at which the diaphragm (the thin sheet of muscle that separates the chest from the abdominal cavity) had been perforated by a bullet. The patient took 30 days to expire.

Abdominal and pelvic wounds

Many with abdominal battle trauma would not live long enough to be observed by our two visitors. Only those with superficial wounds or those 'lucky' enough to have had nature to their aid, would come through. Thomson described eight cases in which a missile had passed into the soft tissues of the thigh, groin or abdomen and had then tracked around the wall of the chest or abdomen to lodge at some distance from the entry wound (rather like those cases in the chest).

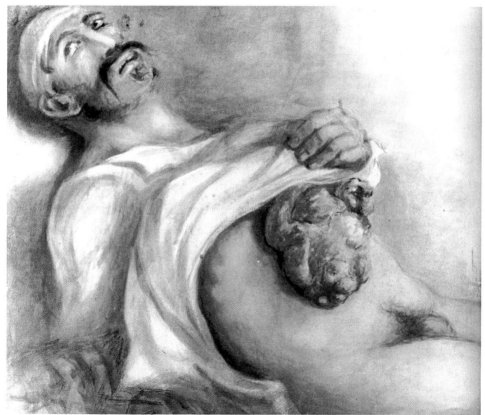

A French cavalry trooper eviscerated after receiving a sabre wound in the abdomen.
(Courtesy of Captain P. Starling, the Army Medical Services Museum)

One case struck him,

> '*A man was struck by the splinter of a shell on the right buttock, ... A hardness and swelling in this case took place over the right hypochondrium [upper right abdomen just under the ribs], and the right side of the epigastric [high central area of the abdomen] region. The tumefaction [swelling] subsiding, a large body was felt between the extremities of the right false ribs and the navel. This body was cut down upon, and a piece of shell, weighing nine ounces and a half, was extracted on the twenty fifth day after the wound had been received.*'[63]

Twelve cases of injuries to the liver were observed, all of who seemed to progress fairly well. In one case the wound discharged bile and in another bile was repeatedly coughed up. This was because the ball had passed through liver tissue and into the chest - a fistula (communication) had formed between the damaged liver and a bronchial tube. Several other cases who had suffered thoracic and liver injuries had occurred.

Thomson did not witness any gunshot wounds of the spleen (an organ with a very rich blood supply), but had been informed of two, who had died of splenic bleeding previously.

As to wounds of the stomach and intestines, Thomson and Somerville observed two surviving cases of gastric wounds, one caused by a lance, the other by a ball - both had stomach contents issue from their wounds, which eventually dried up. Here natural adhesion within the abdominal cavity would eventually 'wall off' the septic injury to the gut, so limiting spread of contaminating bowel contents. As to injuries to the intestine, most would have expired before Thomson arrived - of haemorrhage or peritonitis. Thomson and his friend observed 12 cases. Of these, two patients had a faecal fistula (which would ultimately close and heal over) and in two, the ball had been passed per anum. As with so many observers in later wars, the impression was that small intestinal injuries were more likely to be fatal than those affecting the large gut - the colon. One of the men with a small bowel fistula discharged two ascaris (roundworms) through his wound, reminding us of the frequency of roundworm infestation, through eating poorly cooked pork, infested with the ova.[64]

An interesting observation made by Thomson, clearly quite frequent at these times, was that when the bowel was damaged and opened by a missile, or by disintegration of a dead piece of bowel that had been trapped in a strangulating hernia, the less interference by the surgeon the better. The feeling was that natural adhesion was likely to give a somewhat better, (although only slight) chance of survival, rather than an attempt at surgical repair. We have to accept this doctrine, understanding that without anaesthesia, a full exploratory laparotomy on a muscle-relaxed patient and also without a proper knowledge of modern physiological support, there was little that could have been done anyway. Copious blood-letting, drugs, purgation, emesis and a 'low' diet (i.e. no red meat, alcohol or vegetables), being essential elements of the antiphlogistic (anti-inflammatory) regimen, were considered important elements

---

[63] Thomson J., (1816) p. 96-7.
[64] Thomson J., (1816) pp. 105-6.

of therapy (although we recognise them as having little physiological basis), to minimise a risk of ensuing sepsis.

One case Thomson described had a through-and-through musket ball injury of his abdomen, exiting near his spine. Faeces and urine came through his wounds and the patient also passed air from his bladder when he urinated. The ball had damaged intestine and the urethra, the fine tube that takes urine from the kidney to the bladder. Amazingly, it seems from Thomson's reports likely that the soldier survived this complex and life-threatening injury.[65]

There seemed to be a fair number (around two dozen in all) of lumbar (loin) and back wounds from musket balls, often travelling in a circuitous fashion - tracking around the back or buttocks and apparently causing no serious damage to internal organs or nerves. Abscesses formed in the missile tracks, or where the bullet lodged, occasionally necessitating surgical drainage.[66] The spine, the spinal cord and kidneys, being in the back of the abdomen, were not frequently damaged by missile, lance or bayonet. Such structures could only be injured by deeply penetrating weapon or missile. When a bullet passed across the loins or pelvis, the spinal cord or the sciatic nerve could have been damaged, with ensuing paralysis. Thomson described seven cases - in one a leg was paralysed. Where the pelvic bone was damaged and there was chronic osteomyelitis, the wounds often filled with 'fungus granulations' - i.e. unhealthy, excessive and exuberant healing tissue.

The two visiting doctors observed 14 musket ball wounds of the bladder. In 11 cases the ball had passed right through the abdomen or pelvis and, as a consequence of 'finding an easier way out', urine leaked from one or both wounds (or rectum). To minimise external leakage, urinary catheters lubricated with oil could be passed, but they were stiff (made of silver, pewter or gum elastic) and not only painful to insert, but difficult to retain. One patient was 'most indignant at its being proposed to him', but Thomson commented on the wisdom of such treatment, to those that, 'could be prevailed to wear it'. Since early catheters were difficult to keep in position (unlike the flexible, balloon-retained catheters of today), they were probably used purely on an intermittent basis. One of these patients with a musket ball in his bladder was a case sent home by surgeon Guthrie, for later successful transperineal extraction at the York Hospital.[67]

Wounds affecting the genitalia must have been unbearably painful, embarrassing and disabling. The surgical visitors witnessed around eight cases in Brussels and Antwerp. Several penile wounds appeared to be healing well. One patient exhibited the misery of such a problem,

---

[65] Thomson J., (1816) pp. 106-7.
[66] Thomson J., (1816) pp. 113-6.
[67] Crumplin M, (2010) *Guthrie's War- a Surgeon of the Peninsula and Waterloo*, Pen and Sword publishing, South Yorkshire, pp. 148-9.

'We saw one young man affected with violent hysterical paroxysms, in whom a musket-ball, having passed through both testes, had occasioned great swelling and pain of the organs.'[68]

Where the scrotum and part of the urethra were damaged, a catheter had to be passed to divert the urine away from the wound and, unwisely by modern standards, the healing tissues were approximated, no doubt rather loosely, by adhesive straps and dressings.

Wounds of the upper limb

Wounds of any of the four limbs were frequent and consisted of around three-quarters of injuries treated after the Battle of Waterloo. These were so common since it was possible to survive with them. It was noted that the French casualties were rather reticent to undergo limb ablation, whilst the British often clamoured for it.[69]

Thomson described five cases of fractured clavicle (collar bone). In one of these cases the musket ball broke into three parts on striking bone. The interest in this injury lies in the risk to the lung and major arm blood vessels close by. The apex of the pleural (chest) cavity reaches up to the level of the clavicle and so a musket ball injury to the collar-bone could breach the very top of the lung. One of the five cases he described, was a man shot by a canister round through the right clavicle and who bled profusely on injury then spat blood (haemoptysis) for three weeks - through damage to his lung tissue. The haemoptysis resolved as Thomson left Belgium.[70]

Not far from the shoulder is the axilla (armpit). Here lie further problems. The major blood vessels and nerves from the heart and spine respectively run out of the chest, passing across the armpit into the upper arm. These vital structures were thus prone to injury. Thomson describes five cases where the axilla was damaged, three of which had a degree of palsy of the arm. In a remarkable case a piece of large case shot (measuring one and a half inches) had passed into the region of the shoulder, under the clavicle and had then exited near the scapula (shoulder blade). The subclavian artery escaped damage and was visible, pulsating in the depth of the wound. The soldier had retained finger movements but had a paralysis of the shoulder and arm muscles, through nerve damage.

There were comments that a variety of wounds occurred around the shoulder joint. These had been inflicted by round shot or canister. Some of these patients had had amputation whilst others, commensurate with an increasingly conservative surgical doctrine, had only some of the separated bony fragments removed. Thomson described around a dozen cases of wounding of, or near to, the joint,

---

[68] Thomson J., (1816) p.112.
[69] Cantlie N., (1974), Volume 1, pp 389-90.
[70] Thomson J., (1816), p. 147.

A British casualty of Waterloo with a compound fracture dislocation of the right shoulder caused by small arms fire.
(Courtesy of Captain P. Starling, the Army Medical Services Museum)

'In one case a ball had carried away the integuments [surrounding soft tissues] on the upper and fore part of the joint, together with the deltoid muscle, and had shattered the head of the humerus. The head of the humerus exfoliated [being badly damaged and devoid of a blood supply, became infected and protruberant], and seven weeks after the injury, four inches of the upper part of the bone were removed from the socket. Pains were taken to bring the soft parts together, by means of adhesive straps.'[71]

The patient went on well. Interestingly, Thomson reports that he witnessed some severe injuries of the shoulder-joint, for which amputation had been performed on the field during the action. Probably most operations had been carried out in a field hospital.

As to missile injuries of the arm, several cases were seen with compound fractures of the humeral bone, which had become septic. As a consequence two cases suffered a secondary haemorrhage, requiring ligation of the brachial artery. In one of these two men, the pulse at the wrist had not returned after several weeks, in the other, unusually, sphacelus (dry gangrene) of the arm occurred, necessitating amputation. The usual response to tying off the principal artery to the arm was that a newly formed extra collateral circulation would form. But here, this just had not occured.

Wounds received at the elbow joint were extremely painful and most had been inflicted by sabre, ball or lance. Chronic infection caused some of these, just as in the knee joint, to form what Thomson describes as a 'white swelling'. This is a state of a chronically infected joint that has passed the red, inflamed 'hot' stage of infection and the soft tissues are stretched and distorted by the swollen, smouldering and chronically infected bone and cartilage underneath. Here again Thomson commented on partial bone removal, rather than the patients undergoing full amputation.[72]

In several wounds of the lower arm, amputation for secondary haemorrhage became necessary. With wounds of the wrist, hand and fingers, swelling and great pain followed,

'In one case, a ball had entered about an inch above the wrist, and passed out between the ring and little finger. Great swelling and accumulation of pus were produced in the course of the tendons of the wrist, and [trapped] under the palmar aponeurosis.'[73] [74]

With wrist trauma, aside from the swelling, there was often, 'fungous granulations' (unhealthy excessive vascular and painful healing tissue). This injury was inflicted on Lieutenant Colonel Joseph Muter of the 6th (Inniskilling) Dragoons at Waterloo. He describes his suffering in a letter (as his writing deteriorates in the course of the letter) to his brother,

'You will be anxious to hear how I have got on - badly enough I assure you. There has been an exfoliation of bone, inflammation of the periosteum [membrane enveloping the bone] and a

---

[71] Thomson J., (1816) p. 150.
[72] Thomson J., (1816) p. 157.
[73] A sheet of tough connective tissue lying in the palm of the hand.
[74] Thomson J., (1816) p. 158.

formation of matter in different places - the pain excessive and much fever. Some extraneous matter such as glove pad came out lately. Last night [the 9 July] is the first in which I have had any sleep and I shall now go on well.'[75]

Finally, our visiting Professor comments that wounds of the metacarpal bones (the bones in the palm of the hand) often healed 'readily', whilst damaged fingers, especially the thumb, were accompanied by *'severe local and constitutional symptoms.'*[76] He fails to mention the all-important issue that surgeons should make every effort to conserve as much viable tissue as possible in a wounded hand.

Wounds of the lower limb

Passing on to trauma of the lower limbs, it is unclear from Thomson's visits what the outcomes of hip joint injuries were. The problems with damage to major joints such as the hip were considerable, severe pain, bleeding, discharge of synovial fluid (the clear fluid which lubricates joints), serious constitutional effects, large abscesses and almost certain death. Thomson doesn't let us know.

Thigh wounds were less serious but still carried a high death rate. Often, larger or smaller chunks of muscle were torn away by round shot or canister and the integrity of the leg muscle groups was destroyed by such trauma. Also, the tough fascia lining each muscle group being destroyed, soft muscle herniations took place and bulged out of the wound. Compression bandages were applied to reduce the bulging. Since proper débridement (a thorough cleaning out of all dead or dying tissues) was not practiced, the wounds soon looked sloughy, became infected and if the patient survived, took ages to heal, with glistening unhealthy-looking surfaces.

As musket balls ripped through the thigh muscles, they could pass near to and partially damage the walls of blood vessels, which after five to thirty days could rupture. This was a consequence of the infection along the ball track, which weakened the wall of the artery and then serious haemorrhage would follow. Thomson noted, *'In one case, the haemorrhage had come from the femoral artery, so near to the groin, that it became necessary to cut down upon and tie the external iliac artery'* [above the groin]. Inevitably, tying such large limb vessels could endanger the blood supply to the leg and, even when the vessels lower that the external iliac were tied off, gangrene of the limb could still supervene. With the ligation of higher vessels, such as the external iliac artery, additional collateral blood vessel channels might open up, to provide the leg with sufficient blood supply. Balls split by pelvic bones or other personal debris could land up perilously close to large blood vessels,

> *'...a man had received several wounds from the splinters of a shell which had exploded near him, the feather-spring of a musket-lock was found lying across and pressing upon the femoral artery on the right side.'*[77]

---

[75] Lieutenant Colonel J Muter (1815) Letter written to his brother by the commander of the 6th Inniskilling Dragoons at Waterloo [Cumplin MKH private collection].
[76] Thomson J., (1816) p. 158.
[77] Thomson J., (1816) p. 129.

The real bugbear with thigh injuries received at Waterloo, as always, was the association with compound (open) fractures of the femur (thigh bone), particularly mortal when near the upper part of the thigh, near the hip joint. Chronic infection in the bone (osteomyelitis) or muscles left men suffering recurrent flare-ups of severe infection and limb wounds that rarely healed properly, with significant leg deformity. Hard protruberant swellings occurred in the areas, due to the infected muscle groups and attempts by the femur to reform new, poor quality bone. Counter incisions over these septic swellings were necessary to drain pus and extract dead pieces of infected bone (sequestra). Until all septic fragments of bone were extracted or extruded, there was little chance of fractures ever uniting. One of the frequently described features of severe flare-ups of infection, apart from the hectic fever and unwellness, was diarrhoea.

After admitting such a case, Thomson felt that the damaged limb should be placed in a semi bent position, without any splints or bandages, for about three weeks. That is, until most patients had passed the worst of the 'inflammatory' reaction, then the limb should be straightened and splinted or firmly bandaged. Thomson noted that care was taken to avoid tight bandaging, which might have compromised the blood flow down the leg, by excessive compression.[78] Naturally, if you bandage up an infected thigh injury with a linen roller bandage, access for wound exploration and dressing is difficult, so many-tailed bandages were used. Here, the bandage is intact at the rear, but had many tails that could be rolled around and overlapped on the front of the limb. They could be easily undone for wound access. To properly align the bones, occasional painful manual manipulations to pull the limb straight were carried out, with the patient lying on the side but, unknown to Thomson, were ineffective. He derides cumbersome primitive traction apparatus, yet perversely laudates the French for their care and attention to fracture management, part of which employed fracture boxes, within which traction and counter-traction could be employed to try and keep the limb straight.[79,80]

The two surgical visitors noted, 'more than 60 cases of wounds of the knee-joint', in the main inflicted by musket and canister shot and lance. These wounds were extremely painful, resulted in great swelling and exposed the patient to a significant risk of sepsis, particularly erysipelas and hospital gangrene. Thomson dissected several of these joints after amputation and found fractured bone parts, absorption of cartilage and florid velvety sponge like granulation tissue. Those soldiers lucky enough to survive this terrible injury had white, swollen, painful and stiff knees, not infrequently prone to flare-ups of infection, with discharge of sequestra or portions of dead cartilage. Thomson regarded wounds inflicted below the knee to be very similar to those wounds suffered in the thigh, but, 'In general, however, these symptoms were less severe'[81] There was often much splintering (a comminuted fracture) of bone with injuries of the two bones below the knee, the tibia and thinner fibula. Some balls, noted our surgical visitor, became impacted in the tibia.

---

[78] Thomson J., (1816) p. 133.
[79] Thomson J., (1816) pp. 135-6.
[80] Crumplin M., (2007), *Men of Steel*, p. 238.
[81] Thomson J., (1816) p. 140.

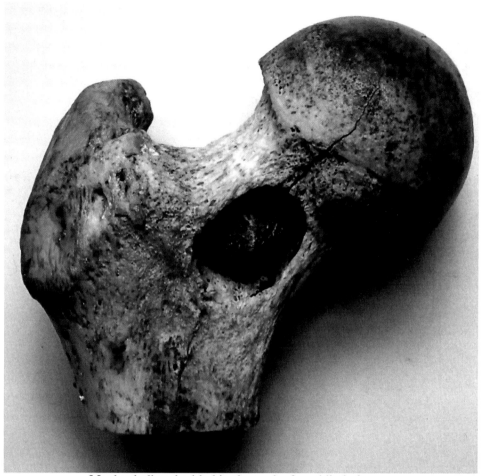

Musket ball embedded in the neck of a soldier's femur.
(Courtesy the Royal College of Surgeons of Edinburgh)

Other missiles, usually spent balls, tracked along the long bones of the leg,

> '*A ball in one case had entered the upper, fore, and outer part of the leg and seemed to have taken a direction backwards to the ham. Various attempts were made to discover it with a probe introduced into the wound, but without success. An abscess after some time, formed over the upper and inner extremity of the gastrocnemius [calf] muscle, from which, upon opening it, a bit of the pantaloons was taken out.*'[82]

What is fascinating about this case was that the ball was not found and apart from some 'fungous granulations' forming in the wound, from sepsis, the wound healed, showing that it was the soiled piece of clothing, not the ball that caused the mischief. Complications were commonplace - infection, non-healing of the fractures and limb deformity. As with thigh fractures, ascending erysipeloid infection (caused by a streptococcal bacterium) of the wounds often was so rapid as to preclude amputation and heralded the demise of the patient. It was noted that a few men suffered

---

[82] Thomson J., (1816) p. 141.

mortification (gangrene) of the leg with these wounds, not having received any damage to the blood vessels of the leg.[83] This most likely signified the complication known as a 'compartment syndrome', where there is so much swelling of the soft tissues, that the increased pressure in the muscle compartments of the leg, squeezed shut the arteries and the blood supply to the leg was obliterated.

As with other contemporary surgical accounts, wounds of the ankle joint were, as noted by Thomson, almost as severe a risk to the patient as injuries of the knee. Many of the convalescing patients with these wounds clearly had serious issues with chronic infection and healing. Some, Thomson considered, would end up with a below-knee amputation. Similar problems assailed those with compound and comminuted fractures of the bones of the foot.

Thomson concluded his report with a short, but interesting and fairly comprehensive treatise on amputation, relating the gradual ascendancy and proper performance of this operation in France,[84] Britain and Prussia, particularly under the influence of the French surgeons Le Dran, Fauré and others, supported by the British surgeons John Ranby and Percival Pott in the mid 18th century. Britain's 'Father of Scientific Surgery', John Hunter, also a physician from Lille - Dr François Boucher by name - had preached caution and careful case selection. By the time of Waterloo, the 'proper' indications for limb ablation had been pretty well worked out - much of this doctrine had been arduously learned in the previous 22 years of war.[85]

Various sources quote incxact data on the total number of amputations performed by all forces over the campaigns of 15 - 18 June, possibly as many as 2,000 - perhaps several hundred of such procedures at Mont St Jean Farm[86] and around 370 or more in the Brussels hospitals.[87] Thomson only referred to British or Allied cases, performed in Brussels and the other Belgian hospitals.

He recorded,

'The cases of [Allied] amputation amounted to nearly 500; and in more than one third of these, the operation had been performed before the supervention of inflammation and fever.'[88]

He rightly points out an important reason for failure,

'The number of those in whom amputation was delayed [i.e. secondary amputation], who died before it could be performed, the protracted pain, suffering, and danger of those in whom that operation became ultimately necessary and practicable, and the far greater proportion even of who died, than of those who had undergone amputation at an early period [primary

---

[83] Thomson J., (1816) p. 229.
[84] Thomson J., (1816) p. 166.
[85] Crumplin M., (2007) Men of Steel, pp. 289-291.
[86] Adkin M, (2001) The Waterloo Companion, p. 315.
[87] Evrard E, Chirurgiens Militaire Britannique à la Bataille de Waterloo et dans les Hôpitaux de Bruxelles en Juin 1815, Waterloo Committee, Brussels, pp. 458-60.
[88] Thomson J., (1816) p. 228.

amputation], were circumstances so evident and striking, as to occasion many regrets among the army surgeons that primary operation had not been more frequently performed.'[89]

Tragically, this reflects the experiences forgotten or never learned from earlier times.

It was well known that compound missile injuries of the upper thigh were particularly risky to the patients, as was amputation at this level. Thomson observed in men that had not undergone amputation,

'Of the few whom we saw who had survived gun-shot fractures in the upper part of the thigh-bone in Belgium, scarcely any one could be said to be in a favourable condition. In all the limbs were much contracted, distorted and swollen, and abscesses had formed round and in the neighbourhood of the fractured extremities of the bones.'

These patients would take months to recover, some even years. Repeated flare-ups of sepsis and exfoliation of dead bone fragments would severely sap their health and, in many, survival was unlikely. Finally, Thomson comments on amputation (disarticulation) at the hip-joint, a procedure successfully carried out by Deputy Inspector George Guthrie on a French prisoner-of-war, a certain François de Gay.[90] Only three cases are known to have survived this huge operation during these wars: one case carried out by Surgeon Dominique Larrey, one by Staff Surgeon David Brownrigg, who served at Waterloo and also Guthrie's patient.

We get the impression that results were probably below average, when Thomson writes,

'The result of the amputations performed in Belgium might, on the whole, be said to be successful, though it certainly was not equally so with that which is stated by M. Larrey and Mr Guthrie to have been obtained in some other countries …'

The renowned military surgeon John Hennen worked for some time with the French wounded in the Gens d'Armerie Hospital. Some of these unfortunate patients were not brought in until eight to thirteen days after the battle! Some had been reduced to eating raw horseflesh. There were 140 compound fractures for Hennen to cope with. Charles Bell recorded some figures, including many late cases. He quoted 146 primary amputations with 40 deaths (27.4%) and 225 secondary (late) amputations with 106 deaths (47.1%). This is a reflection of delayed collection and surgery.[91] As to where these limb removals were performed, probably most were in field hospitals, but as Thomson reported,

'In the actions of the 16 and 18 of June, amputation had been performed upon the field in a 'number' of instances, both by the French and the English [British] surgeons.'

Interestingly, George Guthrie's detailed account of the same group of patients varies slightly from Bell's data, with the latter's mortality figures revealing a higher death rate than Guthrie's (Guthrie's primary amputation mortality rate, 22%; his secondary

[89] Thomson J., (1816) p. 228.
[90] Crumplin M., (2010) *Guthrie's War*, pp. 146-8.
[91] Cantlie N., (1974), Volume 1, p. 391.

amputation mortality rate, 37%).[92] Whilst Guthrie's data was assiduously collected, Bell we know followed up his cases for longer by way of letters interchanged with the surgeons in the Low Countries.

John Thomson's experiences enhanced his Edinburgh teaching for many years. His post was filled by George (later Sir George) Ballingall, the last Regius Professor of Military Surgery there. Ballingall assumed the chair in 1825 and held it until his death in 1855.

---

[92] Guthrie GJ, *Commentaries on the Surgery of the War, in Portugal, Spain, France and the Netherlands*, Sixth edition, 1855, Henry Renshaw, London, p. 158.

Chapter 5:
Allied Generals and Staff Officers' Casualties

The following is a selection of anecdotal reports of wounds and injuries to Allied soldiers received at the Battles of Quatre Bras and Waterloo including, where data has been available, their progress and outcomes. Inevitably many stories are of wounded officers or NCOs and thus in no way is the list comprehensive enough to pay adequate tribute to the thousands of long suffering unranked casualties, whose suffering will never be properly understood.

Neither can the efforts, successes and disappointments of conscientious medical gentlemen ever be fully recalled. The vignettes are ordered in seniority of rank or regiment.

The Prince of Orange assisted by his aides after being wounded by a ball in the left shoulder. (Author's collection)

Wounded Generals
The Prince of Orange
The Commander of the 1st Allied Army Corps at Waterloo, the young 23-year-old Prince, nicknamed 'Slender Billy'(or the 'Young Frog'), with an acne-scarred face, had served with Wellington in the Peninsula from 1811, as a quiet, dutiful and brave member of Wellington's staff. On 11 June 1811, the Prince had been appointed a lieutenant colonel to serve as an extra ADC to the Duke. A senior royal figure in the Low Countries (at that time Holland and Belgium together) and the future King

William II, and commanding a large number of Dutch-Belgian troops, the Prince had to have a significant position in the campaigns of 15 - 18 June. He made some difficult and misinformed decisions at Quatre Bras and at Waterloo and around 1930hrs on the evening of Waterloo, he suffered a wound to his left shoulder, which caused him to be removed from the field.

A junior surgeon, such as an assistant staff surgeon with Wellington's headquarters or a nearby assistant regimental surgeon,[93] carried out first aid. Some accounts relate that it was a severe wound, others not. He was carried to Wellington's headquarters at Waterloo village (the Hotel Bodengien) and subsequently, after wound exploration and dressing by Dr Hume, the Prince was taken to the Royal Palace at Brussels. A staff surgeon by the name of 'Hyde' is mentioned by Evrard as involved in Orange's case, but I find no trace of this man. Certainly, Hume was occupied at this time, being involved with the severely injured Gordon (see below). The Prince travelled to the Belgian capital in the same carriage as the wounded Fitzroy Somerset.[94] The wound was still healing in October.

The great tumulus, built by miners from Lille, (many of them female) stands as a legacy to the Prince's relatively minor wound and the great efforts of the Dutch/Belgian troops. The Duke was not entirely happy with the building of this (Belgic) lion atop a great hill, for it had, he said, 'ruined' his battlefield!

The Lord Uxbridge - later Marquis of Anglesey

This was one of the most notorious and iconic injuries suffered during the Napoleonic Wars. As far as we can ascertain, as Sir Hussey Vivian's Brigade was going down to the charge almost at the end of the day, the Earl of Uxbridge received his wound when riding near Wellington and his remaining staff, to the south east of the farm of La Haye Sainte, following the Foot Guards and Colborne's men down the slope in pursuit of the retiring French Army. Apparently the shot that wounded Anglesey passed over the neck of Wellington's horse, the Duke being on the side of his cavalry commander from which the shot came. Whether the exclamations by the Duke and Paget were apocryphal or not, we shan't ever know. Whilst the Duke was scrutinising the enemy retreat through his glass, Uxbridge observed, 'By *God, Sir, I've lost my leg.*' Wellington momentarily removing his telescope, laconically exclaimed, '*By God, sir, so you have!*' The case round hit Paget in the right knee, passing near the knee-cap tearing open the joint and fracturing the top end of the tibial bone. At first, steadied by the Duke, he was helped off his horse and carried in a carriage to the small farm of Maison Paris (Chateau Tremblant) at the north end of Waterloo village. The owner of the small farm was a certain Monsieur Hyacinthe Joseph-Marie Paris.

---

[93] Units near the staff at this time might be KGL, Brunswick or one of Colin Halkett's Brigade.

[94] Evrard E, *Chirurgiens Militaire Britannique à la Bataille de Waterloo et dans les Hôpitaux de Bruxelles en Juin 1815,* Waterloo Committee, Brussels, p.441-2.

Maison Paris, or Chateau Tremblant, the building in which Uxbridge had his limb amputated - now re-developed as a private dwelling. The monument to the interred limb is to the right of the building. (Courtesy of the late M. Lucien Gerke)

Uxbridge's faithful aide-de-camp, Captain HB Seymour (who reputedly slew more French soldiers than any other individual at Waterloo), led the melancholy party carrying Paget back towards Waterloo village. We are fortunate in having a rare eye-witness account of Uxbridge's wound and rare detail of its treatment unearthed by Gareth Glover, an inveterate researcher and author of the 'French Wars', who included Deputy Inspector John Robert Hume's personal, graphic and rather poignant clinical notes in Part I of his 'Waterloo Archive'. The account of such a notorious wound must be worth relating in some detail, giving much insight into the mind of an experienced contemporary clinician:

> 'On the evening of yesterday, after seeing Colonel Gordon [see below] put to bed [in Wellington's own bed in le Quartier General], Captain Seymour [18th Hussars - ADC to Paget] came to say that, the Earl of Uxbridge had been wounded, he was afraid badly, in the knee, and begging that I would be in the way to see him on his arrival as they were then bringing him in from the field. I offered to go to meet him but my progress through the village of Waterloo [was difficult]. I was stopped by so many wounded men and officers who knew me that it seemed cruel to refuse looking (sic) at their wounds, without assigning some good reason. I had hardly got to the end of the town [where the farmhouse then was] when his Lordship made his appearance in a gig or Tilbury[95] supported by some of his aides-de-camp. I followed him to his quarters and found on inspection that a grape shot had struck him on the right knee close to the lower edge of the patella and entered on the inside of the ligament, and having torn open the capsular ligament had made its exit behind, externally fracturing the head of the tibia end, cutting the outer hamstring in two. The capsular ligament was filled with fragments of bone and cartilage like gravel, but there was no swelling whatever of the

---

[95] A light two-wheeled horse drawn carriage.

joint or limb. His Lordship was perfectly cool, his pulse was calm and regular as if he had just risen from his bed in the morning and he displayed no expression of uneasiness though his suffering must have been extreme; but what struck me as most remarkable was his excessive composure though he had been on horseback during the whole day and personally present in almost every one of the many charges made by the cavalry during the battle, he was neither heated nor did he display the least agitation.'

Now followed the rapid decision-making process in the mind of a senior medical man, who had the life and wellbeing of Wellington's second in command in his hands;

'There could hardly be any doubt of the expediency of amputating the leg but as I was not personally known to his lordship I conceived it was a duty that I owed to his family and to himself to do nothing rashly or without evincing to all the world that amputation was not only necessary but unavoidable.'

Hume recognised the tendency of some officers to refuse surgery. At this point, he took a break and commented,

'I therefore without giving a decided opinion applied a piece of lint wet with cold water over the knee and having desired his lordship to repose himself for a little I went out to endeavour to collect as many medical officers as I could meet [with] that they might see the wound and assist me in the operation.'

Hume knew what should be done but needed decisive support for an action that might result in the death of such a prominent military and social person and mar his own surgical reputation and continued,

I could find no staff surgeon or any other surgeon of the line but I met with several surgeons of artillery[96] who were kind enough to accompany me and from one of them I borrowed a knife [Hume had spent 14 years as a line or staff surgeon, but his current role was that of being Wellington's personal physician] that had never been used as my own had been a good deal used during the day.'

Hume wanted a decent instrument for this patient! He continues,

'We entered Lord Uxbridge's quarters together, his lordship was lying in the same posture as when I left him, and with the most placid smile I ever beheld he said, "Good evening gentlemen!" I went up to him and having removed the piece of lint which covered the wound I was looking round for Mr F…..[97], who seemed to be the senior in order to request him to examine the wound, when a young assistant surgeon pushed himself forward and without taking the trouble to ascertain the extent of the injury[98] said, "My Lord, this is a very nasty wound, it may be long of getting well but a stiff joint will be the only consequence, and there will be no need for taking off the limb." Dumbstruck and his pitch somewhat queered, Hume reprimanded the young man and went on, 'I felt myself so completely confounded and taken aback, however restraining myself I said, "Sir you have not examined the wound,

---

[96] Fogo - also possibly James Powell of the Ordnance Medical Department - see p. 236.
[97] Probably Surgeon Thomas MacMillan Fogo of the Ordnance Medical Department 26 September 1814 - see p. 237.
[98] Thus against protocol, and without much decorum or proper examination.

when you have it will be time enough to give your opinion." Mr P....[99] and two or three of the other gentlemen came forward and examined the injury, I then said 'I hope you have all ascertained exactly what has happened, you see that the ball has passed through the centre of the joint that the head of the tibia is smashed to pieces and that the capsular ligament which is torn open is filled with fragments of bone and cartilage from the middle [of the] external condyle [one of the two large round articulating prominences at the lower end of the thigh bone] of the femur, the outer hamstring is also divided: even were the capsular ligament simply punctured with a sword my own opinion would be against risking the life of the patient under all the circumstances.'

Hume's confidence had been boosted by the 'second opinions' and it was now the patient's turn to respond. Meanwhile, Uxbridge, no doubt highly anxious of the coming event, talked to his staff of the battle. He seemed to be most attentive to everything that passed and said,

"I put myself under your charge and I resign myself entirely to your decision, at the same time whilst I observe to you that I feel as any other man would naturally do, anxious to save my limb, yet my life being of infinitely more consequence to my numerous family, I request that you will without having regard to anything else act in such a way as to the best of your judgement is most calculated to preserve that". I replied, "Certainly my Lord but ..." Uxbridge probably noted a fleeting moment of uncertainty and, 'He stopped me and said, "Why any Buts, are you not the chief? It is you I consult upon this occasion. I said, "We shall retire for a minute and get everything ready in case of necessity". There was but one opinion amongst us, so having prepared the dressings etc, we returned into the room where I announced to Lord Uxbridge that the operation being found necessary the sooner it was performed the better. He said, "Very well I am ready." I disposed the assistants as I thought best to avoid confusion [one assistant to steady the leg, one to support the patient and one to assist Hume and guard the tourniquet] and having applied the tourniquet I took the knife in my hand. Lord Uxbridge said, "Tell me when you are going to begin." I replied, "Now, my Lord." He laid his head upon the pillow and putting his hand up to his eyes said, "Whenever you please." I began my incision without retracting the integument[100] nor in the usual way with one circular sweep, but with my knife I made one cut above[101] from within outwards describing a small segment of a circle and in the same manner below [the thigh bone], beginning at the inner point or horn of the upper and keeping as near parallel as possible. I finished the incision by joining the two points on the outside of the thigh.[102]

I then retracted the skin as much as possible and with a few strokes of the point of the knife had integument sufficient to cover the end of the stump. With one stroke of the knife I divided the muscles all round to the bone and having retracted them on both sides[103] I took the saw. I had sawn nearly through the femur but the person who held the leg being over apprehensive of

---

[99] Most likely Surgeon James Powell of the Ordnance Medical Department who retired half pay on 1 October 1817 - see p. 236

[100] Pulling up on the soft tissues to give more skin, fat and muscle to cover the bone end.

[101] Above the thigh bone.

[102] Hume is using a straight blade and fashioning soft tissue flaps to cover the bone end - this being a better procedure than the so called 'guillotine' amputation.

[103] To keep them away from snagging on the saw blade.

splintering the bone[104] raised up the limb so that the saw being confined could not be pushed backwards or forwards. I did not perceive what was the cause and said angrily, "Damn the saw", when Lord Uxbridge lifting up his head said with a smile, "What is the matter?" These were the only words that he spoke and during the whole of the operation he neither uttered groan or complaint nor gave any sign of impatience or uneasiness. I had only two arteries to tie [using silk or linen ligatures], namely the femoral and a small cutaneous branch [remember that Uxbridge was shocked and probably this limited his blood loss from his now constricted (shut down) blood vessels]. The stump was dressed in the usual manner[105] and his Lordship having drank a very small quantity of weak wine and water was undressed and made as comfortable as the miserable bed upon which he was stretched would allow him to be. His skin was perfectly cool, his pulse which I was curious enough to count gave only 66 beats to the minute, and so far was he from exhibiting any symptoms of what he had undergone in his countenance that I am quite certain had anyone entered the room they would have enquired of him where the wounded man was.'[106]

After surgery, he commented,

'I have had a pretty long run, I have been a beau these forty-seven years and it would not be fair to cut the young men out any longer.'[107]

He requested Sir Hussey Vivian to inspect the amputated leg to ensure that it had been removed for good reason! Vivian regarded the horrid object and agreed on the propriety of the operation.

The remarkable serenity and calm attitude of Uxbridge was either due to an extraordinary stoicism or a blanking out of ascending pain impulses seen in a proportion of patients who have undergone severe trauma. He had continuing neuralgic pains in his stump, which dogged him for years and, in total, was supplied with three elegant, expensive, articulating artificial limbs, made by James Potts of Chelsea. The wound was not properly healed until 1816. These prostheses fitted over his stump with a padded bucket. One of these prosthetics resides in Plas Newydd, the Marquis's home in Anglesey, one in the museum of the Household Cavalry at Whitehall and the third lies in a glass case in the room at Waterloo village, where Wellington slept the night after the battle. As to the disposal of Uxbridge's amputated leg, it was ceremoniously interred in the garden of Chateau Tremblant, a willow tree and a monument inscribed with a memorial poem being planted above it. This attracted many tourists and, no doubt earned M. Paris a considerable sum. After the tree had been uprooted by a storm, exposing the macabre remains, there was a feud between the Paget and the Paris families. The bones were ordered to be re-interred, but were kept hidden and eventually incinerated in Brussels in 1934.

---

[104] That is by pulling down on the supported leg.

[105] Using a Malta cross linen or cotton bandage onlayed over the stump end and large linen roller bandages wound round.

[106] Glover, (2010) *The Waterloo Archive*, Vol 1 British Sources, pp. 213-5.

[107] Anglesey, the Marquess of, (1961) *One leg, the Life and Letters of Henry William Paget, the First Marquess of Anglesey*, p. 150.

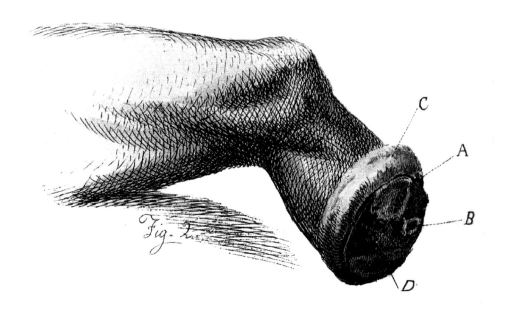

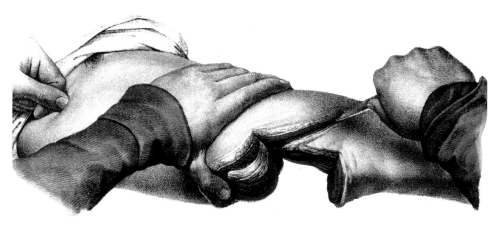

Two images showing the two methods of amputation.
(Author's collection)

The memorial now rests in the garden behind Wellington's Quartier General in the village of Waterloo.

Ci est enterré la jambe
de l'illustré et vaillant Comte Uxbridge
Lieutenant-Général de S.M. Britannique
Commandant en Chef la cavalerie anglaise,
Belge et Hollandaise, blesé le 18 juin.
1815, à la mémorable bataille de Waterloo;
qui, par son héroisme, a concouru au
triomphe de la cause du genre humain;
glorieusement décidée par l'éclatante
victoire du dit jour.'

Some wag had, faintly maliciously scribbled beneath,

'Here lies the Marquis of Anglesey's limb:
The Devil will have the remainder of him.'

The social sang froid of some of the British casualties is well known as various case histories relate - those of Uxbridge, De Lancey, Fitzroy Somerset and Frederick Ponsonby, for example. Costello relates a different and perhaps more usual type of surgical saga concerning a French casualty, who whilst having a wound dilated and explored for debris, was crying out in pain. Close by, a trooper of the Royal Dragoons was undergoing an arm amputation, supporting his own limb, as it was removed by the surgeon. He became irritated by the lusty bellowing of the unfortunate Frenchman. As the trooper's arm came off below the elbow, he hit the Frenchman on the chest with the arm and shouted, *"Here take that and stuff it down your throat and stop your damned bellowing."*[108]

Other members of the Paget family lost limbs in the War against Bonaparte - Major General Sir Edward Paget lost an arm after the crossing of the Douro in 1809 and his daughter lost a hand whilst tending her wounded husband in Spain.

The Duke of Brunswick[109]

The old Duke, Charles William Ferdinand, had served in the Seven Years War and was made a Prussian general in 1773. Five years later, he was promoted field marshal, and commanded the Prussian army, that rapidly and successfully invaded the Dutch Republic and restored the authority of the House of Orange. He was less successful against the highly motivated French Republican army that met him at the Battle of Valmy in 1792. When he counterattacked the Revolutionary French who had invaded Germany, in 1793, he recaptured Mainz, but resigned in 1794 in protest at interference by King Frederick William II of Prussia. Returning to command the Prussian army in 1806 during the War of the Fourth Coalition, his force was routed

---

[108] Costello (1997), *The True Story of a Peninsular War Rifleman* (including the *Adventures of a Soldier*), p. 286.
[109] Friederich Wilhelm von Braunschweig-Lüneburg.

by Marshal Davout at the Battle of Jena-Auerstädt in that year. During the battle he was struck in the face by a musket shot and, as a consequence, lost both of his eyes. Mortally wounded and aged 71, he was led on horseback from the field by his aides, and died in Ottensen two days later - a victim of intracerebral sepsis. His body was returned home for burial.

The Duke of Brunswick being carried off the field mortally injured.
(Courtesy of the Niedersächsische Landsmuseum, Braunschweig.)

Thus the Duchy of Brunswick was no stranger to battle trauma. His son, Frederick William, was no doubt fired up to inflict as much damage as he and his acolytes could muster against the French. The Duchy had been dissolved after Auerstädt and the son of the dead field marshal quit his lands to rest in Austria. After Wagram, in 1809, the Duke took his men to Britain, where they were reformed and fought in the Peninsular War. After returning to his lands in 1814, he promised a division to Wellington, with the help of British supplies and equipment.

The 'Black Brunswickers', led by their Duke, consisted of 6,244 bayonets, sabres and artillery - 4,953 infantry, 919 cavalry and 372 artillerymen. Overall the unit lost 1,446 men during the campaigns, most (846) at Quatre Bras, where the Duke was fatally wounded. He bravely sat on horseback, in the centre of the Allied line, fully exposed to a French cannonading to calm his relatively inexperienced men. Leading his men under intense pressure he rallied what fleeing men he could at the edge of some woods and at around 4.30pm, a French musket ball passed through his right wrist, into the right side of his torso, just above the hip and penetrated the abdomen and liver. After passing through the chest, it exited through the left side of the thorax. He fell from his horse and his friends and aides carried him to safer ground, stumbling over the Duke's sabre and sash, causing the patient great pain.

Others went off to seek a surgeon. The sombre bearer party arrived at a cottage, the Maison Paquet. After being set down, the Duke asked after a friend and then for water. He was then moved to another house, known as La Baracque and Staff Surgeon Pockels declared him dead.[110] His corpse was moved to Brussels and then discreetly carried on to Antwerp, where there were rumours of French victory at Ligny and an influx of casualties.[111] A fine monument on the road to Waterloo from Quatre Bras remains a stalwart tribute to this brave leader.

Lieutenant General Sir Thomas Picton

The redoubtable General Sir Thomas Picton was no novice to injury in combat. He had been absent from the combat at Salamanca, due to a painful wound received at the siege of Badajoz in the spring of 1812. A ball had struck Picton in the groin, just a little above his watch, while leading his men to the foot of the (castle) ramparts. A distinguished officer who was by his side at the time, and to whom we are indebted for much interesting information respecting the events of this night, conceived that this ball had first struck the earth, but still the blow was severe. He did not fall or bleed, but being assisted to the glacis, in a short time became extremely faint and almost insensible. He remained in this state for nearly 20 minutes. After the pain had to some degree subsided, he refused medical aid and again proceeded to direct the attack. He then called on his men to die on the walls if they could not take the castle. The wound Picton had received prevented him scaling the walls after Colonel Ridge, so he remained in the ditch, directing operations. His division had ultimately saved Wellington from ignominious failure at the bloody siege.

Picton lurked in Salamanca, febrile and unwell, either with a septic wound or possibly intermittent fever (tertian malaria), from which he had suffered at Walcheren.

General Ned Packenham had Picton's 'Fighting Third' Division at Salamanca and used them well. Picton's devoted aide, then Lieutenant J Tyler (93rd Foot) waited constantly on Sir Thomas, who was by now emaciated, pale and haggard - so unwell that a period of convalescence in Britain was imperative. He returned to Lisbon, in time for the 1813 spring offensive.

On the morning of Waterloo, one of the questions posed by Napoleon to his staff was, "Où est la division de Picton?" At Quatre Bras, what was generally unknown was that two days previously, Picton had been moderately injured, but had concealed this issue to all but one trusty servant. Around 1415 to 1430hrs on the afternoon of Waterloo, he was struck at the moment when urging his 'rascals' forward to counter d'Erlon's great infantry assault.

---

[110] Robinson M., (2009) *The Battle of Quatre Bras 1815*, p. 260.
[111] Evrard E., p.435.

**Picton (inaccurately dressed) is mortally wounded in the head,
leading his men on to repulse Count d'Erlon's I Corps.**
(Author's collection)

Captain Tyler found his chief's corpse with ease (it may have been robbed after Picton's demise). Upon examination a musket ball had entered the general's left temple and passed into the brain, producing instant 'dissolution'. It must have entered the skull obliquely, since it met 'resistance' and the ball was found under the skin just under the jaw. This notorious missile can be seen in the National Army Museum, London. When Picton's dress was inspected after death, it was observed his coat was torn on one side. According to his biographer,

> '...the truth became apparent:- on the 16th he had been wounded at Quatre Bras; a musket-ball had struck him and broken two of his ribs, besides producing some further bodily, and it is was supposed internal injuries [his body was 'blackened' by it and swollen to a considerable degree, i.e. he was very bruised]: but, expecting that a severe battle would be fought within a short time, he kept this wound secret, lest he should be solicited to absent himself upon the occasion. Regardless of every selfish consideration, he only divulged this secret to an old servant, with whose assistance he bound up the wound; and then, with a command over his feelings almost incredible, he continued to perform his arduous duties.'[112]

Wellington ordered his body to be repatriated to Britain. With due mourning, Picton's remains were removed to London and he was buried in a family vault in the burial ground of St George's church, Hanover Square. Two memorials were raised to Picton; one bust, surmounting a marble column in St Paul's cathedral and some years later, a costly monument was raised by subscription and was built between 1825 and 1828 in Carmarthen. In great ceremony a crowd of townsfolk, Masonic lodge members, dignitaries, soldiers and militia attended the laying of the foundation stone

---

[112] Robinson H.B., (1835) *Memoirs of Lieutenant General Sir Thomas Picton*, Vol. II, pp. 362-3.

in 1825. Beneath the stone were encased gold, silver and copper coins of the year of Waterloo, and, Sir Thomas's own Waterloo medal.

Major General the Honourable Sir William Ponsonby

He was second son of William, 1st Baron Ponsonby of Imokily, County Cork. Ponsonby commanded the Second (Union) Heavy Cavalry Brigade, of the 1st, 2nd, and 6th Dragoons - 1,332 sabres in all at Waterloo. Whilst leading a charge, with Lord Somerset's 1st (Household) Brigade of heavy cavalry to repel d'Erlon's I Corps infantry assault, he was killed by French lancers.

The Death of Sir William Ponsonby at Waterloo.
(Author's collection)

As Count Drouet d'Erlon's I Corps impinged on Picton's Division and others, Lord Uxbridge rode up and after being cheered by the troopers, ordered the two brigades to the front. On the left, led by the Royals, the two brigades trotted forwards and wreaked some havoc on the columns and squares of the French infantry, taking two eagles and around 2,000 prisoners. Ponsonby had notions of limiting the advance to pushing away d'Erlon's men, but failed to restrain the wild pursuit to the French Grand Battery. Hoist by their own petard, the heavy troopers went too far. Inflicting some damage on horses and men, but not the ordnance, they were attacked by French cavalry from the south and east. Ten fresh squadrons of cuirassiers under Marechals de Camp Farine and Travers, five squadrons of lancers and three of chasseurs à cheval under the command of General Jaquinot - around 2,500 horsemen in all - crashed into the blown British cavalry. Ponsonby perhaps unfortunately had not mounted his best charger, since this animal had not yet come up, and as he moved through the heavy wet Brabant mud, he fatally slowed up.

A colonel of French lancers described Ponsonby's end,

> 'I found myself lost for a moment in the powder smoke. When I came out of it, I noticed some English officers surrounding Second-Lieutenant Verrand, eagle bearer. Rallying some horsemen, I rushed to help him. Sergeant Urban [4th Lancers] killed General Ponsonby with a lance thrust to his back. My sabre cut down three of his captains.'[113]

As the lancer caught up with him, Ponsonby knew he was near his end. He handed his pocket watch and a miniature of his dear wife to the major of brigade, Major T Reignolds (2nd Dragoons) to give to his family, but both men were killed. When Sir William's body was found, it contained seven wounds.

A rather youthful William de Lancey and Magdelene de Lancey.
(Author's collection)

---

[113] Adkin M, (2001) *The Waterloo Companion.*

Wounded Staff-Officers

Deputy Quartermaster Colonel Sir William Howe De Lancey

Descended from old and wealthy Huguenots, the De Lanceys originally travelled from Caen, in Normandy to America. This illustrious family produced three celebrated soldiers in the space of 60 years. General Oliver De Lancey, a prominent American Loyalist who had fought with the British in the American War of Independence. He later settled in Beverley in Yorkshire. Another, also an Oliver De Lancey fought in the Carlist Wars in Spain and was killed in the later siege of San Sebastian in 1837.

The third notable soldier in this family was William Howe De Lancey, Deputy Quartermaster General to the Duke's army at Waterloo.

He was born in New York, in 1778, the family afterwards moved to Yorkshire, where De Lancey attended the Beverley Grammar School (reputedly the oldest recorded school in the world - founded in AD 700). When the De Lanceys moved to London, William attended Harrow School for two years. He first joined the army at twelve years of age, becoming a cornet in the 16th Light Dragoons, then transferred to the 80th Foot as a lieutenant in 1793. He was then promoted captain in the 17th Light Dragoons. The image above shows De Lancey as a very young-looking major (aged 21) in the 45th Regiment. He became a most professional soldier, qualifying from the Royal Military Academy, before long serving as an ADC in India, where he was already well known to Sir Arthur Wellesley, a boyhood friend. He joined Sir Arthur Wellesley throughout the Peninsular War. Promoted Colonel, he was knighted for his abilities. These latter had not always been of the best, being at sometime labelled by his harsh taskmaster, the Duke, as 'idle' and 'scatterbrained.'[114]

A true love match ensued between William and a certain Magdalene Hall (daughter of Sir James Hall of Dunglass, a Scottish scientist). They married in Edinburgh in April 1815 - two months before his demise at Waterloo. William was asked to join Wellington for the campaigns in the Low Countries. He was to serve as (Deputy) Quartermaster General (in fact acting as Chief-of-Staff), rather than the favoured Sir George Murray, who was away in Canada, or Sir Hudson Lowe, who was not a favourite of the Duke. He proceeded to Brussels in May, followed a month later by his wife. Surviving Quatre Bras, De Lancey carefully planned out the position of the Allied army at Waterloo - apparently not the extended area finally occupied by Bonaparte's army, but the ridge near La Haye Sainte, considered previously by the Duke.

Later in the action at Waterloo, around 1600hrs, a fierce French cannonading preceded Ney's massed cavalry advances. Whilst riding and talking with his commander, near to the crossroads, on the ridge, where the 'Wellington (elm) tree' was situated, De Lancey was struck tangentially on the left lower chest/upper flank by a ricocheting French round shot. The Duke had been warned away from this rather exposed slight rise in the ground, but had ignored the advice. Falling from his

---

[114] Adkin M (2001), *The Waterloo Companion*, pp. 95-6 and 99.

horse, De Lancey rose up on the ground and fell again. The Duke took his hand and De Lancey then begged to be removed from the crowded place, so that he might die in peace. As he lay, wishing merely to be left alone, his cousin Captain (Lieutenant Colonel) Delancey Barclay of the 1st Foot Guards prevailed on him to be moved. The Duke directed him to be taken to a barn at Mont St Jean Farm. He lay badly injured for 36 hours, relatively undiscovered - most thought he had been killed. When the Duke visited him later, he joked after finding William alive, *"..... you will know what your friends said of you after you were dead."* There was a question as to whether he had been moved to a cottage in Waterloo itself - probably not. On his person was the bloodstained map over which Wellington, Colonel Carmichael Smyth (the senior engineer officer) and De Lancey had poured on the 17 June to plan out the dispositions of the Allied force, south of Waterloo.

A brief synopsis of the abridged diary of Magdalene De Lancey follows, but fails to do justice to her heart-rending account.[115] The poignant work was later enthusiastically applauded by both Sir Walter Scott and Charles Dickens.

Mont St Jean village in 1815. William and Magdelene de Lancey spent their last days together in a small cottage such as one of these.
(Author's collection)

Magdalene arrived in Brussels on the 8 June and passed a few surprisingly peaceful days with Sir William. On one occasion, on the 15 June, she reported that he had found the Duke, dressed only in shirt and slippers talking to a Prussian officer (Major General Baron von Müffling) in full dress. Sir William recommended, for her safety, a removal to a coastal port. Magdalene departed for Antwerp the following day. She was well cared for there, in an inn, one of whose rooms, by coincidence, contained the corpse of the Duke of Brunswick (see above). Lady Magdalene had received distressing and confusing news of her husband just after the battle, and she ultimately believed him alive, but hurt. Passing through Brussels, she proceeded through

[115] De Lancey, Lady, (1906) *A Week at Waterloo in 1815, Lady de Lancey's Narrative.*

Waterloo to Mont St Jean. The roads were choked with wounded and military traffic, often rather aggressive in behaviour. Magdalene smelt gunpowder everywhere and the journey took nearly four hours. When she found Sir William, in a poor farm cottage he said, *"Come Magdalene, this is a sad business, is it not?"*[116] For the next six days, Magdelene sat by him in the poor hovel that was Sir William's sickbay, holding his hand, nursing him and hoping for his recovery.

The love that passed between them was most profound. The surgeons repeatedly bled him (inevitably hastening his demise). He had a painful cough and took little sustenance except tea and moist toast. The Duke, in plain clothes, visited De Lancey and commented on the high price of victory. Apothecary (or assistant surgeon - see below) Mr James Powell acceded to De Lancey's request to have leeches put to the spreading bruise on his side, which Magdalene gently applied. That same day a rather over-jovial Dr Hume, Wellington's personal physician, appeared and said little of comfort. Magdalene and her servant toiled on over their sinking patient. Dr Woolriche (see below) attended assiduously and became concerned at the appearance of De Lancey's blood (i.e. diminished red cell layer and increased 'buffy coat' - indicating a large preponderance of white blood cells - signs of both severe anaemia and sepsis). De Lancey knew that his end was near and most of the time seemed free from pain and at peace. Hume paid another cheerful, noisy and brief visit and recommended another bleeding, (which the patient refused), fomentation of the limbs for comfort and the application of a blister (as a counter-irritant) to his side.[117] Sir William's breathing became laboured and painful and further leeching and blistering were carried out. As he slowly sank, Magdalene lay beside him, washed him and fed him a little. On his last day on earth, he asked to smell some lavender water and looked pleased when Magdalene sprinkled some near him. He gave a small gulp and quietly passed away. Magdalene quietly and sorrowfully returned to Brussels, reflecting on her short very happy life with Sir William.

He had died on the 26 June and Dr Hume dissected the body. Neither his grazed skin nor the coat Sir William wore during the battle had been torn. Hume found eight ribs had been ripped from their rear attachments to the spine, one of them shattered and bits of it had been forced into De Lancey's lung. No doubt his muscles, left kidney and possibly the tail of his pancreas had been pulped into shreds. He was initially interred on the 28 June in a Protestant cemetery at St Joost-ten-Node, but later re-interred in 1887 in the Evere cemetery in Brussels.

Magdalene re-married a Captain Henry Harvey, but tragically died in childbirth with their third baby. Sir Hudson Lowe, later Napoleon's gaoler on St Helena, married William's sister, Mrs Susan Johnson, six months after Waterloo.[118]

---

[116] De Lancey (1906), p.68.

[117] De Lancey (1906), p.89-90.

[118] De Lancey (1906), p.10.

Colonel Sir Alexander Gordon

The place where Gordon was wounded on the battlefield was somewhat to the right of the monument to his death. Prior to Dr Hume's surgical intervention on Lord Uxbridge, the surgeon had to operate on one of Wellington's close friends and aides, Colonel Gordon. He narrates the case history,

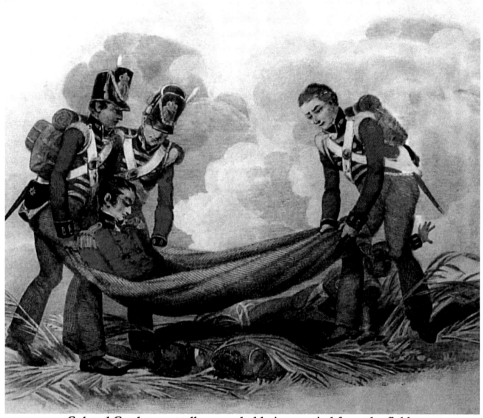

Colonel Gordon mortally wounded being carried from the field.
(Author's collection)

'Sir Alexander Gordon was brought to me [directly off the field] about 7 o'clock in the evening of the 18th by the Sergeant Major[119] & a few of the soldiers of the regiment who were carrying him upon a door, which they had found near the field of battle. I was at that moment occupied in dressing some wounded men near the scene of action [assisting at Mont St Jean Farm] & I suppose I must have seen Colonel Gordon about ten minutes or a quarter of an hour after he had received his wound.

A musket ball had entered on the inside of the left thigh and had wounded the femoral artery a little above where it pierces the biceps muscle & going downwards had shattered the femur in several pieces, lodging in [the] knee near the surface of the integument [just under the skin]. The wound was of such a nature that there was no hope of preserving the limb [the

[119] Sergeant Major Woods of the 2/30th Foot had removed him to Mont St Jean farm.

femur was shattered in many places and the ball had tracked down to lodge near the knee joint]. He had lost a considerable quantity of blood & complained of excessive pain & as the road was crowded with horses and men in great confusion I thought it was better to, amputate immediately [at Mont St Jean] than to wait till he should reach the Duke's quarters at Waterloo since besides the torture that he was then suffering and which he must necessarily suffer from a broken limb during his removal to a distance of upwards of two miles he would run great risk of sinking should haemorrhage come on in consequence of the wound in the artery. I was assisted in the operation by Dr Kenny[120] of the artillery, which I performed entirely to my own satisfaction[121] and notwithstanding that it was necessary to take off the thigh very high up he bore the operation well & though weak was in tolerable spirits asking me several questions about different officers whom he had seen carried from the field wounded and requesting me to tell him how soon I thought he would get well, whether he should not be able to ride.

He said he felt easy and at his own request was removed slowly by the same soldiers who had carried him from the field to the Duke's house in Waterloo which he unfortunately entered at the moment when Mr Gunning [Deputy Inspector John Gunning] was in the act of amputating Lord Fitzroy Somerset's arm.

From that instant he became very restless and uneasy, sighing frequently[122] and begging for a little wine. I gave him a small quantity with water[123] & as soon as Lord Fitzroy and the Prince of Orange[124] set out for Brussels, had him put to bed [in the Duke's bed] & gave him a few drops of laudanum with a little wine. I was sent for about ten o'clock[125] to see Lord Uxbridge whose leg I found necessary to amputate and whilst I was in the middle of the operation I had a message from Sir Alexander to say that his stump was bleeding & [he was] very uneasy but as I could not go to him[126] myself at the moment I sent Mr Cartan[127] surgeon to the 15th Hussars who brought me back word that he was very restless but that nothing appeared amiss with the stump.

As soon as I had finished with Lord Uxbridge I went over to him & as he complained very much of uneasiness & the bandages appeared a good deal tinged with blood. I removed the dressing & examined the face of the wound in the presence of Staff Surgeon Callender[128] and of Mr Cartan the surgeon of the 15th. I found the ligatures on the arteries perfectly secure,[129] but there was very considerable venous oozing [i.e. bleeding from the veins] all over the surface

---

[120] Second Assistant Surgeon Ordnance Medical Department, commissioned 1 December 1810 and served in the Peninsula.

[121] Ensuring the reader of there being no error in technique, see below.

[122] A sure sign called 'air hunger' which indicated hypovolaemic shock, resulting from a low blood pressure.

[123] A common resuscitave manoeuvre.

[124] Who probably had had his wound dressed by Gunning in the same building.

[125] Probably about two hours after being injured.

[126] It was now around three hours since Gordon's operation.

[127] Surgeon 15th Light Dragoons (9 September 1813) - an experienced Peninsular man.

[128] Sic, spelt Callander - Staff Surgeon (permanent rank) 25 October 1814.

[129] Hume had probably performed a 'guillotine' amputation, in contrast to the flap operation carried out on Uxbridge, since the tied off arteries upon Gordon's stump were so easily seen.

of the stump & particularly from the great femoral vein, round which I had put a ligature[130] cleaning away about 8 or 10 ozs of clotted blood, [250-300mls] which had collected about the ends of the muscles and the integument. I again did up the stump carefully moistening the bandage with cold water & I repeated the anodyne draught [tincture of laudanum]. He said he felt easier and lay for some time more composed but about one o'clock in the morning he became restless as before changing his posture, calling every few minutes for his servant and sitting up and laying down in bed almost every moment and in this manner he continued till he became perfectly exhausted and expired soon after daylight I should think about half past 3 o'clock of the morning.'[131]

Gordon had clearly died of continued blood loss. He had probably lost most of his circulating blood volume over the eight hours post injury and his heart and circulation could no longer cope. When his blood pressure had come up after settling in the Duke's bed, a reactionary haemorrhage (when the blood pressure improves, the bleeding recommences) had occurred from smaller vessels and the veins, including the large femoral vein, which had lost its ligature. Ironically, Hume had been correct in not wishing Gordon to travel with a shattered limb. He might, with the benefit of 'armchair' hindsight, have been better (if feasible) to control the bleeding, rested the patient for an hour or two at Mont St Jean, until Gordon's blood pressure had improved and then operated, when blood vessels that were not at first oozing, would have been seen to be bleeding and have been easier to identify and control. In those days, before modern resuscitation techniques, the timing of major surgery was critical. Limb ablations performed too soon or too late were, despite good operative technique, often failures, just for being ill timed.

Lieutenant Colonel Lord Fitzroy Somerset,
Military secretary to the Duke of Wellington
Son of Henry 5th Earl of Beaufort, Somerset was an experienced member of Wellington's staff. As an ADC and as a 'right hand man', he had faithfully and efficiently served the Duke during the long Peninsular campaigns. In 1814, he had married Lady Emily Harriet Wellesley-Pole, a daughter of the Earl of Mornington.

He was wounded in the right arm by a shot fired from one of the rooftops of La Haye Sainte farm, after 1800hrs or so, when it had fallen to the French. The humeral bone having been shattered, his arm had been deftly removed above the elbow, by Deputy Inspector John Gunning, the Principal Medical Officer to the 1st Corps (see below). It was reported that, like so many victims of the blade, he bore the surgery bravely and remained alert during the whole procedure. He lay in a room with the wounded Prince of Orange, who barely noticed the operation on Somerset, for all had been so quiet. Lieutenant Colonel Sir George Scovell AQMG, Assistant Quartermaster General, remained with Fitzroy during the operation and reported that the patient behaved manfully. Somerset did however call out to a hospital orderly,

---

[130] It was not usual practice to tie off veins - often patients were so shocked that there was minimal bleeding from these low pressure blood vessels. He infers that the vein had been tied off at the first procedure - but had the ligature slipped off?

[131] Glover, (2010) *The Waterloo Archive*, Vol 1 British Sources, pp. 216-7.

(and there are various versions of his command) who was removing his arm for disposal, "Fetch me that hand, it has a ring on it that my wife gave me." Then he commanded, "Take off my wedding ring, slip it into my left hand", with a murmured comment, "What would my wife say?"[132]

Fitzroy James Henry Somerset who was later 1ˢᵗ Baron Raglan (1788-1855) wearing his Waterloo Medal by William Henry Haines (1812-1884).
[NGA Archive]

Wellington, when writing to Lord Bathurst, the Secretary of State for War and the Colonies on the 19 June, while praising Lord Edward Somerset's (Fitzroy's brother commanded the Household Brigade of heavy cavalry) brave conduct on the field, also complimented Fitzroy's services,

I was likewise much indebted to the assistance of Lieutenant Colonel Lord Fitzroy Somerset, who was severely wounded.'

---

[132] Sweetman J. (1993), *Raglan, from the Peninsula to the Crimea*, pp. 65-66.

To the Duke of Beaufort, Fitzroy's brother, he wrote,

> '*I am very sorry to have to acquaint you with that your brother Lord Fitzroy is very severely wounded, and has lost his right arm. I have just seen him, and he is perfectly free from fever [it was common knowledge that a fever was the herald of potential disaster], and as well as anybody could be under such circumstances.*'[133]

Six weeks later, his wound was much smaller, but yet unhealed. He progressed well with his left handed writing and determined to follow Wellington's advice to resume the post of Secretary of Embassy in Paris.

Nearly 40 years later on, he was to be made a Field Marshal and Commander in Chief of the British Army in the Crimean campaigns (1854-6). His performance, despite his taciturn manner, political and linguistic skills and albeit in strenuous and difficult circumstances was less than required. He died either of severe dysentery or cholera on the 28 June 1855, saddened by the failures at the assault on the Great Redan in front of Sebastopol. This was ten days after the 40th anniversary of the Battle of Waterloo.

Captain Thomas Noel Harris[134]

Harris was the son of The Reverend Hamlyn Harris of Whitehall, in Rutland. Having campaigned in the Peninsula, he went to Germany and served with the Prussian army from 1813 to 1814. He narrowly escaped death, whilst taking a despatch announcing the fall of Paris in 1814, when he was mistakenly identified as a French officer. He was present at the Battle of Leipzig and all the subsequent battles prosecuted by Blücher. Under fire for much of the 18 June and having lost two horses, he was no doubt close to Vivian, when the diminished brigade was attacking units of the Old Guard, near the end of the action. Harris was hit in the right arm and right side of his abdomen by two musket balls. He was not found (by his cousin, Clement Wallington of the 10th Hussars and Sir Hussey Vivian) until the next morning. He attracted their attention with a low whistle. His story is medically interesting on two counts. Firstly, he was operated on in the farm of Hougoumont and,

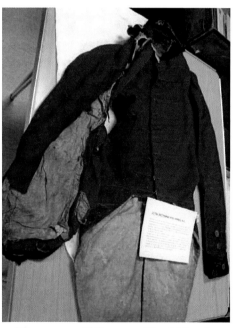

The coat of Thomas Noel Harris worn at the Duchess of Richmond's Ball showing two missile entry wounds and the right sleeve cut up for surgery.
(Courtesy Mr Alan Harrison)

---

[133] Sweetman J., (1993) *Raglan, from the Peninsula to the Crimea*, p. 66.
[134] Major of brigade, serving under Sir Hussey Vivian.

secondly, his coat still exists with the holes created by the missiles and the sleeve slit up by the surgeon.

This notorious relic displays the common surgical practice of cutting up the sleeve of the coat (or trouser leg with lower limb trauma), prior to performing a swift amputation, with the rest of the garment left in situ. Harris asked for the limb to be shown to him after removal as he might shake its hand before parting! The ball lodged in his loin, probably quite near his spinal column and was never removed. He was to suffer significantly from this wound for many years. He had later served as Deputy Adjutant General in Canada, remained a great field sports enthusiast and once, after his yacht sank, swam two miles ashore. Of 14 brigade-majors serving at Waterloo, only six were unscathed.

Captain Thomas Noel Harris of the 18th Hussars.
(Courtesy Mr Alan Harrison)

Major the Honourable Henry Percy of the 14th Light Dragoons[135]

Although his regiment was not present at Waterloo (it had served well in the Peninsula), Percy, the grandson of the 1st Duke of Northumberland and son of the Earl of Beverley, was appointed an ADC to the Duke just a few days before the battle. He had served in a similar post under Sir John Moore - in fact he was one of Sir John's burial party - and had also been made a Prisoner of War. The well-known messenger of the victory of Waterloo, bringing back Wellington's famous despatch to London, he had been, according to family tradition, wounded in a foot by a musket ball, which had become embedded. Dirty and dishevelled, after presenting the two captured eagles and the Waterloo Dispatch, he retired to his father's house in London, to which a surgeon was summoned to remove the missile. The ball was later converted to a ring.[136]

---

[135] ADC to the Duke of Wellington.
[136] Colby R and Percival V, *The Waterloo Despatch*, 1965, the Wellington Museum, Apsley House, HSMO.

Chapter 6:
British Cavalry Casualties

1ˢᵗ Life Guards

Major (and Lieutenant Colonel) S Ferrier

Major Ferrier was said to have led his two squadrons of Life Guards no less than eleven times on the day of Waterloo. He had his head laid open by the cut of a sabre and his body was pierced by a lance. It was reported that most of these charges were not made until he had had these wounds inflicted on him. He was killed in the later part of the day.[137]

Cornet (and Sub-Lieutenant) George Story

Cornet Story had been taken prisoner before the Peace of Amiens and had been kept prisoner in Verdun for seven years. In the very first charge of the Life Guards at Waterloo, Story was about to cut down a Frenchman, when the infantryman threw down his firelock and shouted at Story, " Monsieur ne me tuez pas; je vous connais à Verdun; sauvez-moi la vie en grâce!" Story immediately recognised the speaker, and not only spared the French soldier's life, but likewise that of a comrade, also from Verdun and sent them as prisoners to the rear.[138] He retired about 1825 and died at Maidenhead 20 February 1825.

Corporal Shaw tackles French infantry and cavalry.
(Author's collection)

---

[137] Dalton C, (1890) *The Waterloo Roll Call*, p. 47
[138] Dalton C, (1890) *The Waterloo Roll Call*, p. 47

2nd Life Guards

Corporal John Shaw

Shaw was a charismatic character, somewhat a 'beau' of the regiment, but also a renowned pugilist. Before Waterloo he was seen drinking gin and it was said that he dispatched around ten cuirassiers. He had come to the assistance of Captain Kelly, who was at one time under severe assault. During the bloody struggles, his sabre broke and he promptly hurled the hilt at his opponents. He then used his helmet as a club and was finally cut down and shot. He received a mortal wound from a French cuirassier colonel who thrust him through his body. Before his death, Shaw cut down and killed the colonel with a mighty head strike. Shaw soon crawled away onto a midden to die during the night.

Corporal Shaw's skull - a copy of the original, (from the Household Cavalry Museum at Horseguards), this exhibit is from Abbotsford, home of Sir Walter Scott, an avid collector and enthusiast of the Battle of Waterloo.
(Courtesy of the Abbotsford House Trust)

Royal Regiment of Horse Guards
Lieutenant Tathwell Baker Tathwell
Tathwell was taken prisoner, after an advance by the remains of the Heavy Brigades, late in the battle. He had seized an eagle from the French infantry. His horse was shot from under him and he was captured. The eagle was taken from him and, whilst being escorted to the rear, a wounded French officer on a stretcher carried by four men, called for Tathwell to be brought over to him and then inflicted several kicks on the prisoner. The prisoner's escort seemed very much shocked, but dared not remonstrate.[139] Tathwell escaped two days later and retrieved a French shako plate (of the 123e Infantrie de Ligne) from a dead Dutch infantryman. Speculation perhaps, but had the Dutchman hung on to this plate just in case he might have been captured by the French and could then have pleaded prior service with the Emperor?

1st Dragoon Guards
Troop Sergeant Major Thomas Nicholson
Nicholson was wounded by a penetrating sabre injury, while at the charge and, typical of some discharged Waterloo veterans, he retired to live in York, where he bought the 'Light Horseman Inn' in Fulford Road.

---

[139] Gronow HR, *Recollections and Anecdotes of the Camp, the Court and the Clubs*, 1877 Smith, Elder & Co., London pp. 196-7.

2nd North British Dragoons

Captain Edward Cheney

Consequent on the death or wounding of his three senior officers (Colonel Hamilton, who, after being wounded, rode a high-spirited mare that ran away with him - his body was never recovered - also Majors Clarke and Hankin, who both survived), Edward Cheney commanded the 2nd (North) British Dragoons for the last three hours of the battle. In 20 minutes he had three horses shot from under him.

Letter written by Captain Cheney to his wife on the 20 June 1815.
He commanded the 2nd Dragoons towards the end of the day.
(Author's collection)

Sergeant Charles Ewart

Ewart was a powerful trooper around six and a half feet tall, who rode with his regiment. The 2nd Dragoons were in a reserve position on the left at the advance of the Union Brigade, with the Inniskillings and 1st Royal Dragoons, to counter the massive infantry assault by Count d'Erlon's I Corps.

Charles Ewart in later life
(Courtesy of Mr Stuart Mellor)

The injuries he caused whilst in the act of wresting the eagle of the 45e Infantrie de Ligne (part of General Marcognet's Division) from its unfortunate guardians, well exemplified the typical nature of wounds inflicted by cavalry on both infantry and cavalry. Ewart wrote,

'It was in the first charge I took the eagle from the enemy; he and I had a hard contest for it; he thrust for my groin - I parried it off, and cut him through the head; after which I was attacked by one of their Lancers, who threw his lance at me, but missed the mark by my throwing it off with my sword by my right side; then I cut him from the chin upwards [this must have been a backhanded swipe], which went through his teeth. Next I was attacked by a foot soldier who, after firing at me, next charged me with his bayonet; but he very soon lost the combat, for I parried it and cut him down through the head; so that finished the contest for the eagle.' [140]

Given a commission for his deeds, Ewart became an ensign in the 5th Veteran Battalion in 1816 and retired on a pension of five shillings and ten pence a day. A native of Kilmarnock, he died at Davyhulme, near Manchester in 1846. A memorial exists in front of Edinburgh Castle, which houses the eagle and Ewart's sword and overalls.

Sergeant John Weir

Weir was the pay sergeant of the regiment and 'though normally excused combat, he had requested to remain with the Greys. He was mortally wounded and a certain Corporal Scott, who had lost a leg in the battle, asserts that when Weir's body was recovered, his name was smeared in his own blood across his forehead, since the dying man had no wish for it to be thought that he had absconded with regimental funds![141]

---

[140] Adkin M., (2001) p. 352.
[141] Dalton C, (1890) *The Waterloo Roll Call*, p.228.

6ᵗʰ Inniskilling Dragoons

Lieutenant Colonel Joseph Muter

Joseph Muter was educated at the Royal Military College, High Wycombe and after serving on the Duke of Gloucester's staff, fought in the Peninsula for three years. On 4 June 1813, he was given a lieutenant colonelcy in the 6ᵗʰ Dragoons and a colonelcy a year later. He took over the command of the Union Brigade after Sir William Ponsonby's demise. He suffered five horses killed under him during the day. Later in the day, he was shot through his wrist, a very painful and somewhat disabling injury. He wrote from Brussels on the 10 July of the wound, to his brother, James,

'You'll be anxious to know how I got on - badly enough I assure you. There has been an exfoliation of bone,[142] inflammation of the periosteum [the tough nutrient membrane covering bones] and a formation of matter [pus] in different places - the pain excessive and much fever. Some extraneous matter such as glove pad came out last night. Last night [the 9 July] is the first I have had any sleep and I shall now go on well. In 8 days I shall be able to join [the regiment]. The Regiment has seen nothing since the battle. You'll have observed with pleasure that of the two brigades mentioned as having particularly distinguished themselves, mine was one. I say mine because Sir Wm. Ponsonby was killed at the beginning of the action - my wound was received at 6pm in leading the brigade to the charge - my horse was hit at the same moment. My hurt looked slight; but the consequences have been dreadful, the bones have been injured. I have reason to believe I shall not lose the use of any joints.'

Muter had been ordered by Colonel George Damer, a staff officer, to take the shattered remains (around 250 sabres) of the Union Brigade to make a final charge at the end of the day. Muter was noted to have had his helmet beaten in and with his arm in a sling, he wearily obeyed his last duty at Waterloo. He had survived.

After the wars, Muter took on the surname of Straton upon inheriting an estate from his aunt, Miss Straton of Kirkside, near Montrose. He later become Colonel-in-Chief of the 6ᵗʰ Dragoons, was elected an FRS (Edinburgh), KCH and CB. He died in 1840, leaving £70,000 (£5.5 million in 2010) to Edinburgh University.[143] He also left £500 (£40,000 in 2010) to the regiment and was interred and memorialised in Kincardine.

---

[142] Pieces of dead, infected bone had extruded from the wound.
[143] Dalton C, (1890) *The Waterloo Roll Call*, pp. 60-61.

Brussels, 10th July 1815

My dear Jam[es]

I received yours of the 7th June, & had before apprized you, that I should not want the £100. I am happy to hear that your own prospects of recovering from your Uncle are so brilliant — he seems to have behaved infamously — You'll be anxious to hear, how I have got on — badly enough I assure you — there has been an application of Bone, Inflammation of the Periosteum, & a formation of matter in different places — the pain etc etc etc, & much fever — some extraneous matter such as glass &c. came out lately — Last night is the first, on which I have had any sleep, & I shall now go on well — in 8 days I shall be able to join the Reg.t — has seen nothing since the Battle. You'll have observed with

Letter written by Joseph Muter (who was temporarily in command of the Union Heavy Cavalry Brigade) to his brother, 22 days after the battle. The letter concerns his wound and his writing reflects the disability he suffered with his wrist injury.
(Author's collection)

Troop Sergeant Major Matthew Marshall

One of the most impressive survival stories was that of Matthew Marshall. His troop was cut off during the advance of the Union Brigade, by French cavalry. Marshall was cutting at a cuirassier to his right, when his bridle arm was broken by a cut from an enemy sabre. Some lancers approached and thrust into his flank, throwing him from his horse. While falling he received another body strike, and another which broke his right thigh. His wounded body was tossed about by overriding cavalry. He later espied a horse, but was cut several times by another French trooper. During the French advance later in the afternoon, a French artilleryman rested a foot on Marshall whilst ramming his gun. Marshall lay for three days and two nights on the field unattended. He had suffered 19 lance and sabre wounds, yet he survived and lived in Ireland until his death in 1825.

7th Hussars

Major Edward Hodge

Edward Hodge was killed during the cavalry clash in Genappe, after the action at Quatre Bras on the 17 June. The regiment had a hard contest in the narrow streets of Genappe and received many casualties. Uxbridge ordered in the Life Guards to assist the 7th Hussars. There is a memorial inscription to Hodge in the chapel in the village of Waterloo.

Major William Thornhill

Luckier than Hodge was Major William Thornhill. Having served with the 23rd Foot in the Low Countries and Egypt, he had been severely wounded at Orthez by the point of a standard, wrested from a French soldier. At Waterloo, he was ADC to Lord Uxbridge. He was an experienced officer, who had fought in around 16 general engagements previously and who later, when recalling his experiences, found Waterloo brought him rather indistinct memories, from the confusion of the day and the wound he had suffered. He toured the cavalry outposts with Uxbridge at daybreak on the 18th and was later invited by Lieutenant Colonel Sir Robert Hill of the Blues to join the advance of the Heavy Brigade in their assault on Drouet d'Erlon's Corps. Hill was much amused at the extremely ugly expression that Thornhill made at a cuirassier attacking him. Thornhill fell and was stunned after falling from his shot horse. A bit later, attending Wellington and Uxbridge, he recounted,

> '...I was knocked off the perch by a cannon-shot which carried off a portion of my neck, paralysed my right ear and right nostril, and you will say the right side of my memory also.'[144]

Thornhill probably had his right facial (VII cranial) nerve permanently damaged, giving him a paralysis of his facial muscles. He was personally honoured by the Prince Regent, promoted to lieutenant colonel for his actions at Waterloo and died in 1851.

---

[144] Siborne H.T. (1983), *Waterloo Letters*, pp. 16-17.

William Thornhill in later years.
(Courtesy Mr Clifford Mansfield and the Thornhill family)

10th Hussars

Major the Hon. Frederick Howard

The third son of Frederick, 5th Earl of Carlisle, by Lady Margaret Granville-Leveson, daughter of the 1st Duke of Stafford, Howard was killed whilst leading his squadron during one of the last cavalry advances at the battle. He was ordered by General Vivian to assault a square of the Imperial Guard, a hopeless venture. He was shot in the mouth and fell from his horse where he was bludgeoned to death with a musket butt belonging to one of the Guard. He was buried near the spot where he had fallen, but was later disinterred for re-burial in Streatham, then later at Castle Howard in Yorkshire.[145] As one of the last officer casualties of Waterloo, he is memorialised in Waterloo village.

---

[145] Adkin M. (2001), p. 222.

11th Light Dragoons

Captain James Alfred Schreiber

There were two Schreiber brothers at Waterloo. Captain James Alfred Schreiber the fourth son of William Schreiber, was born at Wickham Market in 1789. He joined the 11th Light Dragoons in 1806. Promoted a lieutenant in 1808, he had Peninsular service. He was badly wounded at Waterloo by a round shot that 'broke his charger's back' at the same moment, thus he probably suffered a torso or leg injury. He died a lieutenant colonel in 1840. His brother, the sixth son, a twin, served in the same regiment and also had his mount shot from under him at Waterloo. He likewise retired a lieutenant colonel after 1867.

Colonel Frederick Ponsonby receives his most serious wound at the hands of a French lancer. (Author's collection)

12th Light Dragoons

Colonel the Honourable Frederick Ponsonby

Colonel Ponsonby, who commanded the 12th Light Dragoons at the battle, was severely hurt and his tale over the night after the battle typifies the behaviour of vengeful, greedy, but also compassionate, combatants. Also one can feel with this man's experiences, the great fear and loneliness of isolation in a hostile environment when injured. Whilst charging into the French, repelling d'Erlon's great infantry assault, Ponsonby received two severe sabre wounds, a lance thrust through the left chest and several other lesser injuries. He described his plight,

'In the mêlée I was disabled instantly in both arms, [he dropped his sabre and his reins] then, next, some of his men were cut down near him and upon,] '…receiving a blow on my head from a sabre, I was thrown senseless on my face to the ground. Recovering, [and able to move away], I raised myself a little to look around, when a lancer passing by exclaimed, "Tu n'est pas mort, coquin," and stuck his lance through my back.' This deprived Ponsonby of his speech. 'My head dropped, the blood gushed into my mouth, a little difficulty in breathing came on [the lance had pierced chest wall and lung tissue, introducing air and blood into his thorax and causing blood to enter his bronchi (air tubes)], and I thought all was over.

Not long afterwards, …. a tirailleur came up to plunder me, threatening to take my life (at this stage he could only make a slight noise, to prove he was alive). I told him that he might search me … he found three dollars (and his cigars) … [He] was no sooner gone than another came for the same purpose; but assuring him that I had been plundered already, he left me … shortly afterwards an officer … stooped down and addressed me, saying, he feared I was badly wounded…. [I] expressed a wish to be removed to the rear. He said it was against the order to remove even their own men (for, he said, the Duke of Wellington was dead and six British battalions had surrendered) … I complained of thirst, and he held his brandy bottle to my lips, directing one of his men to lay me straight on my side, and place a knapsack under my head: he then passed on into the action, and I shall never know to whose generosity I was indebted, as I conceive, for my life - of what rank he was I cannot say, he wore a blue great coat. By and by another tirailleur came and knelt and fired over me, loading and firing many times, and conversing with great gaiety all the while; at last he ran off saying, "vous serez bien aise d'etendre que nous allons nous retirer; bon jour, mon ami" While the battle continued in that part, several of the wounded men and dead bodies near me, were hit with the balls, which came very thick in that place.' It was dusk and there was intense artillery noise, when two squadrons of Prussian cavalry [pursuing the French army off the field] both of them two deep, passed over me in full trot, lifting me from the ground and tumbling me about cruelly; … had a gun come that way it would have done for me ….

I thought the night would never end. Much about this time I found a soldier of the Royals lying across my legs, who had probably crawled there in his agony; his weight, convulsive motions, noises and the air running through a wound in his side [probably another victim of a French lance or sabre], distressed me greatly, the latter circumstance most of all, as the case was [similar to] my own. It was not a dark night, and the Prussians were wandering about to plunder; … several of them came and looked at me and passed on; at length, one stopped to examine me. I told him as well as I could (for I could say but little in German) that I was a British officer, and had been plundered already; he did not desist, however, and pulled me about roughly, before he left me. About an hour before midnight I saw a soldier in an

English [British] uniform coming towards me; Ponsonby told him there would be a reward if the soldier stayed to guard over him. He said he belonged to the 40th Regiment, but had missed it. He released me from the dying man [who actually made it to a hospital the next day]. Being unarmed he took up a [French] sword from the ground, and stood over me, pacing backwards and forwards. (Having begged leave to go off and find the sword, he assured the Colonel, "And then, your Honour, …I'll engage the devil himself won't come near you). At eight o'clock in the morning, some English [British] were seen at a distance … a cart came for me. I was placed in it and carried to a farm-house, about a mile and a half distant, and laid in the bed from which poor Gordon (as I understood afterwards) had just been carried out; the jolting of the cart, and the difficulty of breathing, were very painful. I had received seven wounds; a surgeon slept in my room, and I was saved [!] by continual bleeding, one hundred and twenty ounces [3.5 litres] in two days, besides the great loss of blood on the field.'[146]

On the 10 August Deputy Inspector Hume examined Ponsonby. He described a serious sabre injury to the right arm, exposing bone, an open wound of the right chest, which had broken the sixth rib and several other cuts on his head, shoulder and left arm. Dr Hume was concerned about his slow progress.[147]

The French officer who had assisted Ponsonby was Baron de Laussat and by an incredible coincidence, years later, whilst Sir Frederick was Governor of Malta, he hosted a levée and none other than the Baron was presented to him! Sir Frederick went on to have a successful military career and became a major general.

13th Light Dragoons
Lieutenant George Doherty
There were three Dohertys in this regiment all of whom served at Waterloo. Patrick Doherty was a lieutenant colonel and commanded. This promotion was facilitated by the fact that 22 officers of the regiment died of Yellow Fever in St. Domingo. He died in 1837. Captain Joseph Doherty, the first son of the colonel, was hurt at Waterloo, survived and died prematurely in Bangalore in 1819. The second son of Patrick Doherty had served in the Peninsula. Not quite as lucky at Waterloo as his brother, George was severely wounded in the head, and also was struck by a ball, which was stopped and flattened by the interposition of his watch. He had taken out his watch to remark the time, when the regiment was ordered to advance: and not being able to return it, he put it into the breast of his jacket, and thus providentially his life was saved. He died in Dublin in 1835.

15th Hussars
Major Edwin Griffith
Major Edwin is memorialised on a stone tablet in the chapel at Waterloo. He was shot in the chest, whilst leading the regiment to the charge. Ironically and by sheer

---

146 Mudford W. (1817), *An Historical Account of the Campaign in the Netherlands in 1815, under His Grace the Duke of Wellington etc.*, pp. 287-289.
147 Mudford W (1817), p. 289.

coincidence, his cousin, Watkin Griffith also served as a major of light dragoons (the 29th), and was also killed fighting under Wellington in 1803 at the action of Laswaree, in India. They both received fatal cannon shots in the thorax. Their memorials are in Mold parish church in North Wales.

Sacred to the Memory

of WATKIN GRIFFITH Efq; of Rhual, Major in the 29th Regt of Light Dragoons, which he commanded on the Glorious, but fatal 1ft of November 1803, on the Plains of HINDOSTAN, and having led it on to three moft defperate Charges, was struck by a Cannon ball on the Breaft. and Inftantly expired. in the 30th Year of his Age.

His Remains were Interred, with all Military honours, at the Village of LASWAREE, near the field of Battle.

Peace to the Brave

Memorial to Major Watkin Griffith of the 29th Light Dragoons who was killed by cannon shot at Laswaree in India. (Courtesy of the parish church, Mold)

Sacred to the Memory
Of Thomas Griffith Esqre of Rhual
who died,
June 18th 1811.
Of Henrietta Maria his Wife, who died
June 18th 1813.
And of Edwin their youngest Son,
Major in the 15th Light Dragoons
Who, on a day so Fatal to his family
June 18th 1815
fell, in the thirtieth year of his Age
piercd in the breast by five honourable wounds, while
gallantly leading his Regiment, which he commanded
to a charge of a body of French, in the sanguinary
and ever memorable battle of Waterloo.
His remains were inter'd by his afflicted Compan[...]
in Arms on the field of arduous conflict.
Peace to the Good and Brave.

Memorial to Major Edwin Griffith of the 15th Light Dragoons who was also killed by a cannon shot to his chest at Waterloo.
(Courtesy of the parish church, Mold)

Captain Joseph Thackwell

Brother officer of the above, Joseph Thackwell, of Moreton Court, Worcester had been involved with the 1798 Irish revolt and ultimately served in the 15th, for a total of 32 years, during 12 of which he commanded the regiment. He had behaved gallantly in Granada in the Peninsula, repelling 200 French dragoons with only 50 troopers. At Waterloo, when involved in a charge, he was hit in the left forearm, but he instantly seized the bridle with his right hand, in which was his sword, and still dashed on at the head of his regt., the command of which had devolved on him (Lieutenant-Colonel Dalrymple had been wounded). Another shot struck the same arm, but he immediately seized the bridle with his teeth. At the close of the day, his left arm was amputated close to the shoulder. For this, he received a pension of £300. He subsequently had useful service in Afghanistan and India. He died in 1859.

16th Light Dragoons

Lieutenant Colonel James Hay

Hay had a distinguished career in the Peninsula - at Espesia, he took 70 Lancers de Berg prisoners, and was mentioned in dispatches and awarded a gold medal and clasp. He had his right arm broken at Salamanca. At Waterloo he was so seriously injured (injuries unknown) that he could not be moved from the field hospital for eight days. He died in Ireland in 1854.

18th Hussars

Sergeant John Taylor

A somewhat macabre act of vengeance perhaps underlines the stuff of which tough NCO troopers were made. Taylor served in Captain Ellis's troop and while at the charge against cuirassiers, he made an ineffectual slash at a Frenchman's head. The cuirassier cried out in excited derision, "Ha, Ha!" Taylor parried a hard cut from the Frenchman and thrust his sabre into the mouth of the cuirassier, who fell immediately from his mount. The conqueror loudly reposted, "Ha, Ha!"[148]

Sergeant Taylor wreaks his terrible revenge.(Author's collection)

---

[148] Dalton C, (1890) *The Waterloo Roll Call*, p. 229.

The Inn (Le Roi d'Espagne) in Genappe and upstairs garret, used as a hospital, where Henry Hardinge had his hand amputated on the night of the 16 June - also where General Duhesme died. (Author's collection)

Chapter 7:
British Infantry Casualties

1ˢᵗ Foot Guards

Captain (Lt. Col.) William Miller

Captain Miller was severely wounded at Quatre Bras. While resting after his injury, he sent for his colleague, Colonel Charles Thomas - a hero of Salamanca. He said to Thomas, "I feel I am mortally wounded, but I am pleased to think it is my fate rather than yours, whose life is involved in that of your young wife." After a pause he said, "I should like to see the colours of the regiment before I quit them forever." They were brought and waved around his wounded body. His countenance brightened, he smiled, declared himself well satisfied and was carried from the field. There is a memorial at Waterloo to this gallant officer. Sadly, poor Thomas was also killed - at Waterloo.[149]

Captain (Lt. Col.) Sir Henry Hardinge

Henry Hardinge was the third son of the Reverend Henry Hardinge, the rector of Stanhope, County Durham. He had served throughout the Peninsular campaigns, and was, for most of that time, Deputy Quartermaster General for the Portuguese army. In the campaigns of 1815, he acted as a liaison officer to the Prussian forces, keeping the Duke informed of intentions and events. He was present at the Battle of Ligny, where he was severely wounded in the left hand. One account reads, 'On the night of the 16 June 1815, he lay in a wretched hut with his amputated left hand lying by his left side.' In 1843, he was made Colonel-in-Chief of the 57ᵗʰ Regiment (the 'Die Hards'). In 1846, he was created a viscount and rendered valuable service in the East Indies. Promoted Commander in Chief at home in 1852 and elevated to the rank of field-marshal in 1855, he died the following year.[150]

Lieutenant Robert Adair

Prior to his injury at Waterloo, Adair had dispatched one or two French cavalrymen who had attempted to enter an infantry square. His thigh was irreparably damaged by a roundshot, with splintered bone ends protruding. Assistant Surgeon Gilder had attended Adair probably in the infantry square (although Gilder was but an assistant surgeon, he was just the sort of man to be sent into the front line). Gilder seemed to have had trouble with the operation, since his knife was blunted from previous operations. As Adair's agony went on, he jested grimly with the struggling surgeon, "Take your time Mr Carver." Adair remained in considerable pain after the battlefield amputation. Ensign Rees Howell Gronow visited Adair just before the latter's death in either Waterloo or Brussels. The exhausted Adair had died from exsanguination.[151]

---

[149] Dalton C, (1890) *The Waterloo Roll Call*, p.95.
[150] Dalton C, (1890) *The Waterloo Roll Call*, p.95.
[151] Fletcher, Ian (2001) *A Desperate Business, Wellington, the British Army and the Waterloo Campaign*, p. 72.

Coldstream Foot Guards

Captain the Hon. Edward Acheson

Edward Acheson was the 2nd son of Arthur, 1st Viscount Gosford. He had a fortunate escape while defending part of the chestnut woods in front of Chateau Hougoumont, which were under a severe assault by French infantry,

> 'The enemy made a tremendous attack, and, at the first [counter] charge, the colonel's horse was shot dead. He fell under his horse, and was considerably stunned by the fall, in which situation he must have lain some time, as the enemy passed and re-passed, regarding him as dead. When he recovered he found himself a prisoner by the weight of his horse. He extricated himself with difficulty by drawing his leg out of his boot.'

He survived the 18 June and died in 1828.[152]

3/14th Foot

Ensign George Thomas Keppel, (later the 6th Earl of Albemarle)

George Keppel was to become the 6th Earl of Albemarle and followed in a line of respected and renowned military and naval forbears. A certain Mrs Ward, the daughter of the colonel of the battalion (Colonel Francis Tidy), wrote a memoir of her father and recorded the following of George,

George Keppel, 6th Earl of Albermarle in later life.

(Author's collection)

> 'Mr Keppel was sitting on a drum just in front of my father's mare (i.e. Colonel Tidy's mount) when she was shot - he was even stroking the poor thing's face that the ball struck her down, broke the bit of the bridle and knocked him head over heels, drum and all. The animal plunging in her agony, threw the square into great confusion, and her misery was speedily put to an end by the soldiers' bayonets.'

Albemarle was eventually promoted to a full general and died in 1891.[153] Such incidents remind us of the high morbidity and mortality amongst the equine combatants.

---

[152] Dalton C, (1890) *The Waterloo Roll Call*, p. 102.
[153] Dalton C, (1890) *The Waterloo Roll Call*, p. 116.

Sergeant Samuel Goddard

Occasionally, there were gallant gestures on the field by both sides. Such was the case with Samuel Goddard. He was with an advanced party of skirmishers and at the time of Ney's great cavalry assaults, he and his men were passed by a group of cuirassiers. The men of the 3/14th fired at them and emptied the saddles of a few troopers. One trooper fell after his horse was shot down. A comrade bravely returned at great risk to offer the dismounted man his stirrup. A light infantryman of the 14th, named Whitney had just killed a cuirassier and was reloading to shoot the rescuer. Goddard interfered and shouted out, "No, Whitney don't fire, let him off, he is a noble fellow."[154]

Quarter Master Alexander Ross's wife

When the above Lord Albemarle wrote of his experiences of Waterloo, he also mentioned a stalwart woman of the regiment, Mrs Ross, the wife of the battalion's quartermaster, Alexander Ross. Albemarle wrote,

> 'For some time after the firing had begun, Mrs Ross, our quartermaster's wife, remained with the regiment. She was no stranger to a battlefield, and had received a severe wound in Whitelocke's disastrous retreat from Buenos Ayres [1807] at the time her husband was a sergeant in the 95th. She was at length persuaded to withdraw, and retired to the belfry of Waterloo church.'[155]

23rd Foot

Lieutenant Colonel Sir Henry Walton Ellis

The son of Major General John Joyner Ellis, Sir Henry was a native of Worcester. Walton Ellis was a gallant and much loved commander, who had served in Holland, Egypt, America, the West Indies, Spain, Portugal and France. He was wounded during the sanguinary affair at Albuera on 16 May 1811, having received agonising trauma to his third and little finger of his right (bridle) hand. At Waterloo, he was mortally wounded while in an infantry square, which was receiving cavalry. He was shot in the chest by a French carbine. He refused any assistance from his men who, he said, were much needed where they were. The square opened and as his charger jumped a hedge, he was thrown. One of his men carried him to a small outhouse, where his wound was dressed. On the night of the next day, the hovel caught fire, and he was with difficulty rescued by Assistant Surgeon Munro of the 23rd. He died the following day and was buried at Braine l'Alleud, within a few hundred yards from where he fell. He is memorialised in Worcester Cathedral.[156]

---

[154] Dalton C, (1890) *The Waterloo Roll Call*, p. 225.
[155] Dalton C, (1890) *The Waterloo Roll Call*, p.116.
[156] Broughton-Mainwaring R (1889), *Historical Record of the Royal Welch Fusiliers*, pp. 140-1.

Memorial to Colonel Sir Henry Walton Ellis in Worcester Cathedral.
(Author's collection)

27th Foot

The 27th Foot took severe punishment at Waterloo (casualty rate, 478 of 698 - 69%) and this is well reflected in the attrition rate of the officers. Nine of nineteen officers were killed or wounded (56%). Captain George Holmes was the senior officer killed in the battle. A small French ball from a shell's air-burst entered his right chest, near his spine. He would have bled into his chest and had a significant air leak (pneumothorax) from disruption of his lung tissue. Sadly, he died and his wife created a rather tender, but macabre, memorial to her husband. She had the vertebral bone, which had been damaged by the missile, removed from his body, dried and varnished. The body of the vertebra was hollowed out and set in silver. The whole was mounted in a red morocco case, along with the round that ended his life.

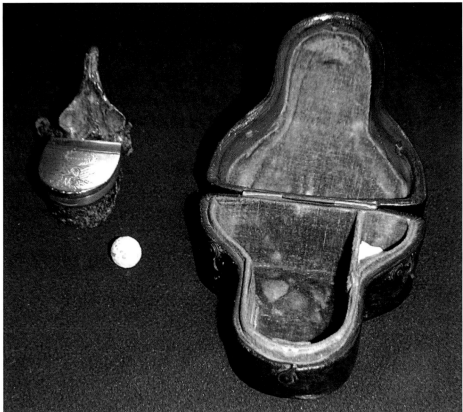

The second thoracic vertebra of Captain George Holmes, killed by a lead ball from a shell exploding near him. The missile tore away the right hand pedicle of bone, which articulated with the second rib. The round entered his chest and caused a fatal haemopneumothorax (a collection of blood and air).
(Author's collection)

Lieutenant Thomas Craddock

Son of William Craddock of Loughborough, in Leicestershire, he had served with the battalion through the Peninsula. After the surrender of the garrison at Badajoz, Lieutenant Craddock entered the town at the head of his regiment. He survived the assault on New Orleans in 1815. At Waterloo, a ball passed right through his cheeks carrying away the roof of his mouth. He survived this unpleasant wound, was appointed a Knight of Windsor in 1842 and died in 1851.[157]

28th Foot

Lieutenant James Deares

This zealous officer accompanied the cavalry in pursuit of the enemy at the end of the day. He was on foot and attacked every Frenchman he met. He was severely wounded, taken prisoner and stripped of all of his clothes except his shirt, in which state of dress he joined his regiment the next day.

Lieutenant George Ingram

This fellow officer of the above had played a distinguished role at Albuera. He was wounded in the thigh at Waterloo and suffered an amputation of his leg, which was followed by a surgical misadventure. Clearly the postoperative bleeding was not adequately controlled, so a tourniquet was placed above the operation site. Demonstrating the dangers of poorly controlled arterial haemorrhage, the canvas strap must have snapped, shifted, or the buckle may have become unfastened during the night and the officer bled to death. Memorialised at the village of Waterloo.[158]

2/30th Foot

Lieutenant Colonel Alexander Hamilton

This officer had performed well in Egypt and in the Peninsula. Hamilton had received the gold medal for Salamanca. He received a severe leg wound at Quatre Bras, after which he received a personal commendation from Sir Thomas Picton. It is speculation, but I feel he was probably nursed in the large farm at Quatre Bras and there prepared for amputation. Three times the screw tourniquet was applied and three times it was removed again, since the surgeon (probably Surgeon Elkington) had been called away to more urgent cases. Since the leg had ceased to bleed and was stable in its damage, the surgeon(s) decided to take a chance. The patient and his limb recovered. His whole life service had been with the 'old three tens'. He died in 1838.

---

[157] Dalton C, (1890) *The Waterloo Roll Call*, p. 121.
[158] Dalton C, (1890) *The Waterloo Roll Call*, p. 125.

Young Lientenant Lockwood
(Courtesy Mr Clifford Mansfield)

Purefoy Lockwood was another Quatre Bras casualty. Hit in the left forehead, a musket ball had been split in two as it crashed into his frontal bone, entering a frontal (air) sinus. The risks of infection, epilepsy and chronic discharge of purulent material were high. One of the surgeons of the 30th explored the head wound at the Quatre Bras farm field hospital and retrieved a part of the split missile. His wound was dressed and he was sent back to Brussels. There he was trephined, further portions of bone and the rest of the ball were extracted. He was not content with the ugly dent in his head, which was clearly visible and wished to cover the skull defect. The wound was infected and lay partially open with intermittent discharge. He decided the best way to protect and hide the area was to have an oval silver plate made, perforated with small holes to let the wound 'breathe' and let out any thin sero-purulent discharge. On the plate he had inscribed, with robust humour, 'bomb-proof! The plate was held in place with a black silk bandana. He was later appointed Captain of Invalids of Kilmainham Hospital. King George IV asked to meet 'Bomb proof Lockwood', when visiting the hospital.

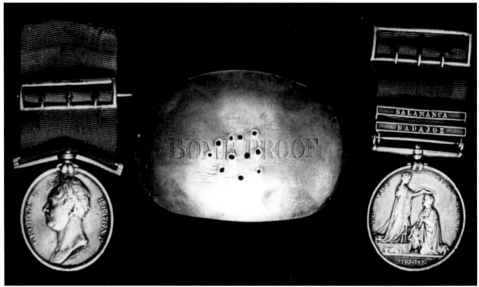

Plate and medals of Young Lockwood. (Courtesy Mr Clifford Mansfield)

33rd Foot

Captain Joseph M. Harty

Harty had joined the army in 1807 and had served at Bourbon and the Île de France, (1810) also in the campaigns in Germany and Holland, including the capture of Bergen-op-Zoom. He had survived the severe contest at Quatre Bras, where the regiment had been hard pressed. He was a company commander at Waterloo, where he suffered a musket ball injury in one of his thighs. The missile probably missed bone since he was not amputated.

The gorget worn by Major Harty, wounded in the thigh at Waterloo.
(Author's collection)

Captain John Haigh

When the 33rd formed square during the action at Quatre Bras, they became very exposed to French ordnance. Lieutenant Arthur Gore, a tall officer of the grenadier company was struck in the head by a round shot, covering some fellow officers in blood and brain tissue. Captain John Haigh, soon observed a side of the square formed by number five company folding in. He encouraged his men and shouted out,

> *"Keep up, keep up; I say keep up". The words were vibrating on his lips, when a cannon ball hit him on the abdomen, and cut him nearly in twain. He fell on his back; the separation between body and soul was most appalling. His eyes strained as if they would leap from their sockets, and the quiver of the lip with the strong convulsion of his whole frame, showed unquestionably how unwilling his spirit was to be driven in this ruthless way from her clay tenement.'*

Thomas Haigh, John's brother, was devastated by the loss of his brother thus. He was later killed himself.[159]

1/40th Foot

Captain William Fisher

This officer had his head removed by a round shot at Waterloo, during the afternoon, whilst standing next to the battalion's colours. Perhaps exhibiting the occasionally frail relationships between the rank and file with their misdemeanours and the less popular company officers, a private of Fisher's company sardonically remarked, "There goes my best friend." This motivated a nervous, warm-hearted but rather naïve subaltern of the same company in a moment of nervous support, "I will be as good a friend to you", as he took the place of the dead captain. The men of the company gave a grim laugh as they knew what the young officer did not, namely that the private, an unkempt soldier 'though brave in combat', had constantly been harangued by Fisher, who had tried to improve the private, named Marten.[160]

---

[159] Hope Pattison F, (1997) *Personal Recollections of the Waterloo Campaign*, (edited by Elmer R), pp.6-7.
[160] Lawrence W, (edited by Bankes, NG) (1886), *The Autobiography of Sergeant William Lawrence, a Hero of the Peninsular and Waterloo Campaigns*, pp. 210-211.

42nd Foot

Lieutenant Colonel Sir Robert Macara

Robert Macara was born in 1759, in Atholl, so was 56 when commanding the 42nd at Quatre Bras. A somewhat harsh disciplinarian, he had served in Ireland, India and the Peninsula. After arrival at Quatre Bras he led a spirited charge of the battalion, but then a confused mass of French and Brunswick cavalry crashed down on the 42nd amongst tall rye crops and whilst properly forming square, Macara was left outside, as the rear face closed up. He was hit by friendly fire, which he had ordered his men to pour on the French horse. So wounded, he was carried away by four privates, who were aiming for the field dressing station at Quatre Bras. The circumstances of his death exhibit all the worst type of behaviour in excited and desperate combat. A squadron of French lancers surrounded the sad party, having realised that this was an important field officer and, totally ignoring the unwritten decencies of war, lanced to death the wounded Macara and his escorts. A French lance had entered Macara's brain from under the chin.[161]

Colonel Macara is killed whilst severely wounded at the action at Quatre Bras.
(Author's collection)

Captain George Davidson

In the same battalion, there was just one major, Robert Henry Dick, yet in an interesting account of a major's plight at Quatre Bras, it is commonly presumed that the following saga referred not to Dick, but to Brevet Major George Davidson. There was another account, ascribing this tale to Captain Archibald Menzies of the same regiment, who had been severely wounded, but, this officer was not then of brevet rank. The story went,

---

[161] Grant C. and Youens M. (1971), *The Black Watch*, Osprey Publishing, p. 22.

'Major ---, of the 42ⁿᵈ preferring to fight on foot, in front of his men, had given his horse to hold to a little drummer-boy. After severe fighting, he fell wounded near a brave private, Donald MacIntosh, also injured. The drummer left his horse to attend to his friend Donald. A French lancer attempted to seize the horse, on which the prostrate Donald exclaimed, "Hoot man, ye mauna tak that beast, it belongs to our captain here."

The lancer, little heeding this, seized the horse. Donald with a last expiring effort, loaded his musket and shot the lancer dead. A French cavalry officer [a cuirassier], seeing the major bestirring himself, rode up and attempted to dispatch him with his sword. As he stooped from his saddle, the major seized his leg, and managed to pull him off his horse upon him. Another lancer observing this struggle, galloped up and tried to spear the major and relieve his officer; but the former, by a sudden jerk, and desperate exertion, placed the French officer uppermost, who received the mortal thrust below his cuirass and continued lying upon the major's body for near ten minutes sword in hand. A pause in the battle permitted some men of the 42ⁿᵈ to carry their officer into the square of the 92ⁿᵈ, [where presumably there was a surgeon less busy] where he was found to have received sixteen wounds.'

Davidson did not recover from his injuries and died shortly afterwards, in Brussels.[162]

2/44ᵗʰ Foot

Lieutenant Colonel John M Hamerton

Typifying the loyalty to and devotion of some NCOs for their senior officers (and no doubt with some hope of recognition!), was the story of Lieutenant Colonel John Hamerton of the 2/44ᵗʰ at Waterloo. Hamerton, a cornet at 15 years of age, had served in the Low Countries, West Indies, Egypt and the Peninsula, during which he commanded the 1/44ᵗʰ Foot. At Waterloo he took over command of the 2ⁿᵈ battalion. He was presumed dead after receiving severe head and thigh wounds. A devoted sergeant, named Ryan brought the colonel's lifeless and limp body to (probably) the farm of Mont St Jean, where he slowly recovered and was convalesced home. Reaching the rank of general, Hamerton died in Ireland in 1855.

Ensign James Christie

One of the most agonising and notorious wounds of Quatre Bras, indeed of the whole campaigns, was that inflicted on the senior ensign of the 2/44ᵗʰ, James Christie. A bold French lancer charged at the colours of the 44ᵗʰ, one of which was held by Christie. A lance passed through the young man's left eye, from above down, passing out through the lower jaw. The Frenchman tried to seize the colour, but incredibly, with this agonising wound, Christie threw himself down on the colour, thus making it difficult for the lancer to retrieve it. As Christie fell the lance tore out a fragment of the silk colour, which was a slight trophy for the lancer to escape with. This was not to be. He was shot and fell from his mount and was then bayoneted by Christie's men. Amazingly, Christie survived and today he surely would have been awarded the highest award for gallantry.

---

[162] Dalton C, (1890) *The Waterloo Roll Call*, p.141.

2/69th Foot

Ensign (Volunteer) Christopher Clarke

A brave role model for a volunteer was Ensign Christopher Clarke, who was a cadet at the RMC. He killed three cuirassiers at Quatre Bras, but paid for his tenacity, by receiving 22 sabre cuts. He died in 1831, as a subaltern in the 33rd Foot.

Quartermaster Matthew Stevens

Several units had a claim to have served under both Wellington and Nelson. In an interesting and illustrious career, Stevens was a soldier, who 18 years prior to Waterloo, fought at the action off Cape St Vincent (14 February 1797). Whilst serving under Commodore Nelson, he had, with his musket butt, smashed in the upper quarter gallery window of the 84-gun Spanish line of battle ship, *San Nicholas*. He thus gained entry for Nelson, into the Spanish captain's cabin and thus accessed the quarter-deck of the vessel. A Scot with a wicked turn of humour, he was a man whose senses were probably dulled by years of combat. On the day of Waterloo, when a round shot decapitated a man, presumably with little battle experience standing by Steven's side, he was heard to remark quietly, "Aweel, it is time for a respectable non-combatant to gang awa!"[163] Stevens died in India, still a quartermaster, in 1821

71st Foot

Lieutenant Robert Lind

Lieutenant Robert Lind belonged to a 'respectable' family from County Antrim. He received a round of case in his chest at Waterloo. The missile was successfully removed, having been cut from his shoulder region. It weighed 10ozs and Lind had it mounted and enclosed in a band of silver. He lived until 1851 and died at Waterloo Cottage, Cookstown, County Antrim.

---

[163] Dalton C, (1890) *The Waterloo Roll Call*, p.156.

2/73rd Foot

Lieutenant Colonel William George Harris

Another great example of indomitable courage and leadership was shown by Colonel William Harris at Waterloo. Whilst serving under his father, General Sir George Harris, of Seringapatam renown, William had been one of the first men into the breach of that city. The 73rd Foot were decimated at Waterloo, sustaining 336 of 568 casualties (60%). At one stage there was a delay or hesitation in the 73rd closing a gap on one side of their square, which had been cut out by the 'relentless iron'. Harris drew up his mount and pushing his horse lengthwise across the gap proclaimed, "Well, my lads, if you won't, I must." It was said that the horse was then led back to its proper position and the ranks closed up by men, 'still more devoted than before.' He was fortunate not to be killed.[164] Colonel William became Lieutenant General Lord Harris and died in 1845.

Lieutenant Joseph William H. Strachan

Sergeant Morris's *Recollections* remind us of 'blue on blue' injuries. Lieutenant JWH Strachan had just caught up with his battalion and was marching behind his company. The company then retired in line and as the men had all right-about faced, he was now in front of his men. These files were carrying their muskets at the trail. The firelock of the man immediately behind Strachan (Private Jeremiah Bates) discharged by accident and the ball passed into the officer's back and fatally pierced his heart. Surgeon Duncan McDiarmid (see below) pronounced the poor man dead. The trigger (it is interesting that the flint was at full cock) had been forced back by an entangled stalk of corn.[165]

79th Foot

Surely one of the hardest hit battalions on the fields of Quatre Bras and Waterloo, the 79th suffered 479 casualties of 675 effectives (71%). However, the striking issue is the officer casualty rate, 30 (five killed) out of 41 combatant officers, a staggering 73%.

---

[164] Dalton C, (1890) *The Waterloo Roll Call*, p.162.
[165] Morris T, (Edited by Selby J) (1967) *The Recollections of Sergeant Morris*, p. 72.

1/95th Foot (Rifles)

Ned Costello

Wounded in the action on the Coa River in the summer of 1810, where he had received a ball in the right knee and also a spent ball in his thigh, Ned Costello was hit again two days before Waterloo. As he emerged from a wood at Quatre Bras on the 16 June, 'a regiment of French infantry on our right received us with running fire. I was in the act of taking aim at some of our opposing skirmishers, when a ball struck my trigger finger, tearing it off. It also turned the trigger aside. A second shot passed through the mess-tin on my knapsack.' He made his way to a farm building in the rear, which was soon crammed with the wounded of Costello's division (the 2nd). That night lying on a bed of hay, he commented, 'To sleep was impossible with the anguish of my shattered hand, and the groans of my fellow-sufferers.'[166]

Captain William Johnstone

A native of Dumfriesshire, William joined the 52nd Foot in 1805 and subsequently was promoted to lieutenant in the 95th. He commanded one of four companies at the action at Barba del Puerco in the spring of 1810 and was one of the storming officers at Cuidad Rodrigo. Surviving unscathed from this, he preceded the forlorn hope at Badajoz, in order to lasso the chevaux-de-frise. He and his whole group were shot down before they even reached the obstacle. Johnstone was hit in the arm, and survived. He was wounded at Quatre Bras and also at Waterloo and yet again lived to tell the tale - the nature of his wounds unknown. He died in 1836.[167]

2nd Lieutenant Allen Stewart

A chivalrous and daring highlander, who singled out a French officer at Waterloo and had a contest with him. Stewart's sword broke off at the hilt, but he closed with the Frenchman, whom he 'finished in an instant'. He later served in the Buffs, but ended his life in the Norwich Lunatic Asylum in 1847.

1st Lieutenant George Simmons

Simmons had started training for medicine before he joined the army. He had served as an assistant surgeon in the South Lincolnshire Militia, but was commissioned into the 95th. He was another victim of the action on the Coa River in 1810. He had received a ball in the thigh and, while reaching for his own field tourniquet strap, he passed out. Captain Napier took off his neckerchief and gave it to a sergeant, who used a ramrod to tighten the cloth round Simmons's thigh. Both the sergeant and Napier were wounded whilst rescuing Simmons. After convalescence at Belem, Simmons returned to active duty. At Waterloo, he served as a lieutenant in Captain Beckwith's company, in which all the officers had become casualties during the battle.

This experienced young officer was hit on the trunk by a ball during the action. The missile passed in through the right side of the lower chest wall, it then went on through the lower chest/diaphragm and the very top of the abdomen. It came to rest

---

[166] Costello (1997), p. 281.
[167] Dalton C, (1890) *The Waterloo Roll Call*, p. 172.

under the skin near the right nipple. A surgeon companion of Simmons cut down on the ball and with ease extracted the ball. He then bled Simmons a quart of blood (1080ml). Incredibly, Simmons rode around 12 miles to his billet, where he was bled another quart and wrapped in poultices. Inevitably, he became septic and was bled another four quarts over the next three days! He was so weak (from sepsis and profound anaemia) he could not lift his head from his pillow without fainting. Despite this, and we do have to marvel at the faith of soldiery in the illogical practice of venesection, he remarked, 'the lancet was the only thing to save me so I was bled again very largely.' His abdomen was swollen and painful and, 'bleeding was the only remedy for it'. The surgeon became reticent to bleed his patient much more so (having obtained a second opinion and also being fearful for his patient's life) applied 30 leeches (which would have extracted around 600 ml more blood). These caused him agony, when placed over the wound, 'I kicked, roared, and swore and tried to drag them off, but my hands were held.' He was now given up for dead by a surgeon friend. As he lay dying his thoughts were for the provision for his family. Three days later, a month or so after wounding, a massive subphrenic abscess (a large collection of pus under the diaphragm) discharged from his abdomen into the bed. Three months later, he was up and about, weak, emaciated with massively swollen legs (a result of protein deficiency, chronic heart failure, and severe anaemia). He was observed walking around supported by two young ladies! If we can believe the therapy meted out to this very brave soldier, he had been venesected (bled) around five to six litres of blood during his treatment over a week or so.[168] Simmons was, before long, evacuated back to Britain - a remarkable survivor of a severe injury.

2/95th Foot (Rifles)

Captain John Garlies McCullock

Captain McCullock was badly wounded in the shoulder, whilst on the chase after Massena's force, which was quitting Portugal in 1811. This wound deprived him of the use of the arm. Late in the afternoon of the 18 June, he lost the other arm. He received promotion to major, but as he later explained to the Duke of Wellington, '… *having no longer an arm to wield for his country,'* he was, *'yet being anxious to serve it'.* He was posted to the 2nd Garrison Battalion in December 1815. He died in 1818.[169]

Private Tom Plunkett

Tom, who had dispatched General Colbert near Cacabelos on the retreat to Corunna in late 1808, was wounded at Waterloo. While he was fighting with the 2nd battalion 95th Rifles, a ball ripped the forepeak of his cap, and,

> '*tore his forehead across, leaving a very ugly scar. I (Ned Costello) had gone wounded to the rear [via Mont St Jean Farm to a Brussels hospital] and there saw him [Plunkett] in the hands of the surgeon.*'[170]

After Waterloo, Plunkett was invalided to Britain, where he was upset at a mean pension of merely 6d a day. No doubt this dissatisfaction was fuelled by the fact that

---

[168] Crumplin M (2007), *Men of Steel*, p. 283.
[169] Dalton C, (1890) *The Waterloo Roll Call*, p. 175.
[170] Costello (1997), p. 284.

his facially disfigured wife (burned in an ammunition wagon explosion at Waterloo), had received 1 shilling a day! Tom emigrated for a brief period to Canada and returned to Britain, where he died in the mid to late 1830s.

3/95th Foot (Rifles)

1st Lieutenant Thomas Taylor Worsley

A member of an old Yorkshire family, which resided at Hovingham, Thomas had served through the Peninsular, receiving nine clasps to his General Service Medal. Worsley received such bizarre injuries, that they are almost unbelievable. At the desperate assaults on Badajoz, a ball entered his neck under his right ear, injuring the muscle that extends obliquely forward in the neck. The ball tracked out to the opposite side of his neck and was extracted. The damage to the muscle shortened it, which twisted Worsley's neck to the right (and down a little), so he suffered a 'wry' neck. He recovered however and continued serving. At Waterloo, he received a near identical injury in the opposite side of his neck, from a spent ball. This somewhat straightened his twisted neck![171] His family retained the two missiles for a while.

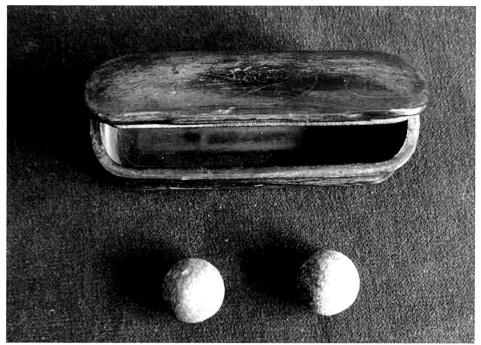

The missiles that twice damaged Lieutenant Worsley's neck.
(Author's collection)

---

[171] Crumplin M. (2007), *Men of Steel*, p. 44.

Chapter 8:
Royal Artillery Casualties

Roger's Brigade, Royal Artillery
2nd Lieutenant Richard Goodwin Wilson
Richard Wilson acquired notoriety by being very close to Picton, when the latter received his fatal wound. He became superintendent at Shoeburyness during the Crimean campaigns and died a major general in 1876.

Mercer's Troop, Royal Horse Artillery
Lieutenant John F Breton
An anecdote of this officer was recorded in Captain Cavalié Mercer's Waterloo Journal, which again reminds the reader of the sad toll amongst horses (around 2,000 equine casualties at Waterloo - about 1,500 killed),

> *'Lieutenant Breton, who already lost two horses and had mounted a troop horse, was conversing with me during a leisure moment. As his horse stood at right angles to mine, the poor jaded animal dozingly rested his muzzle on my thigh; whilst I, the better to hear amidst the infernal din, leant forward, resting my arm between his ears. In this attitude a cannon ball smashed the horse's head to atoms, and the headless trunk sank to the ground.'*

It is interesting to note that the highly successful and very wealthy civilian Sergeant Surgeon to the monarch, Sir William Astley Paston Cooper, was so moved by the horse casualties after Waterloo that he took in 20 wounded convalescent mounts to graze on his estate.

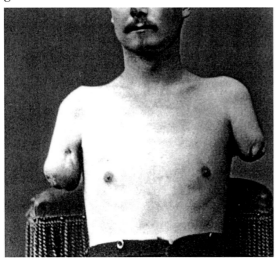

A mid 19th century bilateral arm amputation suffered by a gunner from a cannon discharge whilst the unfortunate man was ramming his piece of ordnance - similar fatal injuries were suffered by Gunner Butterworth.
(Courtesy the United States Army)

Gunner Butterworth
Butterworth was acting as a rammer on a nine-pound piece at Waterloo. Mercer recounted this poor man's fate in his journal. Butterworth had,

'just finished ramming down the shot, and was stepping back outside the wheel, when his foot stuck in the miry soil, pulling him forward the moment the gun was fired. As a man naturally does when falling, he threw out both his arms before him, and they were blown off at the elbows. He raised himself a little on his two stumps, and looked most piteously on my face. To assist him was impossible - the safety of all, everything depended on our not slackening our fire, and I was obliged to turn from him.'

Mercer soon determined that Butterworth had got up and had retired towards Mont St Jean field hospital. He exsanguinated by the side of the chausée, just missing a chance of survival.[172]

Ramsay's Troop, Royal Horse Artillery
Captain William Norman Ramsay,
Norman Ramsay was immortalised by his 'run' at Fuentes de Ônoro in 1811. He had joined Major Bull's battery RHA and served in that unit from 1811 to 1813. On 5 May 1811, Allied cavalry support was locally overwhelmed and Ramsay's battery was cut off. At the head of his battery, he cantered through the French horsemen and returned to his lines. At Vitoria, he disobeyed an order by Wellington to wait ''til he was ordered up', but some 'general' sent an aide to move him and Ramsay felt morally obliged to save a unit under threat and so moved his battery. Wellington had him arrested for disobeying orders. There was a great consternation at this and it mightily demoralised the mortified Ramsay. He was soon released and resumed his service. At Waterloo, he commanded H troop, and he was fatally shot and buried on the spot during a lull in the action, by Sir Augustus Frazer. Ramsay's last words were those of praise for two of his junior officers. His head had been carried away by a round shot. His body was re-interred in Edinburgh, as a small consolation to his grief-stricken father, who had lost his three sons in just eight months of this long war.[173]

Rocket Troop, Royal Horse Artillery
Captain Edward Whinyates,
Rising eventually to the rank of general, Edward Whinyates also became Colonel Commandant of the Royal Horse Artillery. A Devonian, who joined the artillery in 1798, he served at the Helder, the Low Countries, Madeira, Cathcart's expedition to Copenhagen and in 1810, embarked for the Peninsula, where he distinguished himself at Albuera and also in the cavalry action at Ribera. Promoted First Captain in 1813, he returned to Britain and proceeded to Belgium, where he commanded his rocket troop, which frightened many a Frenchman and horse at Waterloo. Here he had three horses shot from under him and was badly wounded in the leg and, towards the end of the day, in the left arm.[174]

---

[172] Mercer C., (1985) *Journal of the Waterloo Campaign*, pp. 172-3.
[173] Dalton C, (1890) *The Waterloo Roll Call*, pp.189-90.
[174] Dalton C, (1890) *The Waterloo Roll Call*, p.186.

Chapter 9:
King's German Legion Casualties

2nd Brigade King's German Legion

Colonel Baron Christian Ompteda (Brigade Commander)

Colonel Christian Ompteda obtained lasting admiration for his gallant and selfless performance at Waterloo. Following the capture of the farm of La Haye Sainte by the French, Wellington's centre was under considerable threat from French artillery. Around 1830hrs, when French infantry units were building up in front of him and cuirassiers lurked in support, General von Alten ordered Ompteda's brigade to attack the enemy infantry. Ompteda remonstrated, pointing out the proximity of the French cavalry. Unfortunately, von Alten and the Prince of Orange pressed home their order, wrongly advising that the cavalry to their front were Dutch! Ompteda's two nephews were with the Colonel and Ompteda requested they should be cared for by the battalion commander of the 5th Line Battalion KGL. The 5th then began its suicidal advance, at the walk, then charge, down on the French infantry. The French cavalry slaughtered all but 24 men of the German unit. Ompteda's two nephews were unwillingly led back out of danger, but the Colonel rode on, alone straight into the French infantry. As muskets were presented to bring down the gallant colonel, French officers knocked them up. Ompteda then cleared a hedge at the rear of the farm and lay about the infantry around him. Soon his horse sank and he with it. His body was later recovered, a singed ball hole in the collar of his coat implied that he had been dragged from his horse and shot in the neck at close range.[175] So tragically ended the life of one of the bravest officers of the day.

To omit the names of thousands of brave Frenchmen in their heroic sacrifice for their emperor seems callous and in no way demeans their effort and sacrifice, but space simply does not permit. Two names however have to be included as they have such a revered place in Waterloo's saga.

---

[175] Fletcher I. (2001), pp.147-9.

Chapter 10:
Two French Casualties

Service de Santé and Dr (Baron) Jean Dominique Larrey[176]

The most meritorious doctor in the French Army was Jean Larrey, who had served his Emperor faithfully and hard, right throughout this war. At Waterloo he had returned to Napoleon's call and acted as surgeon to the Imperial Guard. The aging and rather enfeebled Percy had been promoted Surgeon in Chief over Larrey's head. Bonaparte, aware of Larrey's unhappiness over this move, appointed him Surgeon to the Guard and General Headquarters. He had slept the night before, with the Emperor's staff in the farm of Le Caillou, along with Surgeon François Percy. Where Larrey spent most of his time during Sunday is uncertain. Most likely, at the start of the battle, he was on the field and later, back at the field hospital. We know that Larrey had worked some of the time in the open field, since he was seen there by Allied witnesses. He had an ambulance (a collection of medical support staff, as well as vehicles) around La Belle Alliance or at Rossome. Initially he concentrated on the wounded line soldiers, since, for the early part of the day, the Guard received few casualties. During the action, Wellington noticed Larrey and enquired, "Who is that bold fellow over there?" "That's Larrey", said some officer. Wellington then ordered, "Tell them not to fire at him. Give the brave fellow time to pick up his wounded." So saying he raised his hat in the direction of Larrey. "Whom are you saluting?" asked the Duke of Cambridge. "The honour and loyalty you see yonder," the Duke replied, pointing at the surgeon with his sword.

But mercy was not only the prerogative of the Allied Commander. Colonel Samuel Waymouth of the 2nd Life Guards, then a lieutenant, was at one time surrounded by French cavalry and was to fall prisoner. He was covered with blood and the brains of the corporal who had ridden by his side and who had just met an ugly death. A French infantryman levelled a musket at Waymouth, but Larrey knocked the firelock down. Later Larrey showed Waymouth the amputation knife he used, made in Cockspur Street, London.

At dusk on the 18th, having been advised to retire with the army and while riding in the dark, Larrey was surrounded by a few Prussian lancers. Sabre in hand (medical officers were required to remain armed at these times), Larrey fired his pistols, one at a time, at the enemy horses and darted for a gap. While he was hotly pursued, his horse was shot and he was surrounded and struck on the head and shoulders by Prussian sabres. The Prussians cantered off after the others of Larrey's party, leaving the French surgeon for dead. Larrey feebly remounted his horse, which had recovered, and as he approached the River Sambre, he was again surrounded and taken prisoner by Prussian horsemen. Some of his clothing, arms and purse, containing 40 gold napoleons, were taken. Larrey was mistaken for Bonaparte, on account of his grey watch coat and build. After being tied up, he was taken to another senior Prussian officer, who had realised that he was not the Emperor, nevertheless decided to have Larrey shot. As the firing party made ready, a Prussian regimental

---

[176] Surgeon in charge if the Imperial Headquarters and the Guard.

surgeon about to cover Larrey's eyes with adhesive tape, recognised the captive and begged for Larrey's life, the Frenchman was taken to the Grand Provost of the Prussian Army, Count von Bülow. Standing in front of the Prussian general, dishevelled and wearing only pantaloons, an overcoat, with his head swathed in bloody bandages, Larrey was sent to Marshal Blücher himself.

Larrey had saved Blücher's son's life after the latter had been severely wounded and taken prisoner during a former campaign in Austria. Blücher gave him lunch, 12 gold Frédérics d'or and sent Larrey to Louvain, with a Prussian aide. After lodging in a poor woman's house, Larrey was later moved to a wealthy advocate's dwelling. He assisted Belgian surgeons at the local hospitals for a while, then moved on to Brussels. Here, at the city's military hospital, he assisted Dr Seutin (see above), with the French casualties. He visited the British hospitals, where he noted François de Gay (see below) and recommended the patient to the care of,

> '…my honourable confrère M. Guthrie, Chief Surgeon to the English armies, whom I was unable to meet as I had to return to Louvain urgently.'

Larrey noted (no doubt reflecting the former allegiance of many Belgian folk to Napoleon),

> 'At Brussels, as in Louvain, the inhabitants vied with each other in taking in as many of the French wounded as they could; they lacked for nothing, and the most tender care was lavished upon them.'[177]

François de Gay of 45e Ligne

This courageous wounded French infantryman was amongst the casualties retrieved after the advance of the British heavy brigades of cavalry. He was probably shot whilst in the act of returning to the French lines. A round of small case or a firelock ball crashed through his buttock and exited after irreparably damaging his hip joint. Surgeon George Guthrie after due deliberation and initial hesitation by de Gay, preceded with the only and highly risky surgical option, to remove the man's right leg by disarticulation at the hip joint, a truly massive operation.

The operation was a success and the Frenchman survived. The patient had lost around a pint and a half of blood, and the wound healed after some inevitable infection. He was evacuated to the York Hospital, Chelsea, where he was visited and admired by many notable visitors. He was later removed to Paris, where he remained a convalescent at Les Invalides. There he resided, a visible tribute to Guthrie's surgical skill.[178] When de Gay announced that he was to be married, Guthrie thought it a most unwise move!

Finally, to the thousands of wounded men of all armies, our deep sympathy must go out. These few representative examples of suffering and courage enumerated above, also the efforts of all medical men, must surely complement the great military

---

[177] Dible J.H. (1970), *Napoleon's Surgeon*, p. 242.
[178] Crumplin M. (2010), *Guthrie's War - a Surgeon of the Peninsula and Waterloo*, pp. 146-8.

achievements of the Allied Armies and the sacrifice of the French Army at the hard-fought Battle of Waterloo.

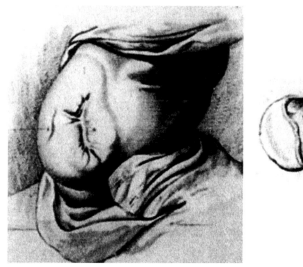
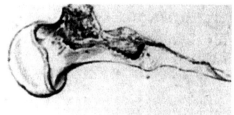

The entry wound, operation scar and detached head of the right thigh-bone (left).
(Authors collection)

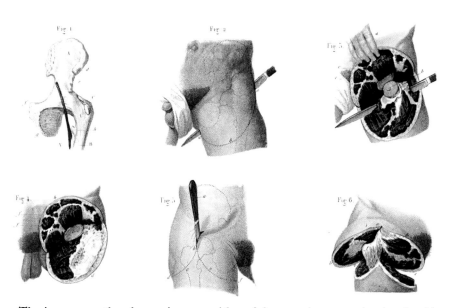

The images on the above give some idea of the massive operation involved in removing de Gay's right leg at the hip-joint. (Author's collection)

Chapter 11:
Epilogue.

The Battle of Waterloo essentially marked the end of a long and bitter war against Republican and Imperial France. After the battle, many casualties would die later of chronic infection, poverty and deprivation. Medical care was meted out in military hospitals, workhouse infirmaries and by urban and country surgeons or surgeon-apothecaries, family and friends. Apart from disability pensions awarded to wounded officers and men, prosthetics (artificial limbs), were provided by private firms also Chelsea and Kilmainham Hospitals, but often with great delay. One soldier of the 2/30th, from Athy, who had lost a leg at Waterloo, waited 15 years for his artificial leg from Chelsea Hospital!

**Care and compassion being meted out by the
citizens of Brussels in the Grande Place.**
(Author's collection)

As far as the army doctors were concerned, some would stay on in the service, others would go on to half-pay, some resigned and would have a struggle to worm their way back into the nation's medical society. Many attended courses of lectures and sat examinations to refresh their knowledge of civilian practice and to remain competitive in their future careers. One of the main problems for them was the burgeoning number of ex-service medical men who would flood the market.

A good proportion of these hardened medical campaigners had enormous confidence, gleaned by dint of harsh experience. They had learned to refute erstwhile rigid surgical dogma. The best of them found employment and many made a significant success of their post-war lives. Their experiences had given them learning, ability, confidence and reputation - so moving them up in surgical society, often with considerable wealth in addition to well-deserved status. This is well documented in much detail in a publication from the Oxford University Press, issued in 2006, *Advancing with the Army*.

Such abilities gained from the long and bitter wars against France, heightened resentment about lack of recognition, status and the award of honours heaped on their military compatriots. However, the seeds of their successes were to germinate slowly and gradually strengthen the long battle for better medical influence within the army hierarchy, ultimately resulting in the formation of an influential unit just over 80 years later - the Royal Army Medical Corps.

The greatest tragedy for the surgeons returning from the Brabant battlefields was that many valuable lessons learnt in Portugal, Spain, France and Belgium were soon forgotten after Waterloo and so tragically were to be repeated in the disastrous war against Russia (1854-6) in the Crimea, just 40 years and two generations of surgeons later.

Appendix I:
Medical Staff present at or after the
Battle of Waterloo

Much of the basic data on the members of the Army Medical Department below is taken from Johnston's seminal work, published in 1917. Additional data have been added, where possible.

There must have been many a military medical man who wished he had been present at this monumental battle. The staff who were there, were mostly surgeons, both in regimental and staff posts. Some arrived late and would not receive the coveted Waterloo medal and two years added pension rights. Some of the medical officers shifted to other regiments, many were promoted after the battle and not a few went on to have distinguished military or civilian careers. In this chapter, we have made a significant effort to cull all the medical gentlemen who were there on the day or who arrived later, including some eager civilian medical staff.

At the end of the Peninsular campaigns, there were almost 1,300 medical men in the Army Medical Department;

Table 4: The Army Medical Department in 1815.[179]

	Men
Medical Staff Officers[180]	354
Regimental Surgeons	313
Regimental Assistant Surgeons	573
Garrison/Assistant Surgeons	23
Miscellaneous	11
TOTAL	1,274

Many of these men who had long served in Portugal, Spain and France went on to half-pay and were only too glad that the war was 'ended'. Many of them had been worn out with their exertions or disease. Almost all of those who served in the 1815 campaigns escaped battle trauma. Only two medical staff seemed to have received injury at Quatre Bras and Waterloo, Physician George Denecke (KGL) and Assistant Surgeon John Stewart of the 92nd Foot. This may partly reflect sensible positioning of the medical staff.

---

[179] Army list, 1815
[180] Includes other medical officers on the staff e.g. 47 Purveyors

Director General of the Army Medical Department

He was appointed 13 June 1815 (Based in the United Kingdom)

Sir James McGrigor[181]

Born at Cromdale, Inverness-shire, 9 April 1771, the son of an Aberdeen merchant;
MA (Marischal College Aberdeen) 1788;
Surgeon 88th Foot (by purchase) 25 September 1793; served in Flanders 1794-5; served in Grenada and St Vincent 1795-6; served in Egypt 1801 (awarded Turkish Order of the Crescent); McGrigor was superintending surgeon to Sir David Baird's force, sent from India to assist in Sir Ralph Abercrombie's assault on the French in Rosetta and Cairo; McGrigor was commissioned as an HEIC medical officer so as to regularise his position with those other HEIC medical men. He was the first of the AMD to hold such an appointment;
Surgeon Royal Horse Guards (Blue) 9 February 1804;
MD 1804;
DIH 1805;
IG 1809; served in Walcheren 1809;
Physician to Portsmouth Garrison 13 June 1811 (**IG** Southern Command); on the 10 January 1812, he joined Wellington's army at the siege of Cuidad Rodrigo and served in the Peninsula 1812-14 (GSM - five clasps) as PMO to the British Army; awarded Commander of the Portuguese Order of the Tower and Sword;
KB 1814; he thus served in the Peninsula, through from 1812 to the Battle of Toulouse in 1814.

McGrigor's administrative abilities, courage and self-reliance gained in Iberia (1812-14) soon gave him Wellington's confidence. The great efficiency of the Army Medical Department of the Peninsular army under his direction was well shown by Napier, who stated that in ten months after the disastrous retreat from Burgos, 95,348 casualties and sick passed through the hospitals, and yet before the Battle of Vitoria, the sick list was below 5,000, and after Vitoria, without reinforcements from Britain, the army mustered within 30 men as strong as before, the ranks having been recruited by convalescents; retired half pay in 1814 (special rate of £3 per diem); on full pay as **DG** of the Army Medical Department on 13 June 1815 (relative rank of major-general at a salary of £2,000 per annum). At the end of the war, Wellington declared his satisfaction with McGrigor and stated, *"He is one of the most industrious, able and successful public servants I have ever met with."*[182] After the war, the medical officers who had served under McGrigor presented him with a service of plate valued at 1,000 guineas. His tenure of the office of Director General was associated with great benefit to the Army Medical Service as well as to the Army as a whole. He started the system of medical reports and returns from all military stations, which later formed the basis of *The Statistical Returns of the Health of the Army.*

---

[181] Referred to in the DNB, Gurwood (1861) *Wellington's Despatches*, etc. *Autobiography of Sir James McGrigor, Bart*; Richard L Blanco *Wellington's Surgeon General*; Mary McGrigor, *The Scalpel and the Sword*; Michael Crumplin, (2007) *Men of Steel* by and Martin Howard, *Wellington's Doctors*.
[182] Gurwood (1867), *Despatches, Correspondence, and Memoranda of Field Marshal Arthur Duke of Wellington KG*, Vol VII, p. 643.

LL.D. (Edinburgh) and **FRS** 1816; appointed as **Physician Extraordinary** to HRH the Prince Regent 1816.

Director General of the Army Medical Department, Sir James McGrigor FRS.
(Courtesy Aberdeen Medico-chirurgical Society)

He founded the Museum of Natural History and Pathological Anatomy at Fort Pitt, Chatham, which was transferred later to Netley Hospital (formerly on Southampton Water) and then to the RAMC College at Millbank. He presented 1,500 books to the Fort Pitt library, which were later housed at the Army Medical Officers' library at Millbank. In 1816, he founded the Army Medical Officers Friendly Society for the relief of widows of army medical officers. When he retired the fund contained around £80,000 and provided for 120 widows. This fund now flourishes as the Army Medical Officers Widows' and Orphans' fund. He also founded the Army Medical Benevolent Fund, which assisted the orphans of medical officers. These funds were perhaps the most enduring of the monuments to the memory of this great army medical officer.

FRCS (Edinburgh) and **MRCS** (London) 1825;
FRCP (Edinburgh) and Rector of the University of Aberdeen 1826, 1827 and 1841;
Member of Council University of London;
Created a **Baronet** 1830;
Created **Queen's Honorary Physician** in the year of her coronation, 1837;
Retired on pension on the 6 February 1851. He was then 80 years old and had served his country for 57 years.

McGrigor wrote much, including

(1801) *A Memoir on the Health of the 88th and Other Regiments,* Bombay;

(1804) *Medical Sketches of the Expedition to Egypt from India,* London;

(1830 and 1838) *A Memoir on the Health of the Army in the Peninsula,* in *Transactions of the Medico-Chirurgical Society,* London vol. VI; *Reports on Sickness, Mortality and Invaliding in the Army;*

(1861) an *Autobiography,* London;

(1865) a *Letter to the Commissioners of Military Enquiry,* London.

His portrait by Sir David Wilkie hangs in the Officers' Mess of the 2nd Brigade Training Depot at Strensal and another by William Dyce (1806-64) hangs in the post graduate medical centre, where the Aberdeen Medico-Chirurgical Society meets. This society was founded in 1798 by James McGrigor and James Robertson, who were then two medical students. A statue, erected by his many friends and admirers and formerly at Chelsea, was later housed at the Royal Army Medical College at Millbank and is now near the entrance of the erstwhile Army Staff College, at present the regimental headquarters of the RAMC in Camberley. In Aberdeen, his alma mater, there stands in Duthie Park, a stately granite obelisk erected in his memory. He died in London on the 2 April 1858 and was interred in Kensal Green Cemetery.

Principle Medical Officer
During the Waterloo Campaigns and of the Army of Occupation, France.

Sir James Robert Grant (Field Equipment PMO)[183]
Born in 1771 at Forres in Morayshire to Duncan Grant of Lingeston, he was brother to the distinguished soldier, Major General Colquhoun Grant, who served on Wellington's staff and who was wounded at Waterloo. James Grant was one of the few men to have served throughout the whole war, from 1793-1815.

Regimental Mate 11th Foot 22 January 1792; served in Flanders 1793;

Surgeon 21st Dragoons 12 September 1794;

Staff, Foreign Service, 18 March 1795; served that year in the Cape; retired on half pay 17 May 1803; on full pay 23 July 1803;

DIH 16 April 1807; Walcheren 1809;

IH (Later **IG**) 14 July 1814;

MD (King's College Aberdeen) 1814;

PMO during the Waterloo Campaigns, where, annotated in Grant's diary with others as belonging to Field Equipment Department, he rode with the senior staff entourage. We learn surprisingly little of this senior medical officer in various medically aligned accounts of the battle.

Kt. (2nd Class) St. Anne of Russia 1814. He received this latter award from the Emperor, for his services to the Russian forces in France.

KH 1816;

Knight Bachelor 1819; retired on full pay 25 March 1819. Retired on full pay about 1847, afterwards residing in Cumberland. **CB** 1850 Died 10 January 1864.

---

[183] For image, see page 13.

Deputy Inspectors

William Taylor
Hospital Mate 26 March 1795;
Assistant Surgeon 10th Dragoons 23 March 1797;
Surgeon 10th Dragoons 27 August 1803;
Staff Surgeon 20 June 1811;
DIH 25 July 1811; served in the Peninsula 1813-14; retired on half pay 25 September 1814 and on full pay 25 April 1815; the most senior DIH present at Waterloo, where he served the cavalry divisions; retired on half pay 25 February 1816. Died at Turnham Green 9 January 1820.

John Gunning (PMO 1ˢᵗ Corps)[184]
John Gunning (junior) was born in 1773. John Gunning's uncle was a contentious colleague and rival of the celebrated John Hunter and may have been implicated in the bitter rows that preceded Hunter's death. Within 24 hours, Gunning Senior, with no military experience had been appointed Surgeon General after Hunter;
Hospital mate prior to being commissioned;
Temporary Staff Surgeon with the Earl of Moira, 20 November 1793; served in Holland and Flanders 1793-5; retired on half pay 25 April 1799;
Permanent Staff Surgeon 12 September 1799; retired on half pay 22 October 1801; on full pay 25 July 1803; superseded, having been ordered on foreign service, desired leave to resign, 13 August 1805; reinstated 9 June 1808;
DIH 17 September 1812; At Waterloo, where he was Principle Medical Officer of the Allied 1st Corps, he amputated Fitzroy Somerset's (later Lord Raglan) right arm at Wellington's HQ in the village.[185] After Waterloo, he directed a large convoy of 48 spring wagons to the battlefield, just as they were heading off on the Nivelles road. These wagons had been busy taking the casualties from Quatre Bras, but their transit had been delayed by the cluttered state of the roads on the 18 June;
IH (continent of Europe only) 1 February 1816; retired on half pay 1 October 1816; went with Wellington's army to Paris, where he resided;
CB (military) 1850. Died in Paris 11 January 1863, aged 90 years.

Stephen Woolriche
Born 3 June 1770;
Regimental mate 1794;
Surgeon 111th Foot 30 May 1794; retired on half pay 1 March 1798; served in Holland 1799; on full pay 4th Foot (exchanged) 22 May 1806;
Staff Surgeon 18 June 1807 served at Copenhagen 1807; served in the Peninsula 1812-14;
DIH 26 May 1814; retired on half pay 25 September 1814; on full pay 25 April 1815; served at Waterloo in the Field Equipment Department, attending Sir William Howe

---

[184] *Dictionary of National Biography*, s.v. John Gunning, surgeon of St George's Hospital and Master of the London Company of Surgeons and who died in 1798, whose nephew he was, also *Lancet* (17 January 1863).
[185] Sweetman J. (1993), *Raglan, from the Peninsula to the Crimea*, p. 65.

De Lancey in the latter's last few days in the hamlet of Mont St Jean; retired on half pay 25 July 1816;

IH (brevet) 9 December 1823; on full pay 13 December 1826; retired on half pay 25 May 1828;

IG 22 July 1830;

CB (military) 1850. Died 29 February 1856.

John Robert Hume (Personal Physician to the Duke of Wellington)[186]

Born 1782;

Hospital Mate 28 October 1798; served in Holland 1799;

Assistant Surgeon 92nd Foot 9 May 1800; served in Egypt 1801;

Surgeon 14th Battalion of Reserve 9 July 1803; **Surgeon** 79th Foot 25 March 1805; served in the Peninsula 1808; served at Walcheren 1809;

Staff Surgeon 17 August 1809; served in the Peninsula 1810-14;

DIH 26 May 1814; at Waterloo served as the Duke's personal physician and surgeon, in which capacity he amputated Henry Paget, Lord Uxbridge's right leg (later Marquis of Anglesey). After the battle, Wellington sat down to a lonely supper with only one member of his staff, Miguel Alava, as a companion. We read an account by Lord William Lennox of the meeting of Hume and Wellington on the evening after the battle. After the battle, Wellington rode to Brussels, and the first person who entered his room on the morning of the 19th was Dr Hume,

> *"He had, as usual," says the doctor, "taken off his clothes, but had not washed himself." As I entered, he sat up in bed, his face covered with the dust and sweat of the previous day and extended his hand to me, which I took and held in mine, whilst I told him of Gordon's death. He was much affected. I felt his tears dropping fast upon my hand, and, looking towards him saw them chasing one another in a stream over his dusty cheeks. He brushed them suddenly away with his left hand, and said to me, in a voice tremulous with emotion - "Well, thank God, I don't know what it is to lose a battle, but certainly nothing can be more painful than to gain one with the loss of so many of one's friends."*[187]

The Duke, in a rare display of distress, had been clearly deeply upset by the losses after this hard-pressed action. Hume also amputated Colonel Alexander Gordon's right leg (his patient subsequently died) and briefly attended Sir William De Lancey, before his death;

MD (St Andrew's) 1816;

FRCP (Edinburgh) 1816; practised in London after peace was declared in 1815;

IH, afterwards

IG 3 December 1818; on full pay 27 April 1820; retired on full pay 25 April 1821;

DCL (Oxford) 1834; was Examining Physician to the Honourable East India Company 1835-45; he was appointed one of His Majesty's Commissioners in Lunacy in 1836;

FRCP (London) 1836;

CB (military) 1850; was for many years private physician to the Duke of Wellington. Died in London 1 March 1857, aged 75 years.

---

[186] Written about in the *Dictionary of National Biography* and in Munk's *Roll*, iii. 212-3.

[187] Fletcher I, (2001) *A Desperate Business*, p. 170.

William Curtis

Assistant Surgeon 1st Foot Guards 25 December 1796;

Surgeon to the Flank Battalion of Brigade of Foot Guards 2 October 1806; **Surgeon** Grenadier Battalion of Brigade of Foot Guards 21 August 1809;

Battalion Surgeon 1st Foot Guards, afterwards Grenadier Guards, 5 October 1809; served in Bergen-op-Zoom 1814.

DIH (local rank in the Netherlands) 11 May 1815; he served with the 1st Division at Waterloo. Died in London 25 April 1824.

Summers Higgins (late arrival)

Born in 1777. He was one of five sons of a subaltern, all of whom served in the army with distinction. His brothers were: Colonel Sir Samuel Gordon Higgins KCH. 3rd Foot Guards; Colonel Warner Westenra Higgins KH 21st Light Dragoons; Major General Lewis Higgins, formerly Carabineers and General Gordon Higgins, RA.

Assistant Surgeon 23rd Dragoons 1 September 1797; **Assistant Surgeon** 22nd Dragoons 1 December 1797; served in Egypt 1801; on half pay 25 June 1802; **Assistant Surgeon** 59th Foot 25 December 1802;

Surgeon 3rd Foot 15 October 1803; **Surgeon** 6th Dragoon Guards 17 July 1806;

Staff Surgeon 5 January 1809; served in the Peninsula 1809; whilst serving at Talavera, he was left with the British wounded, taken prisoner and later released by Bonaparte, for services he rendered to the French casualties. Twenty-three wounded British officers presented him with a handsome drinking vessel (the 'Talavera Cup'), which with his portrait, was left to the officers of the Army Medical Staff, by his son. These were originally housed at Millbank Hospital, now at the headquarters of the Royal Army Medical Corps, on the site of the old Staff College, Camberley; served again in the Peninsula 1811-14;

DIH 12 November 1812; served in North America 1814; at Waterloo, he was unattached, but was in charge of the hospitals in Brussels and Antwerp;

M.D. (Marischal College, Aberdeen) 1816; on half pay 25 July 1819;

IH (brevet) 27 May 1825;

IG 22 July 1830. He died at Cheltenham 5 April 1843.

George Frederick Albert (late arrival)

Born 18 December 1771;

Staff Surgeon 30 August 1799; retired on half pay 24 June 1802; on full pay cavalry depot, Maidstone (exchanged) 17 March 1803;

DIH 4 November 1813; on half pay 25 November 1815;

MD (Edinburgh) 1823. Died on 5 April 1853.

Donald McNiel (late arrival)[188]

Hospital Mate 22 October 1794; served in Holland 1799-1800;
Surgeon 85th Foot 16 September 1795;
MD;
Staff Surgeon 22 September 1802;
DIH (local rank in the West Indies only) 18 May 1809; **DIH** 21 January 1813; served at Guadeloupe 1815; retired on half pay 25 March 1817. Died at Jersey 24 February 1824.

Thomas Thomson (late arrival)[189]

Born 7 November 1776;
Hospital Mate, Chatham Barracks June 1796;
Assistant Surgeon 3rd Dragoons 19 July 1797; **Assistant Surgeon** 17th Dragoons 21 December 1797; retired on half pay 27 September 1798; re-commissioned **Assistant Surgeon** 21st Dragoons 20 March 1799; served in Egypt 1801;
Staff Surgeon 23 June 1808; served in Martinique in 1809; Guadeloupe 1810;
DIH West Indies (local rank) 8 March 1810; **DIH** 21 January 1813; served in the Peninsula 1813-4; served in North America (New Orleans) 1814;
MD (Paris) 1816; retired on half pay 15 April 1817;
IH (brevet) 27 May 1825;
IG 22 July 1830 - retired the same date;
FRCP (London) 1843. Died at Tunbridge Wells on 4 August 1853.

George James Guthrie (late arrival)

Born in London 1 May 1785;
Acting Assistant Surgeon (mate) York Hospital 1799/1800;
Hospital Mate 23 June 1800 (warranted only);
MRCS (London) 5 February 1801;
Assistant Surgeon 29th Foot 5 March 1801;
Surgeon 29th Foot 20 March 1806 (at Halifax, Nova Scotia, in Canada); 17 August 1808 served at Roliça, was wounded on 21 August 1808 at Vimeiro; served at Oporto, during the crossing of the Douro, at which action he saved a Portuguese regiment from destruction and captured a piece of French artillery. After Talavera in 1809, he isolated his own cases in houses separate from the general hospital;
Staff Surgeon (to 4th Division) 1810; served at Cuidad Rodrigo, three sieges of Badajoz,

Daguerreotype of Deputy Inspector George James Guthrie FRS in 1851.
(Courtesy the Royal College of Surgeons of England)

---

[188] Named 'McNeil' in *Army Lists* of 1798-1802 and 'M'Neill' in *Army Lists* (Medical Department) of 1812-13.
[189] Wrongly named 'Thompson' in the *Army Lists*, when in the 25th Foot and in some London Gazettes. Munk's *Roll*, iii. 169.

Salamanca, Madrid and Lisbon; ill and sent home 18 October 1811;

DIH afterwards **DIG** 16 September 1813; served at Santander, Pyrenees and Toulouse; retired on half pay 25 September 1814; Initially declined service in the Waterloo Campaigns, but arrived 3 July - came of his own accord, acting as a consultant and curious to learn more about some military trauma issues and remained around a week; he operated on only two patients in Brussels, serving only in the city's hospitals; founder and senior surgeon of the Royal Westminster Eye Hospital 1816; commenced a series of lectures, given gratis, in 1816 to the medical staff of the Armed Services and Hon. East India Company;

Assistant Surgeon Westminster Hospital 1823;

MD (King's College Aberdeen) and Member of Council of the Royal College of Surgeons of London (England) 1824;

elected **FRS** 1826 (refused a knighthood this year);

Surgeon Westminster Hospital 1827;

Hunterian Orator 1830; resigned 1843;

Professor of Anatomy and Surgery RCS (London) 1828-31;

FRCS (London) 1844;

Vice President of same College five times;

President in 1833, 1841 and 1854. He had been instrumental in the revision of the new Charter for the Royal College of Surgeons of England (formerly London) in 1843 and bringing about the Anatomy Act of 1832.

Contributed and wrote much to the evolution and practice of military surgery after the war. His greatest book was *Commentaries on the Surgery of the War*, which ran to six editions and was of use in both the Crimean campaigns and the American Civil War. He wrote 11 other books as well as numerous other publications. Married twice, his first wife predeceased him, dying of cholera in 1846. He had four offspring, one by his second marriage. His two sons predeceased him.[190] Guthrie died of bronchiectasis or chronic cardiac failure on 1 May 1856.

William Somerville - visitor from United Kingdom

Born 22 April 1771;

Hospital Mate 25 March 1795;

Staff Surgeon Cape Town Garrison 17 March 1796;

MD (King's College Aberdeen) 1800;

DIH 25 March 1805; Senior Medical Officer in Scotland, he travelled out with his friend, Sir Charles Bell;

Principle Inspector 28 December 1815; retired on half pay December 25 1816;

FRS 1817;

Physician, Royal Hospital Chelsea 11 November 1819. He was an explorer, and was the first white man to visit the Orange River. He married Mary Somerville, the authoress and mathematician. Died in Florence on 25 June 1860.

---

[190] Hurt R (2008), *George Guthrie, Soldier and Pioneer Surgeon*, pp. 114-5.

Royal Staff Corps

James Gordon Cavenagh (late arrival)[191]

Warranted **Regimental Mate** of 83rd Foot;

Hospital Mate,

prior to his commission as **Assistant Surgeon** 63rd Foot 31 January 1799;

Surgeon Staff Corps, afterwards Royal Staff Corps 21 February 1800; retired on half pay as **Surgeon** 62nd Foot, 25 August 1825. Died at Wexford 11 September 1844.

Physicians

George Denecke (KGL)

MD Wurzburg 1801;

Assistant Surgeon KGL 12 January 1805;

Surgeon 2nd Line Battalion, KGL 25 May 1805; served at Copenhagen 1807; served in the Peninsula 1808; served at Walcheren 1809;

Staff Surgeon 6 July 1809; served in the Peninsula 1811-13;

Physician 17 June 1813; served again in the Peninsula 1813-14; slightly wounded at Quatre Bras and his horse was severely injured, 1815; in charge of the medical care for the 3rd Division at Waterloo;

DIH (brevet - Continent only) 27 February 1816; retired on half pay 15 July 1824;

DIH, after **DIG** 26 October 1826. Died in the Isle of Wight 19 August 1838.

Edmond Sigismund Somers (Foreign Service - late arrival)[192]

MD (Edinburgh) 1783;

Physician (Foreign Service) 18 March 1795; served at the Cape of Good Hope 1795; served in the Peninsula 1810-14; unattached at Waterloo;

DIH 18 January 1816; retired on half pay the same day. Died in Lisbon 3 February 1824.

Edward Walsh (late arrival)[193]

Born at Waterford 1756;

MD (Glasgow) 1791;

Regimental Mate 65th Foot 22 August 1796;

Assistant Surgeon 29th Foot 3 May 1797; served at the Irish Rebellion 1798 and the Helder expedition 1799;

Surgeon 49th Foot 28 August 1800; served at Copenhagen 1801 (wounded); **Surgeon** 62nd Foot 2 October 1806; **Surgeon** 6th Dragoon Guards 5 January 1809; served in the Peninsula;

Physician 12 August 1813; served in Holland 1814; retired on half pay (?)1814; on full pay 25 April 1815; served unattached at Waterloo; retired on half pay 25 July 1816. He was a poet, artist and author. He wrote and illustrated *A Narrative of the Expedition to Holland*, London, 1800, 4to. - also, *Bagatelles* (poems) 1793.

---

[191] In the *Army Lists* of 1801-13, he is named as 'Walter'

[192] Munk's *Roll*, ii, 419. Also, appears in *Gore's Story*.

[193] A portrait of Edward Walsh was painted by John Comerford (DNB).

John Dwyer (late arrival)[194]

Hospital Mate 23 July 1805;

MD (Edinburgh) 1805;

Assistant Surgeon 58th Foot 20 March 1806; **Assistant Surgeon** 90th Foot 22 October 1807; **Assistant Surgeon** 6th Dragoon Guards 3 March 1808; **Assistant Surgeon** 6th Foot 13 December 1810;

Physician 18 April 1813; served in the Peninsula 1813-14 and in America 1814-15; served unattached at Waterloo; retired on half pay 25 October 1816; on full pay 25 October 1819; retired on half pay 25 January 1827. Died in Dublin 7 May 1829.

William Galbraith Wray (late arrival)

Hospital Mate previous to being commissioned;

MD (Edinburgh) 1805;

Assistant Surgeon 27th Foot 20 November 1805;

Surgeon 27th Foot 6 August 1812; served in the Peninsula 1813 (wounded);

Physician 26 May 1814; retired on half pay 25 September 1814; on full pay 21 April 1815; served unattached at Waterloo. Died in Barbados 21 January 1817.

John Eyre (late arrival)[195]

MD (Edinburgh) 1806;

Physician 6 July 1809; retired on half pay 25 October 1814; on full pay 25 April 1815; retired on half pay sometime after Waterloo. Died on half pay in Rome 15 November 1819.

John MacKenzie (late arrival)[196]

Hospital Mate 6 May 1805;

MD (St Andrew's) 1805;

Assistant Surgeon 1st Dragoons 13 November 1806; served at the Cape of Good Hope 1806; served in the Peninsula 1809-11;

Surgeon 39th Foot 1 February 1810;

Physician 15 July 1813; served again in the Peninsula 1813-14; served in New Orleans 1814-15; retired on half pay 25 July 1815; on full pay (by exchange) 11 January 1819. Died in Jamaica 31 May 1819.

Francis Home (late arrival, a resigned army physician)[197]

MD (Edinburgh) 1800;

Ensign in the 3rd Foot Guards 20 December 1803;

Physician 12 September 1805 - resigned his medical commission 1806;

Lieutenant then **Captain** in 3rd Foot Guards 22 May 1806; served in the Peninsula; **Captain** and **Lieutenant Colonel** 1814; served in the 3rd Foot Guards at Waterloo; retired by sale of commission 1818.

Son of Professor Francis Home.

---

[194] Munk's *Roll*, iii, 94.
[195] Munk's *Roll*, iii, 56.
[196] Munk's *Roll*, iii, 115.
[197] Munk's *Roll*, iii, 4.

James MacDougle (late arrival)[198]

Born at Berwick-on-Tweed;
MD (Edinburgh) 1801;
Hospital Mate 26 May 1804;
Assistant Surgeon 39th Foot 3 August 1804; **Assistant Surgeon** 13th Light Dragoons 21 August 1806; resigned 6 August 1807; served at Walcheren 1809;
Re-commissioned as **Physician** 25 August 1809; served in the Peninsula 1810-13; served in Holland 1814;
DIH (unattached) then afterwards, as **DIG** 7 September 1815; retired on half pay 25 February 1819; on full pay 11 October 1827; retired on half pay 7 November 1829. Died in London 1843.

Charles Graham Tice (late arrival)[199]

Assistant Surgeon 3rd Dragoon Guards 31 August 1797; retired on half pay 25 December 1797 to 20 June 1798; **Assistant Surgeon** Coldstream Guards on 21 February 1800 and resigned on 23 October 1800;
MD (Edinburgh) 1802; re-commissioned **Physician** 28 November 1805 (unattached); served in South America 1807;
DIH 20 May 1813; served in the Peninsula 1809-14; retired on half pay 25 September 1814; on full pay 25 March 1815; on half pay 25 February 1816. Died in Bruges 1 September 1819.

James Forbes[200,201]

Born 1779; **MA** (Marischal College, Aberdeen) 1794; **MD** (Edinburgh) 1803;
Hospital Mate 8 October 1803 to 8 February 1804;
Assistant Surgeon 30th Foot 9 February 1804; **Assistant Surgeon** 15th Dragoons 26 October 1804; served in the Peninsula 1808-9;
Surgeon 95th Foot 15 June 1809;
Staff Surgeon 13 July 1809; served at Walcheren 1809; served in the Peninsula again in 1810-14;
Physician 5 November 1812, where he served as Staff Officer to Sir James McGrigor in the Peninsula; retired on half pay 25 October 1814; on full pay 25 June 1815; **DIH**, after, **DIG** 23 May 1822;
IG 22 November 1836; retired on half pay 1 June 1837; in charge of the large General Hospital at Colchester, which received sick and wounded from Waterloo; Later, Superintendent of the Chelsea Hospital and Medical Director of Fort Pitt, Chatham. He founded the officers' mess at Fort Pitt. He later moved to Netley Hospital and then to Millbank Hospital, where in the officers' mess, there used to hang a portrait of him. Died in London 7 November 1837 (aged 58 yrs).

---

[198] Munk's *Roll*, iii, 61.
[199] Munk's *Roll*.
[200] Noted in DNB. His granddaughter married Lieutenant Colonel DV O'Connell RAMC and his great grandson, Lieutenant JF O'Connell MB, was killed in action at the Battle of the Aisne in 1914, buried at Verneuil, near Vailly, France.
[201] He was not present at Waterloo or Brussels, but particularly involved in the care of repatriated Waterloo casualties.

Appendix II:
Staff Surgeons (to the Forces)

Staff Surgeons

David Brownrigg
Hospital Mate 25 March 1800;
Assistant Surgeon 15th Dragoons 18 April 1800;
Surgeon 69th Foot 9 August 1803;
Staff Surgeon 18 June 1807; retired on half pay 24 June 1808; on full pay 24 January 1809; served in the Peninsula 1809-12; retired on half pay 28 February 1812; on full pay 22 October 1812; retired on half pay 25 June 1816; on full pay 25 July 1816; retired on half pay 25 January 1817;
DIH (brevet) 17 July 1817; on full pay 25 December 1827; retired on half pay 29 March 1833. Although it was not properly recorded, Brownrigg was probably the first surgeon in the British Army to have successfully removed a leg at the hip joint, of a soldier in the Peninsular War - with survival of the patient. The soldier, wounded near Merida in December 1811, had a successful hip disarticulation a year later.[202] Brownrigg was clearly a very competent and experienced surgeon. George Guthrie also was successful in such a case but his case was well recorded, the patient being returned to his native France (see above). Died in Dublin, November 1836.

Henry Gresley Emery (PMO 2nd Corps)
Henry was born on 22 May 1776, at Banwell, North Somerset; apprenticed to a surgeon apothecary at Bristol Infirmary; apparently served at the Irish Rebellion, Wexford 1798, possibly as a **Warranted Mate**;
Hospital Mate 25 September 1799, serving at Colchester and the York Hospital;
Assistant Surgeon 32nd Foot 3 December 1800;
Surgeon 3rd Battalion Light Infantry of the Line 28 April 1804; **Surgeon** 53rd Foot 30 May 1805. Serving at Shrewsbury, he saved the life of a boy thought dead from drowning and was rewarded by the town;
Staff Surgeon 11 August 1808; he remained behind with British casualties at the hospital at Lugo, during the retreat to Corunna. Made prisoner, he was permitted by the French to return home; served at Walcheren 1809; served in the Peninsula 1809 to 1813, during which he participated in the arduous retreat from Burgos;

Staff Surgeon Henry Gresley Emery, Principle Medical Officer to the Allied 2nd Corps at Waterloo.
(Courtesy of Mr David Milner)

---

[202] Crumplin (2007), *Men of Steel*, p. 338.

MD (Marischal College, Aberdeen) 1811; he worked at the general hospital at Plymouth; at Waterloo he acted as PMO to the 2ⁿᵈ Corps;
DIH 7 September 1815; retired on half pay 25 February 1816. Died, worn out with war, probably of pulmonary tuberculosis at Banwell near Bristol in 1826.

Thomas Draper

Hospital Mate 25 April 1795 to 24 April 1799;
Assistant Surgeon 1ˢᵗ West India Regiment 25 April 1799; **Assistant Surgeon** 87ᵗʰ Foot 11 November 1799; **Assistant Surgeon** 14ᵗʰ Foot 25 January 1800;
Surgeon 78ᵗʰ Foot 17 April 1804; served at Maida 1806; served in Egypt 1807;
Staff Surgeon 1 September 1808; served in the Peninsula 1808-11, he attended Sir John Moore, prior to the latter's demise at Corunna; having served at Waterloo, he received the thanks of the Government;
DIH, after, **DIG** 18 January 1816; retired on half pay 18 January 1816; on full pay 14 February 1822;
IH, after, **IG** (brevet) 27 May 1825; served in the West Indies as **IG** (local rank only) 24 February 1837 to 23 February 1840;
IG (substantive) 24 February 1840; retired on half pay 2 October 1840. Died at Instow, Barnstable 28 June 1850.

Michael Andrew Burmeister (or Burmester)

Hospital Mate 14 September 1799; served in Holland 1799;
Assistant Surgeon 82ⁿᵈ Foot 27 April 1801; **Assistant Surgeon** 53ʳᵈ Foot 3 September 1803;
Surgeon 2ⁿᵈ Division Light Infantry Militia in Ireland 28 August 1804; **Surgeon** 8ᵗʰ Garrison Battalion 18 December 1806; **Surgeon** (by exchange) 66ᵗʰ Foot 21 January 1808;
Staff Surgeon 4 January 1810; served in the Peninsula 1810-14; retired on half pay 25 September 1814; on full pay 25 April 1815; retired on half pay 25 January 1819; on full pay 25 December 1819;
MD (Marischal College Aberdeen) 1821. Died in Jamaica 3 November 1823.

Robert Grant[203]

Born 29 May 1777;
Assistant Surgeon 10ᵗʰ Dragoons 15 June 1797; retired on half pay 25 December 1797; on full pay as **Assistant Surgeon** 60ᵗʰ Foot 31 May 1798; **Assistant Surgeon** 69ᵗʰ Foot 19 April 1799; resumed as **Assistant Surgeon** 10ᵗʰ Dragoons 30 August 1799;
Surgeon 28ᵗʰ Foot 9 July 1803;
Staff Surgeon 22 August 1811; served in the Peninsula; retired on half pay 1814; on full pay 25 March 1815; since serving in the cavalry, he may, shortly after Waterloo, have stood in for Surgeon Charles Morison of the 10ᵗʰ Hussars, absent from the battle (see below); Grant retired on half pay 1818. Died 13 May 1837.

---

[203] His name first appeared in the *Army List* of 1812.

John Maling (2nd Division)[204]

Hospital Mate 3 July 1799 and again when he entered the service on 5 April 1805; **Assistant Surgeon** Royal Horse Guards (Blue) 3 October 1799; left the service around 30 May 1803; re-commissioned as an **Assistant Surgeon** 52nd Foot 20 June 1805; served in Egypt 1807; in January 1809 he attended Sir John Moore as the wounded general was carried past Maling's battalion en route from above the village of Elvina to his headquarters at 16, Canton Grande in Corunna, where Moore died. Here Maling, another surgeon and the Guards Brigade Chaplain attended Moore in his last two hours;[205] **Surgeon** 8th West India Regiment 20 April 1809; **Surgeon** 52nd Foot 15 June 1809; served at Walcheren 1809; served in the Peninsula 1810-14; **Staff Surgeon** 3 September 1812; retired on half pay 1 June 1817; whilst attending the wounded Earl of March after the Battle of Orthez, Maling, dozing in a chair, observed Wellington quietly entering March's room and briefly visiting his family friend - Wellington did not notice Maling; on full pay 25 September 1818; retired on half pay 25 March 1819; on full pay 25 June 1823; **DIH** (brevet) 27 May 1825; **DIG** 22 July 1830; retired on half pay 12 November 1830; on full pay 9 November 1831; retired on half pay 9 June 1832. Died at Southampton 29 September 1835.

Andrew Halliday (later Sir Andrew Halliday)[206]

Halliday was of humble parentage, but of good blood, being descended way back from 'Thomas Halliday, my sister's son so dear', and mentioned by none other than the great Scots patriot, Sir William Wallace. He was educated for the church, but finding he had an aptitude for medicine, he adopted the latter profession.
MD (Edinburgh) 1806;
Hospital Mate 30 July to 16 September 1807;
Assistant Surgeon 13th Dragoons 17 September 1807; **Assistant Surgeon** 4th Dragoon Guards 17 March 1808;
Staff Surgeon (local rank in Portugal only) serving in Portugal under Lieutenant General Sir W. Carr Beresford 17 August 1809; served in the Peninsula 1809-12; retired on half pay 25 August 1812; on full pay as **Staff Surgeon** (substantive rank) 29 April 1813; served in Holland 1814; retired on half pay 25 April 1816;
Created **Knight Bachelor** 1821;
KH;
FRCP (Edinburgh) 1827;
DIG 22 July 1830; retired on half pay 22 July 1830; on full pay 1833;
FRS; retired on half pay 1836. Died in Dumfries 7 September 1839.

---

[204] John Maling's 1796 Officer's pattern blued light cavalry sabre is on display in the Hunterian Museum at the Royal College of Surgeons, Lincoln's Inn Fields, near Holborn.
[205] Crumplin (2007), *Men of Steel*, p. 33.
[206] Cited in the *Dictionary of National Biography* and Munk's *Roll* iii, p. 211.

A prolific writer, he wrote on

> *Emphysema: Lunatics and Lunatic Asylums.*
> *The Portuguese Army: A Memoir of the Campaign of 1815.*
> (1820) *A History of the House of Brunswick.*
> (1826) *Annals of the House of Hanover.*
> (1837) *The Natural and Physical History of the West Indies.*

John Gideon van Millingen[207]

Born at Westminster on 8 September 1782, the son of a Dutch merchant; he lived in Paris during the French Revolution and studied medicine there.

Assistant Surgeon the Queen's German Regiment, afterwards the 97th Foot 27 January 1802;

Surgeon 31st Foot 17 November 1809; served in the Peninsula 1808-14;

MD (St Andrew's) 1812;

Staff Surgeon 26 May 1814; retired on half pay 25 September 1814; on full pay 25 March 1815; at Waterloo, he was attached to the cavalry, also at Waterloo, Assistant Surgeon Haddy James of the 1st Life Guards, had to borrow some rollers and lint from van Millingen, since James's equipment had not arrived! Retired on half pay 25 July 1816; on full pay 2 April 1818; retired on half pay 9 October 1823.

Perhaps van Millingen is best remembered for his efforts to bring about some issues of reform in the Army Medical Department. In 1819 he wrote *The Army Medical Officer's Manual Upon Active Service*, which included a recommended Corps of Ambulance. This consisted of a unit of 20 men for a battalion (60 for a brigade), who would work in pairs as bearers - each carrying half a stretcher. This was emulating the French brancardiers or stretcher-bearers. Also he suggested two designs of ambulance, long cars for sitting wounded and spring wagons for more serious casualties. Musicians working as bearers would take the wounded to a regimental aid post. From there, the ambulance corpsmen would take the casualties on to a brigade hospital, where other regimental surgeons would commence definitive treatment. Each of these units was to serve a battalion and when there was no combat, the corpsmen would be used in hospitals. Inevitably, in the post war austerity, van Millingen's ideas were not taken up. Such resistance to sensible development was sadly realised during the Crimean campaigns, in which Lieutenant-Colonel Anthony Sterling, the author of, *The Story of the Highland Brigade in the Crimea*, expressed a telling and rueful criticism,

> *'In France there is a permanent wagon train always organised, a permanent commissariat, and also a permanent ambulance: these three departments hang very much upon one another. The English people having destroyed these above-named departments, which existed during the Spanish War, or which rather were then formed, its Government, on deciding upon war, should have instantly begun to organise them again. This is a matter of time as well as money; there has now been time enough allowed to slip away; but nothing is really organised yet.'* [208]

---

[207] He is recorded in the DNB.
[208] Judd D. (1975), *The Crimean War*, p. 131.

How frustrated Gideon van Millingen must have felt as an old man reading of the lessons that had not been learned by senior military men and government! Not afraid to air his views, van Millingen expressed his disapproval of appointing military commandants to general hospitals, since they seemed unacquainted with their administrative and purveying duties. After leaving the army, van Millingen became resident Physician at the Lunatic Asylum, Hanwell; he wrote a novel, several dramas and farces and the libretto for a musical play. He also published books on homeopathy, hereditary insanity and on the treatment of the insane. His best-known books are;

> (1837) *Curiosities of Medical Experience*, London.
> (1839) *Stories of Torres Vedras*, 3 vols.
> (1841) *The History of Duelling*, 2 vols.
> *Recollections of Republican France from 1790-1801.*

He was Domestic Physician to William IV, when Duke of Clarence. Died in London in 1862.

George Beattie (late arrival)

Hospital Mate 8 September 1803;

Assistant Surgeon 92nd Foot 25 September 1803; served at Copenhagen 1807; prisoner of war for eight months (exchanged or repatriated), after his ship was wrecked off the coast of Holland November 1807;

Surgeon 60th Foot 4 January 1810; **Surgeon** 79th Foot (by exchange) 1 March 1810; **MD** (Marischal College Aberdeen) 1812;

Staff Surgeon 9 September 1813; retired on half pay 24 September 1814; on full pay 25 April 1815; retired on half pay 24 February 1816; on full pay 5 November 1818; retired on half pay 25 January 1820. Died 13 August 1837.

Samuel Barwick Bruce (late arrival)[209]

Born January 8 1786; studied in Barbados, under his father Barwick Bruce; served on HMS 'Spartiate' under Lord Horatio Nelson, (then chasing Admiral Villeneuve around the West Indies), prior to his service in the British Army; In Dalton's *Waterloo Roll* he, 'saw some of his earliest service afloat under Lord Nelson in 1805';

Hospital Mate 19 July 1804; may have served at sea around 1805; served in Martinique 1809, was awarded the Military General Service Medal with two clasps, Martinique and Guadeloupe, where he worked at St Thomas, St Croix and Fort Desaix;

Apothecary 5 April 1810; served in Guadeloupe 1810; served in the Peninsula 1813;

MRCS (London) in 1814; served in America 1814-15, where, serving under Sir Edward Packenham, he worked at New Orleans and Fort Bowyer;

Staff Surgeon 25 May 1815; after Waterloo, he was present at the capture and downfall of Paris; retired and apparently objected to being placed on half pay; on half pay 16 March 1816; on full pay (by exchange) 26 October 1832, but commuted to half pay 22 January 1833. Died suddenly of an 'apopleptic seizure' (i.e. a stroke) on 24 December 1852.

---

[209] There is a memorial plaque to Bruce and his descendants in Ripon Cathedral, placed there in 1902.

James Alexander Campbell *(late arrival - unattached)*
Regimental Mate 2 February 1796;
Assistant Surgeon 89th Foot 25 December 1796;
Surgeon 58th Foot 1801;
Staff Surgeon 19 March 1812; served in the Peninsula 1812-14; retired on half pay 1814 or 1815; on full pay 25 March 1815;
DIH (brevet) 17 July 1817; retired on half pay. Died in Ireland 28 May 1822.

John Callander *(late arrival)*
Born 13 March 1875;
Hospital Mate 30 December 1805;
Assistant Surgeon 4th Foot 1807; served in the Walcheren campaign July 1809;
Staff Surgeon (Portugal only) in Portugal, serving under Lieutenant General Sir William Carr Beresford and Inspector of Hospitals (Portugal only) Dr William Fergusson 17 August 1809; served in the Peninsula 1809-14; **Staff Surgeon** (permanent rank) 25 October 1814; retired on half pay 25 December 1814; on full pay 25 April 1815; retired on half pay 25 November 1815;
Surgeon 7th Dragoons 30 May 1816; retired on half pay 25 June 1829. Died 21 July 1854.

Samuel Cooper *(late arrival)*[210]
Born 11 September 1781, son of a wealthy West India merchant;
Hospital Mate May 1801 until 1802; **Hospital Mate** 7 January 1813; served in the Peninsula 1812-13;
Assistant Staff Surgeon 14 October 1813;
Staff Surgeon 26 May 1814; retired on half pay 25 July 1816;
one of the first **FRCS** awards (1844);
Vice-President (in 1843/44), then **President** of the Royal College of Surgeons of London (England) 1845;
FRS 1846;

Surgeon and **Professor of Surgery** to University College London - the first London University Medical School. He eventually fell out with the University over the appointment of James Syme as Professor of Clinical Surgery. Nicknamed the 'Surgical Johnson', he had many publications; *First Lines of the Practice of Surgery*, also many essays and dissertations. *A Dictionary of Practical Surgery* first published in 1809. This tome, produced by Cooper single-handedly, was translated into three other languages and went to many editions. It is a veritable cornucopia of terminology, surgical history and philosophy and technique, most of it reflecting surgical lessons learned in the Peninsula - it is a most valuable resource for those researching the evolution, comparisons and rationale of surgical procedures. It was, for many years, the standard text of surgery for medical students. Died of gout at Shepperton 2 December 1848.

---

[210] Noted in the DNB.

Professor Samuel Cooper FRS.
(Courtesy of the Royal College of Surgeons of England)

James Matthews (late arrival)

Born 12 December 1770;

Hospital Mate 8 July 1799;

Assistant Surgeon 52nd Foot 19 December 1799; **Assistant Surgeon** 4th Dragoons (by exchange) 8 October 1802;

Surgeon 1st Battalion of the Reserve 9 July 1803; retired on half pay 24 February 1805; **Surgeon** 8th West India Regiment 12 September 1805; **Surgeon** 3rd Foot 17 July 1806; served in the Peninsula, probably from 1808 to 1814; he was awarded £100 for injuries received in Portugal;

Staff Surgeon 9 September 1813; retired on half pay 25 September 1814;

MD (St Andrew's) 1814; on full pay 25 March 1815; at Waterloo he was attached to the 4th Division; retired on half pay 25 October 1816. Died at Oestrich, Nassau 9 March 1844.

William Flamank Blicke (late arrival)[211]

Assistant Surgeon 86th Foot 5 May 1805;

Staff Surgeon 20 September 1810;

Surgeon 10th Foot 30 April 1812;

Staff Surgeon 13 May 1813; retired on half pay 8 February 1815; on full pay 25 April 1815; he performed the only other case of disarticulation at the hip joint - the other being carried out by George Guthrie - Blicke's case sadly died on the eighth postoperative day; retired on half pay 25 February 1816. Died 13 August 1838.

John Boggie (late arrival)

Born 8 March 1779;

warranted **Hospital Mate** before his commission;

Assistant Surgeon 28th Foot 8 January 1801; served in Egypt in 1801;

Surgeon 45th Foot 15 October 1807; served at Copenhagen 1807; **Surgeon** 28th Foot 22 August 1811;

Staff Surgeon 15 October 1812; served in the Peninsula 1813-14; on half pay 25 September 1814; on full pay 25 April 1815; retired on half pay 25 February 1816;

MD (Edinburgh) 1817.

Hugh Bone (late arrival)

Hospital Mate 8 to 16 September 1803;

Assistant Surgeon 5th Foot 17 September 1803;

Surgeon 6th Foot 13 July 1809; served in the Peninsula, possibly from 1812 to 14;

Staff Surgeon 26 March 1812; on half pay 25 September 1814; on full pay 25 April 1815;

MA and **MD** (Glasgow) 1815;

Physician 7 September 1815; on half pay 1 August 1816; on full pay 10 April 1817;

DIH (brevet) 27 May 1825; **DIH** afterwards, **DIG** 1 November 1827;

IG (local rank only in the West Indies) 2 October 1840; **IG** (Substantive rank) 2 October 1843; retired on half pay 24 November 1845.

---

[211] In the *Army Lists* of 1813-18 inclusive, his second name is given as 'H------' instead of 'Flamank'.

John Cole (late arrival)

Assistant Surgeon 68th Foot 23 May 1800;

Surgeon 68th Foot 25 June 1803; served at Walcheren 1809;

Staff Surgeon 3 September 1812; served in the Peninsula 1812-13; on half pay possibly 1813;

MD (Marischal College, Aberdeen) 1817; on full pay (by exchange) 25 June 1819; retired on half pay 24 September 1821. Died at Boulogne 29 May 1826.

Charles Collier (late arrival)

Born 16 July 1785;

Medical Cadet and **Hospital Mate** 25 September 1805 until 1 October 1806;

Assistant Surgeon 13th Foot 2 October 1806;

Surgeon 60th Foot 10 August 1809; served in Martinique 1809; 70th Foot (by exchange) 1 February 1810;

Staff Surgeon 4 June 1812; served in the Peninsula 1812-14; on half pay 25 September 1814; on full pay 25 April 1815; on half pay 25 May 1817; There are extant letters concerning the progress of casualties after Waterloo, written to Sir Charles Bell, by Collier, after Bell had left Brussels.[212]

DIH (brevet) in Ceylon 3 February 1825; **DIH** (brevet) in Mauritius 1 October 1829; **DIG** 22 July 1830; retired on half pay 9 June 1838;

MD (St Andrew's) 1840.

Thomas Donahoo (late arrival)[213]

Born 1769;

Regimental Mate before being commissioned;

Assistant Surgeon 9th Dragoons 1 May 1797;

BA (Trinity College Dublin) 1799;

Surgeon 38th Foot 4 September 1806;

MD (St Andrew's) 1809;

Staff Surgeon 3 September 1812; served in the Peninsula possibly from 1812 to 1814; on half pay 25 April 1814; on full pay 25 March 1815;

Physician 7 September 1815; retired on half pay 25 June 1816. Died at Torquay 16 February 1838.

Francis Downing (late arrival)

Hospital Mate 10 September 1799;

Acting Assistant Surgeon 10th Dragoons 1799;

Staff Surgeon 1800; served on the expedition to Ferrol 1800-1; on half pay 1802; on full pay 1803; served as PMO to the 6th Division in the Waterloo campaign;

DIH 7 September 1815; retired on half pay 1816. Died 1 March 1830.

---

[212] Crumplin and Starling (2005) *A Surgical Artist at War, the paintings and sketches of Sir Charles Bell 1809-1815*, p. 63.

[213] In records in the Dublin PRO and the *Army Lists* 1798-1806, referred to as 'James Donaghoe'; in the *London Gazette* 1806 and in *Army List* 1807 'James Donahoe'. In the *London Gazettes* of 1812 and 1815 and *Army lists* of 1808-1817, he was named 'Thomas Donahoo'. Munk's *Roll* iii, 130.

Theodore Gordon (late arrival)[214]

Born 22 April 1786;

Hospital Mate 28 November 1803 to 2 March 1804;

Assistant Surgeon 14th Reserve Battalion 3 March 1804; **Assistant Surgeon** 91st Foot 23 November 1804; served at Buenos Aires

Surgeon 89th Foot 6 July 1809; **Surgeon** 4th Foot 28 March 1811; served in the Peninsula 1812-1813

Staff Surgeon 9 September 1813;

MD King's College (Aberdeen) 1814;

Physician, afterwards **AIH** 7th September 1815;

DIG 29 January 1836;

FRCP (London) 1838; this distinguished doctor had a long and meritorious career. He was wounded on three occasions, on the last time when he had been called to the front line to treat his commanding officer. He had suffered much from eye trouble and had lost the sight in one eye. He had been eventually compelled to retire. He was awarded a special annual pension of £600 - a testimony to his arduous term of service.

Died at Brighton 30 March 1845

John Hennen (late arrival)[215]

Born at Castlebar Ireland 21 April 1779; apprenticed in the county (Mayo) Infirmary, he acted as a dresser; was a student of Monro Secundus and Dr Black in Edinburgh, later qualifying as **MRCS** (Edinburgh);

Hospital Mate (Edinburgh) 24 March 1800;

Assistant Surgeon 40th Foot 4 April 1800; he worked in Malta and Minorca;

Assistant Surgeon 3rd Dragoons 15 October 1801; served in Egypt 1801;

Surgeon 3rd Battalion Irish Light Infantry 12 November 1803; retired on half pay 24 August 1806; **Surgeon** 7th Garrison Battalion 18 December 1806; **Surgeon** (by exchange) 2nd Battalion 30th Foot 31 December 1807; he was publicly thanked by Major General Dunlop for his exertions at Fuentes de Õnoro and was senior surgeon (**PMO**) to the 5th Division;

Staff Surgeon 24 October 1811; served in the Peninsula 1809-14, where he had gained a strong reputation as a dextrous surgeon; retired on half pay 25 October 1814, when he entered into private practice in Dumfries and wrote a paper on hospital gangrene - no doubt based on his huge experience with this infection at Bilbao in 1813; on full pay 25 March 1815; after the Waterloo campaign Hennen was in charge of the Jesuit's Hospital in Brussels, where he remained until September 1815. He also operated at the Gens d'Armerie Hospital;

DIH 7 September 1815; he returned to Britain and became in charge of the South Western district of England, based in Portsmouth; he later moved to Edinburgh;

MD (Edinburgh) 1819; in the winter of 1820, he gave lectures with Professor Thomson, based on hospital cases; in 1821 he was given charge of the medical department of the Mediterranean Hospitals, based at Malta and Corfu;

---

[214] See *Gordons under Arms* by Skelton and Bulloch.
[215] Recorded in the DNB and in *Gore's Story*.

IH (brevet) 11 December 1823; he was then, in 1826, given command of the medical services at Gibraltar. In August 1828, a fever epidemic broke out and on the 28 October, Hennen was seized with the contagion. Although very sick he continued to work. He was vomiting copiously, became jaundiced and then went into renal failure. He died at 6am on the 3 November.

He was an extremely talented surgeon and wrote, (1818) *Principles of Military Surgery, comprising Observations on the arrangement, police, and practice of Hospitals'*; after the publication of the second edition of his principle work, the Emperor of Russia presented him with a magnificent diamond ring. He also wrote a valuable book, (1830) *Medical Topography of the Mediterranean*, also texts on venereal diseases and sanitation. There is a memorial erected by subscription of Hennen's colleagues from many places, under the leadership of Sir George Don the then Governor of Gibraltar, to the memory of this gallant surgeon in the King's Chapel Gibraltar. Its inscription finishes with a fitting tribute. This surely the greatest approbation any committed doctor would care to receive.[216]

> *This tablet is erected by his personal friends, - not with a view of perpetuating his name, for that lives in the more imperishable memorials of his own genius, but as a testimony of regard for a man whose zeal was indefatigable, and who, in the day of general calamity, sacrificed all consideration of his own safety for the public weal.'*

Thomas Inglis (late arrival)

Hospital Mate previous to his commission;
Assistant Surgeon 62nd Foot 19 December 1799; on half pay 1802; **Assistant Surgeon** 6th Foot 23 July 1802;
Surgeon 71st Foot 20 March 1806;
Staff Surgeon 8 June 1809; served in the Peninsula;
DIH (brevet) 26 November 1818; retired on half pay 1818; on full pay 1 December 1824; **DIH** 2 December 1824. Died in West Africa either on 11 or 12 July 1825.

Thomas Kidd (late arrival)

Born 25 August 1777;
Regimental Mate 49th Foot 17 June 1796 to 23 January 1797;
Hospital Mate 24 January 1797 to 5 April 1797;
Assistant Surgeon 13th Foot 6 April 1797; **Assistant Surgeon** 14th Light Dragoons 15 March 1799;
Surgeon 4th Battalion 60th Foot 25 April 1799; **Surgeon** 63rd Foot 25 July 1799;
Staff Surgeon 1803; served in the Peninsula 1810 to 1813;
DIH afterwards **DIG** (brevet) 1817; retired on half pay 1819;
MD (Aberdeen) 1819;
FRCP (Edinburgh) 1823; on full pay 1833;
DIG 1837;
IG 16 December 1845; retired on half pay 16 December 1845. Died 14 December 1849.

---

[216] Hennen J, (1830) *Principles of Military Surgery*, 3rd Edition London, p. xii.

Richard O'Connell (late arrival)

Assistant Surgeon 4th Battalion Light Infantry of the Line, Ireland 22 December 1804; on half pay thereafter for an uncertain period; on full pay as **Assistant Surgeon** 7th Garrison Battalion 15 January 1807; **Assistant Surgeon** 38th Foot 18 February 1808; **Assistant Surgeon** 43rd Foot 7 July 1808;
Surgeon 45th Foot 25 March 1813; served in the Peninsula 1813-14;
Staff Surgeon 9 September 1813; retired on half pay 25 October 1814; on full pay 25 April 1815; retired on half pay 25 June 1816. Died in Ireland 18 October 1817.

John Rice (late arrival)

MD (Montpellier) 1792;
Hospital Mate 18 October 1800; served in Egypt 1801;
Assistant Surgeon 39th Foot 3 August 1804;
Surgeon 89th Foot 6 March 1806;
Staff Surgeon 8 June 1809; served in Walcheren 1809; served in the Peninsula 1812-14; retired on half pay 25 February 1816. Died 16 October 1828.

Jordan Roche (late arrival)

Hospital Mate before commission - probably 26 September 1793;
Surgeon 89th Foot 5 May 1794; **Surgeon** 13th Light Dragoons 7 September 1796; retired, probably on half pay 1 January 1799;
re-commissioned **Staff Surgeon** 6 February 1812; served in the Peninsula 1812-14. Died 26 July 1821.

Thomas Sandell (late arrival)

Hospital Mate 5 October 1799; served in Egypt in 1801;
Assistant Surgeon 8th Foot 17 May 1803;
Surgeon 53rd Foot 1 September 1808; served in the Peninsula 1809-14;
Staff Surgeon 9 September 1813; retired on half pay 25 September 1814; on full pay 25 April 1815; retired on half pay 25 July 1816. Died 24 June 1835.

William Thomas (late arrival)

Assistant Surgeon 3rd West Yorkshire Militia; **Assistant Surgeon** 67th Foot 12 November 1807; served in the Peninsula 1812-13;
Surgeon 37th Foot 28 July 1814; served in Holland 1814; he was known to have served in Brussels after the battle and may have moved there after hearing of the conflict; retired on half pay 18 June 1817;
MD (Edinburgh) 1820; commuted half pay 3 September 1830.

Professor John Thomson (late arrival)
Born at Paisley 15 March 1765;
FRCS (Edinburgh) 1793;
Hospital Mate 1803;
Regius Professor of Military Surgery, University of Edinburgh 1806;
MD (King's College, Aberdeen) 1808;
Staff Surgeon 21 September 1815; retired on half pay 25 March 1821;
Consulting Physician to the Edinburgh new-town dispensary,
Professor of Surgery at the Royal College of Surgeons of Edinburgh,
Professor of General Pathology, University of Edinburgh 1832.

John Thomson MD, Regius Professor of Surgery at the University of Edinburgh.
(Courtesy the Royal College of Surgeons of Edinburgh)

He wrote a most valuable account of the hospitals, the casualties, the wounds, their management and several post mortem findings during a tour of Brussels. The work is titled, (1816) *Report of Observations made in the British Military Hospitals in Belgium after the Battle of Waterloo with some remarks upon amputation,* Blackwood of Edinburgh.[217] Other published works were;

  (1798-1800) *Elements of Chemistry and Natural Philosophy,*
  (1808) *Lithotomy,*
  (1813) *On Inflammation*
  (1827 edited) *Works of William Cullen MD.*

Died in Edinburgh 11 October 1846.

Owen Lindsey (late arrival)

Born 17 March 1785;

Assistant Surgeon 2nd Dragoon Guards 31 December 1803; served in Walcheren in 1809;

Surgeon 72nd Foot 2 November 1809; **Surgeon** 74th Foot 28 December 1809; served in the Peninsula 1810-14; **Surgeon** 5th Dragoon Guards 16 January 1812;

Staff Surgeon 5 November 1812; retired on half pay 25 October 1814; on full pay 25 April 1815; on half pay 9 June 1817; on full pay 14 August 1817;

MD (Glasgow) 1827;

DIG 22 July 1830; retired on half pay 13 December 1830; recorded as on half pay for the last time on Army List in 1863. This man travelled out to Ostend from Ramsgate with Assistant Surgeon John Haddy James (see below). He was certainly in Flanders at the time of the campaign, but there remains uncertainty as to whether he was around at the time of the battle.

---

[217] This report forms the basis of Chapter 4 of this book.

Assistant Staff Surgeons

James Dease[218]

Hospital Mate (general service) 29 September 1812;
Assistant Staff Surgeon 11 March 1813; served in the Peninsula 1813-4; served with the 3rd Division at Waterloo.
Staff Surgeon 7 September 1815;
MD (Edinburgh) 1825. Died at Edgesworthtown, Ireland 18 October 1827.

William Twining[219]

Born in Nova Scotia 1790; served in the Royal Navy for two years before being commissioned;
Hospital Mate (general service) afterwards
Hospital Assistant 6 February 1812; served in the Peninsula 1812-4;
Assistant Staff Surgeon 10 March 1814; served with Headquarters at Waterloo;
Supernumerary Assistant Surgeon, India 12 June 1823; retired on half pay 25 December 1823; joined the Honourable East India Company Service (Bengal) as an **Assistant Surgeon** 12 August 1824; commuted half pay 7 December 1830;
Registered as **FRCS** (London.) - this must be incorrect, since we note that he had died before the Fellowship had been instituted in the London (later, English) College. Author of (1822) *Diseases of Bengal* and *Diseases of the Spleen* and *Cholera*. Died at Calcutta 25 August 1835.

Thomas McWhirter (late arrival)[220]

Assistant Purveyor Holland 1794 (taken prisoner of war);
Ensign and **Assistant Surgeon**, then **Lieutenant** and **Assistant Surgeon** to the West Lowland Fencibles until disbanded in 1798;
Hospital Mate, serving in the Helder expedition of 1799 (prisoner of war); resigned after 1800;
MD (Edinburgh) 1800; entered civilian practice in Newcastle 1803;
he was employed as a **Temporary Physician** at Deal, after the Walcheren debacle in 1809;
Hospital Assistant 9 August 1813; served in the Peninsula 1813-14;
Assistant Staff Surgeon 26 May 1814. Died in 1836.

---

[218] Name wrongly spelt in the *London Gazette* as 'Richard Jones Dease'
[219] *Dictionary of National Biography* and *Bengal Obituary* 1848, pp. 23 and 112.
[220] Munk's *Roll*, iii. 88.

Appendix III:
Hospital Assistants (and Hospital Mates)

Hospital Assistants to the Forces
These were in all but name, similar to the above.

Thomas William Cahill (acting by warrant)
MD (Paris) 1814;
Acting Hospital Assistant, Brussels 5 May 1815;
Hospital Assistant 7 September 1815; retired on half pay 25 July 1816; commuted half pay 26 August 1831.

William Cannan
Alumnus, Glasgow 1808;
Hospital Mate 9 November to 22 March 1815; saw Peninsular service;
Hospital Assistant 23 March 1815; attached to the 4th Division; retired on half pay 25 December 1818; on full pay 25 June 1820; on half pay 25 April 1823;
Assistant Staff Surgeon 25 October 1833;
Assistant Surgeon 76th Foot 15 November 1833; retired on half pay 15 July 1836. Died in Glasgow 6 July 1839.

Robert Caverhill
Hospital Mate 21 December 1811; served in the Peninsula 1812-14;
Hospital Assistant 23 March 1815;
Assistant Staff Surgeon 28 December 1820.
Died in Barbados, on 9 December 1820, prior to this appointment reaching him.

George Evers
Born 18 February 1787;
Hospital Mate 26 November 1813 to 23 September 1814, when he was discharged with a gratuity; he had served in the Peninsula;
Hospital Assistant 3 June 1815; on half pay 25 March 1816; on full pay 25 May 1816;
Assistant Surgeon 14th Foot 23 December 1824; retired on half pay 15 December 1825; granted a pension for loss of sight. Died before 1881.

John Freer (probably late arrival)[221]
Hospital Mate 7 April 1813;
Hospital Assistant 25 April 1815; retired on half pay 25 April 1819; on full pay 25 June 1820;
Assistant Surgeon 21st Foot 9 May 1822; dismissed the service 3 June 1824 'for negligence and professional incapacity'; two men who had each received 1000 lashes under his superintendence having died from the effects of the punishment. Died at Sutton Coldfield, Warwickshire 1857.

---

[221] See Sir John Hall (1911) *Life and Letters*, p. 87.

Andrew Gibson

Hospital Assistant 3 June 1815; on half pay 25 February 1816; on full pay 12 June 1818; dismissed the service by court marshal at Halifax 1821; readmitted as **Hospital Assistant** 20 October 1825;

Assistant Staff Surgeon 29 December 1825; **Assistant Staff Surgeon** for the Veteran Companies of New South Wales 15 February 1826; retired on half pay 25 April 1829;

on full pay as **Surgeon** 3rd Foot 20 January 1832; name last shown on the Army List of 1836.

John Huggins

Hospital Mate 10 January 1814; served in the Peninsula 1814;

Hospital Assistant 25 April 1815;

Assistant Surgeon 2nd Battalion 30th Foot 28 December 1815; on half pay 25 April 1817; on full pay as **Assistant Surgeon** (by exchange) 92nd Foot 6 November 1817; retired on half pay 25 December 1818; on full pay as **Assistant Surgeon** 58th Foot 9 August 1831; retired on half pay 2 August 1833. Died 15 October 1877.

Thomas Lough

Hospital Assistant 12 May 1815; served at Waterloo in the field equipment service; on half pay 25 July 1816; on full pay 25 September 1817; retired on half pay 23 October 1823. Died 1826.

William McChristie

Hospital Assistant 9 November 1813;

Assistant Surgeon 69th Foot 25 April 1814; served at Bergen-op-Zoom 1814, here, he was left in charge of the wounded who could not be moved. For this duty, he was duly thanked by his Commander-in-Chief. He was forced to resign in 1814, having fought a duel with an officer of the same battalion; resigned 15 December 1814; reappointed **Hospital Assistant** 9 February 1815; retired on half pay 25 January 1819; on full pay 25 December 1823; superseded 18 November 1824.

Denis Murray[222,223]

Born January 1793;

Hospital Mate (General Service);

Afterwards, **Hospital Assistant** 9 November 1812; retired on half pay 25 August 1814; on full pay 25 March 1815;

Assistant Surgeon 16th Light Dragoons 22 June 1815; retired on half pay 25 December 1818;

MD (Edinburgh) 1820; on full pay 25 May 1822;

Assistant Surgeon 31st Foot 10 November 1831;

---

[222] May have been seconded to the 16th Light Dragoons during the Battle - see below

[223] His Christian named was spelled with one 'n' but in several *Army Lists* it was spelled with two.

Surgeon 46th Foot 23 November 1832; **Surgeon** 13th Foot (by exchange) 2 June 1833; **Surgeon** 10th Light Dragoons 14 December 1841; **Surgeon** 44th Foot 20 March 1846;
Staff Surgeon (1st Class) 18 September 1846; retired on half pay 10 September 1847.

Daniel Silver
Hospital Assistant 14 February 1814. Presumed a late arrival at Waterloo.

John Hutchinson Walsh
Hospital Mate 1807;
Assistant Surgeon 1st Foot 31 March 1808; served in the Peninsula 1808; **Assistant Surgeon** 4th Foot 29 June 1809; served in the Walcheren Campaign 1809; served in the Peninsula 1810-12; dismissed the service 5 November 1812; re-commissioned as an **Hospital Assistant** 6 December 1813; retired on half pay 25 February 1816; on full pay 29 May 1823;
Assistant Staff Surgeon 5 January 1826. Died on half pay in London 7 December 1827.

Richard Walshe
Hospital Mate 6 March 1812;
Hospital Assistant 23 March 1815; retired on half pay 25 February 1816. Died at Lambeth 7 December 1827.

William Williams
Hospital Mate (general service) 12 July 1810;
Assistant Surgeon 7th Foot 29 August 1811; served in the Peninsula 1810-14; discharged the service 26 May 1814;
re-appointed as **Hospital Assistant** 6 May 1815; he served with the field equipment service at Waterloo; retired on half pay 25 February 1816; on full pay 13 May 1817;
Assistant Surgeon 27th Foot 30 June 1825. Died at St Vincent 29 December 1827.

John Davy
Born 24 May 1790 in Cornwall;
MD 1814;
Hospital Assistant 19 May 1815 - he wrote home to a friend, Mrs Fletcher, from Paris, of his experiences following the battle in Brussels hospitals,
> *The wounded came in immense numbers; the hospital was soon filled. They still continued coming, every place was occupied, so that it became difficult to walk, even in the passages without treading on them. The streets were crowded with wagons and cavalry, all bearing the wounded.'*

Davy wrote rather disparagingly,
> *The horrors of the hospital continued to increase, the cries of the wounded were terrible, especially those of the Belgians. The English [!] in general, bear pain heroically, so do the French. I have seen little difference between them in this respect, but the same cannot be said*

of other troops. The Prussians, Hanoverians and Belgians seem to me deficient in fortitude.'[224]

Davy describes the careful attention given to the wounded by the citizens of Brussels, his work hampered by the distribution of wounded officers in private houses. The door of each house containing wounded was designated by a figure, which chalked the number of wounded housed in that dwelling. Like many Davy was exhausted and,

'The first rest I had was on the 19th when I went by canal barge to Antwerp, in charge of about 200 men, whose wounds were slight, allowing of their removal to make room for the severer cases crowding the hospitals in Brussels.'

When Davy returned to Brussels he found his quarters so crowded with wounded officers that he had difficulty finding a place to lay his head. He describes his work,

'I was now attached to a smaller hospital, in charge of a staff surgeon and here I was initiated in operative surgery. Most of the patients were French soldiers and as composed as our own men. I was struck by their superior intelligence and provident care of themselves. Most of the capital [major] operations, such as amputations of the thigh proved fatal. I well remember after a hard day's work amongst the wounded, the pleasure I had in the late evening when going to rest when all was quiet except the song of the nightingale then in full song and nightingales abounding in the neighbouring park.'[225]

Assistant Staff Surgeon 9 November 1815; on half pay 2 November 1820; on full pay 25 December 1820;
Surgeon 15th Foot 1 February 1821;
Staff Surgeon 29 March 1821;
Physician afterwards, **AIH** 8 November 1827; he served in India, Ceylon (Sri Lanka) and Barbados;
DIG 13 October 1840;
(local rank of) **IG** 13 October 1840 to 10 January 1842; on half pay 11 January 1842; on full pay 30 May 1845 (local rank of) **IG** 30 May 1845 to 21 December 1848; **IG** 22 December 1848; retired on half pay the same day!

John Davy was a noted physiologist and anatomist, and the younger brother of the distinguished chemist Sir Humphry Davy (1778–1829). He was one of the most prolific medical experts of his day. First published in 1862, Davy's book, *On some of the more important diseases of the Army; with Contributions to Pathology,* discusses the prominence of fever, dysentery, cholera, liver disease, pneumonia, and other diseases common to the army, estimating that 45% of deaths in the British Army serving abroad were caused by disease rather than by conflict. Davy also records his observations on putrefaction of bodies, particularly the vital organs, emphasising the need to determine the normal condition of human organs so that abnormal, diseased organs can be easily identified. Died 1868.

---

[224] Glover (2010), *The Waterloo Archive*, Vol I: British Sources, p. 219.
[225] Glover (2010), *The Waterloo Archive*, Vol I: British Sources, pp. 220-1.

Henry Home Blackadder (late arrival)
Hospital Assistant 14 August 1813; served in the Peninsula; retired on half pay 25 August 1814; on full pay 25 March 1815; referred to in letters written by Sir Charles Bell, who enquired concerning patients who had been operated on by Bell;
Assistant Staff Surgeon 21 September 1815; retired on half pay 25 December 1819. Died 13 January 1830.

David Donaldson (late arrival)
Hospital Mate 5 July 1813;
Hospital Assistant 12 May 1815; on half pay 25 February 1816; on full pay 27 June 1821. Died at Isle de Los 12 October 1822.

George Finlayson (late arrival)[226]
He was the brother of Assistant Surgeon Donald Finlayson of the 33rd Foot - probably murdered en route to Paris after the Battle of Waterloo (see below).
Hospital Assistant 3 June 1815; probably arrived in Brussels between 21 and 22 June;
Assistant Surgeon 8th Dragoons 24 September 1818; on half pay 1823; on full pay as **Staff Surgeon** 19 June 1823; he later died at sea on his passage home from India. Correspondent and friend of DIH William Somerville (see above).

Ninian Gilmour (late arrival)
Hospital Assistant 9 August 1813; retired on half pay 25 August 1814; on full pay 25 March 1815; retired on half pay 13 May 1817. Died April 1819.

William Grier (late arrival)
Hospital assistant 6 May 1815; retired on half pay 25 June 1816; on full pay (by exchange) 5 February 1818. Died in Jamaica 25 September 1819.

John Hall (late arrival)[227]
Born 15 November 1795;
Hospital Assistant 24 June 1815; he joined the army six days after Waterloo and was posted to a general hospital in Brussels for duty; on half pay 25 February 1816; on full pay 25 September 1817;
Assistant Staff Surgeon 12 September 1822;
Staff Surgeon 8 November 1827;
Surgeon 33rd Foot 28 July 1829;
Staff Surgeon (1st Class) 26 February 1841;
MD (St Andrew's) 1845;
DIG 25 September 1846; he served in the Kaffir War 1847 also in 1850-1;
IG 28 March 1854;

---

[226] See, *The Mission to Siam and Hué the Capital of Cochin China in the year 1821-22. From the (1826) Journal of the late George Finlayson Esq., Surgeon and Naturalist to the Mission with a Memoir of the Author by Sir Stamford Raffles*, p. 427.)
[227] *Dictionary of National Biography*, also, SM Mitra (1911), *Life and Letters*.

He served as **PMO** in the Eastern Mediterranean during the Crimean War - spending most of his time on the Crimean Peninsula. Expressing initial caution in the use of chloroform and not always in harmony with Miss Florence Nightingale, he and his department came under frequent criticism for many inefficiencies, not all of his own making.[228] Considered by many as not being quite up to his tasks, he retired on half pay 1 January 1857;

KCB 1857;

awarded **FRS** (Edinburgh);

Legion of Honour; Medjidie (3rd Class).

He was one of the first three persons annotated in the Army List, awarded the **Reward for distinguished and meritorious service** (abbreviated **[R]**). Died at Pisa 17 January 1866.

Inspector General Hall - Principle Medical Officer in the Eastern Mediterranean
- a controversial senior medical officer in the Crimean War (1854-6).
(Courtesy Dr and Mrs J. Carey-Hughes)

---

[228] Shepherd J, *The Crimean Doctors, A History of the British Medical Services in the Crimean War*, Volume I, 1991, Liverpool University Press, pp161-7.

Henry James (late arrival)

Hospital Mate 19 August 1813; served in the Peninsula 1813;
Hospital Assistant 25 April 1815. Died at St Lucia, the West Indies 3 January 1824.

Isaac James (late arrival)

Hospital Assistant 12 May 1815; whilst describing his work after the battle and reflecting on the wealth of experience to be had by young surgeons in wartime, James wrote,

> 'I have been extremely fatigued having so many wounded to attend. I was up on only the three first nights after the engagement. We have had lots of legs and arms to lop off. The inhabitants are most particularly kind to the wounded; their attention to them is unremitting.'[229]

Retired on half pay 24 December 1815; on full pay 21 July 1821;
Assistant Surgeon 7th Foot 19 November 1821;
Staff Surgeon 12 September 1824. Died at Malta 19 July 1825.

Robert Knox (late arrival)[230]

Born 4 September 1791;
MD (Edinburgh) 1814;
Hospital Assistant 16 June 1815; a brilliant critical and rather irritable anatomist, surgeon and zoologist of Edinburgh, he may well have travelled out to Brussels in the company of Sir Charles Bell, whose work after the battle he criticised severely. On first appointment in Brussels, where he attended the wounded after Waterloo, he worked at the Gens d'Armerie Hospital. Here he witnessed a French Imperial Guard grenadier, who was so delighted with his recovery from a head strike by a musket ball, that he commented he would gladly go through it all again for his Emperor! After the battle he returned to Hilsea to work.

He served in April 1817, possibly as **Assistant Surgeon** with the 72nd Foot at the Cape of Good Hope, where he made valuable ethnological,

Dr Robert Knox teaching - in later years.
(Courtesy Royal College of
Surgeons of Edinburgh)

---

[229] Glover G, *The Waterloo Archive*, Volume I: p. 223.
[230] See DNB and *Life of Knox*, by Henry Lonsdale, 1870, with portraits.

geographical, meteorological and medical researches; returned to Britain in 1820; conservator of the Museum of the Royal College of Surgeons of Edinburgh 1825;

FRS (Edinburgh) 1823;

FRCS (Edinburgh); he became a most distinguished teacher of anatomy in Edinburgh, but his purchase of 'subjects' from the murdering 'resurrectionists' or 'sack-em-up men', Burke and Hare, in 1828, made him very unpopular. He wrote many works, chiefly on anatomy, physiology, zoology and ethnology; retired on half pay 1830; commuted half pay 1833. Died in London 20 December 1862.

William Lloyd (late arrival)

Born 19 January 1791;

MD (Edinburgh) 1814;

Hospital Assistant 12 May 1815;

Assistant Staff Surgeon 9 November 1815; served during the Kandyan rebellion 1817; retired on half pay 25 December 1819; on full pay (by exchange) 2 November 1820;

Surgeon 36th Foot 18 September 1835; retired on half pay 11 June 1841. Died 13 February 1870.

Michael McDermott (late arrival)

Hospital Assistant 7 February 1814; served in the USA 1815; retired on half pay 25 February 1816;

MD (Trinity College Dublin) 1820; on full pay 12 April 1821;

Assistant Surgeon Ceylon Regiment 25 December 1823; **Assistant Surgeon** 83rd Foot 22 June 1825; **Assistant Surgeon** 61st Foot 2 November 1826;

Staff Surgeon 23 June 1837;

Surgeon 89th Foot 5 April 1839; retired on half pay 4 November 1853. Died in Dublin 1 March 1859.

James Mitchell (late arrival)

Born in 1792, in Fife;

Hospital Assistant 7 June 1813; he served in the Peninsula and then at New Orleans in 1814, later in Holland;

Assistant Surgeon 48th Foot 29 June 1820; served in Australia and retired on half pay 1822; established a slate factory then a tweed factory and became involved in a copper works and was the original owner of the Hunter River Railway Company; commuted half pay 13 September 1833. He died after 1851.

James Rowland Morgan (late arrival)

Hospital Mate 21 February 1814;

Hospital Assistant 25 April 1815; on half pay 25 February 1816; on full pay 28 February 1822;

Assistant Staff Surgeon 25 January 1824. Died at Point de Galle 16 September 1825.

Robert Thin (late arrival)

MD (Edinburgh) 1813;
Hospital Assistant 26 May 1815;
Assistant Surgeon 2nd Ceylon Regiment 23 November 1815. Died at Colombo 26 or 27 July 1819.

Charles Thompson (late arrival)

Hospital Assistant 16 June 1815; employed in Brussels after the Waterloo campaign; retired on half pay 25 February 1816; on full pay (by exchange) 25 September 1817; **Assistant Surgeon** 92nd Foot 25 June 1823. Died at Fermoy 22 June 1829.

Henry William Voysey (late arrival)

Hospital assistant 12 May 1815; retired on half pay 6 February 1823. Died before 1825.

Frederick Wilmore (or Willmore - late arrival)

A certain 'Frederick Willmore' (probably the same person) was gazetted **Hospital Mate** (general service) 12 October 1809; he served in the Peninsula;
Hospital Assistant 19 May 1815; retired on half pay 25 February 1816; commuted half pay 7 December 1830.

William Maurice (late arrival)

Hospital Mate (general service), afterwards
Hospital Assistant 25 April 1811; served in the Peninsula 1812-14; on half pay 25 August 1814; on full pay 25 March 1815; attached to the Royal Horse Guards, in Netherlands **after** Waterloo, then in Paris (with rank of **Hospital Assistant**);
Assistant Surgeon 7th Light Dragoons 9 November 1815; retired on half pay 25 December 1818; commuted half pay 26 October 1830.

Hospital Mates (warranted)

William Daniel Watson
MD;
Hospital Mate 1815, where he worked in the 5th Division;
Hospital Assistant 1 February 1816; on half pay 25 July 1816; on full pay 19 April 1821; resigned the service 21 July 1821.

WD Clarke (late arrival)
Hospital Mate prior to his commission;
Hospital Assistant 24 August 1815.

John Finlayson Nivison (late arrival)
Hospital Assistant 24 June 1815; on half pay 25 April 1816; on full pay 10 October 1822;
Assistant Surgeon 5th Foot 30 June 1815;
Staff Surgeon 6 July 1826; served in Canada 1837-1838;
Surgeon 25th Foot 20 September 1839;
Staff Surgeon (2nd Class) 4 April 1845; retired on half pay 8 January 1847. Died c1863.

Appendix IV:
Apothecaries

William Lyons
Hospital Mate (General Service) 27 June 1811;
Apothecary 9 September 1813; served in the Peninsula 1814; retired on half pay 25 September 1814; on full pay 25 March 1815; served at Waterloo in the Field Equipment Department;
Staff Surgeon 11 June 1818; on half pay 1820; on full pay 25 September 1824;
MD (Edinburgh) 1827; retired on half pay 24 April 1828;
On full pay as **Surgeon** to 34th Foot 17 March 1834, but never joined, since he must have been ill. Died at Quebec 26 July 1834.

Richard Matthews (late arrival)
Born 7 May 1763;
Hospital Mate 20 December 1803; served at the Cape of Good Hope 1805; served at Montevideo in the expedition to Rio Plata 1806; served in the Peninsula 1808-13;
Apothecary 6 April 1809; served in Holland 1814; retired on half pay 25 February 1816. Died 24 March 1846.

James Powell [231]
Hospital Mate 1 February 1796;
Assistant Surgeon Depot (Hospital) Isle of Wight, 10 July 1801;
MD (Marischal College, Aberdeen) 1802;
Apothecary 8 July 1813; retired on half pay 25 April 1817.

John Shower (late arrival)
Dispenser of Medicines 6 April 1812; served in the Peninsula 1812-14; served at New Orleans 1814;
Apothecary 7 September 1815; retired on half pay 25 February 1816; on full pay 25 April 1816. Died at Malta 29 October 1834.

James Wooley Simpson (late arrival)
Born 10 September 1788;
Hospital Mate from 24 June 1811 to 19 August 1812; clerk in the Statistical Department of the Army Medical Board office 20 August 1812 to 17 May 1815;
Apothecary 18 May 1815; on half pay 1 December 1822; on full pay 9 January 1835; retired on half pay 5 December 1856.

---

[231] There is some doubt that James Powell was present at this campaign or, indeed, was a late arrival. His name and service record are included as there is a reference to his possible presence at Sir William Howe De Lancey's bedside, prior to the latter's death. (see above)

James Taylor (late arrival)
Apothecary 9 September 1813;
Previously served as **Dispenser of Medicines** 29 July 1812; served in the Peninsula 1812-13; on half pay 25 July 1814; on full pay 25 April 1815; retired on half pay 25 October 1816; on full pay 25 December 1816. Drowned on passage to Barbados, 28 April 1822.

Appendix V:
Purveyors

Purveyor
William Usher (late arrival)
Born 21 February 1774;
Purveyor's Clerk prior to being commissioned;
Deputy Purveyor 13 November 1800; served in the Peninsula 1808-9; served at the Walcheren expedition 1809;
Purveyor 2 June 1814; retired on half pay 25 February 1816. Died c. 1867.

Deputy Purveyors
George Robinson
Born 16 April 1786;
Purveyor's Clerk prior to being commissioned; served in the Peninsula and at Waterloo (Department of Field Equipment) in this capacity;
Deputy Purveyor 7 September 1815; retired on half pay 25 October 1816. Died 18 May 1852.

Charles Surtees (late arrival)
Purveyor's Clerk prior to being commissioned;
Deputy Purveyor 15 April 1813; served in the Peninsula 1813-14; on half pay 25 September 1814; on full pay 25 April 1815; retired on half pay 25 February 1816. Died September 1823.

George Winter (late arrival)
Born 19 May 1789; probably
Purveyor's Clerk prior to being commissioned; served in the Peninsula 1808-14;
Deputy Purveyor 15 October 1812; retired on half pay 25 December 1816. Died 30 September 1876.

John Saunders (late arrival)
Purveyor's Clerk prior to being commissioned;
Deputy Purveyor 31 August 1809; reduced 25 September 1810; on full pay 30 May 1811; served in the Peninsula 1811-14; on half pay probably 1814; on full pay 25 April 1815; retired on half pay 25 March 1817. Died at Valenciennes c. October 1822.

Jonathan Croft (late arrival)
Born 13 March 1784;
Clerk in the office of the Army Medical Board 3 July 1804-15 April 1812;
Deputy Purveyor 16 April 1812; served in the Peninsula 1812-14; on half pay 25 February 1816; on full pay 23 October 1818; retired on half pay 25 April 1819; on full pay (by exchange) 12 October 1826; retired on half pay 20 August 1850.

George Pratt (late arrival)
Purveyor's Clerk 25 September 1809 to 2 June 1813;
Deputy Purveyor 3 June 1813; served in the Peninsula 1813-14; on half pay 25 March 1819; on full pay 25 June 1819; retired on half pay 25 June 1820; on full pay (by exchange) 25 March 1821;
Purveyor 27 April 1853.

Appendix VI:
Civilian Staff

These assisted with the wounded (or visited the battlefield) in Belgium, after the Battle.

Sir Charles Bell
Consulting Surgeon to the Middlesex Hospital (from 1814)

Charles Bell was born in Edinburgh in November 1774, the fourth son of the Reverend William Bell and Margaret Morice, the latter descended from a line of church ministers. Margaret was left to bring up her sons with very little money. She educated Charles herself and it was from her that he acquired his artistic talent.

Charles elected to follow his elder brother John into medicine and undertook his studies at Edinburgh University. Whilst there he attended his brother's anatomy lectures gaining sufficient knowledge to eventually teach anatomy. He was formally apprenticed to John. In 1798, his last year of studies, he wrote *A System of Dissections Explaining the Anatomy of the Human Body,* which was illustrated by his own drawings. Charles graduated in 1799 and in the same year was elected to the College of Surgeons of Edinburgh, becoming a surgical attendant at Edinburgh Infirmary.

In 1802 Charles published a series of engravings of the brain and nervous system to accompany his brother's lectures and then in 1804 published jointly with John, *Anatomy of the Human Body.* That same year, seeking further advancement, Charles left Edinburgh and arrived in London in the autumn. His published works had brought him to the attention of many eminent London doctors and before long he was accepted into their social scene but this still did not bring him immediate employment. Eventually he settled down in Leicester Street and began lecturing on anatomy and surgery to the medical fraternity and anatomy to artists.

The Corunna oil paintings

Mention of the wars against Napoleon in the early 18th century and one not only thinks of the hard fought victories in Spain and Portugal but the great retreat of the British Army under Sir John Moore (himself the son of a Glaswegian physician) to Corunna in early 1809. After a march of almost 300 miles undertaken in 18 days and nights, often in unimaginable weather conditions, starving, disease ridden and harried by the enemy, the British Army entered Corunna on 11 January 1809. It would not be before 17 January that the army was able to embark, after it had defeated the French force, sadly losing their commander to enemy fire.

When the British fleet, carrying the remnants of the army, arrived off the English coast, they brought some 6,000 tattered, sick and wounded men home, causing considerable consternation in Britain.

Economy had dictated that the general hospitals at Gosport, Plymouth and Deal had previously been closed, leaving insufficient hospital beds ready to receive the sick and wounded. Luckily the Portsmouth area had a highly efficient Inspector of Hospitals in Dr James McGrigor, who quickly set up temporary hospitals in barracks and used hospital ships and hulks to house the sick. The lack of doctors was compensated for by military surgeons (from the Foot Guards) being ordered from London and by civil surgeons volunteering their services. One of the civil surgeons was Charles Bell. He administered to the wounded and afterwards made sketches of his cases, eventually completing them in oils. These paintings are now in the possession of the Royal College of Surgeons of Edinburgh and hang in the Playfair building.

After his brief experience of the world of military surgery, Bell returned to London and in 1811 married Marion Shaw and they moved into 34 Soho Square. Marriage, he found, suited and stimulated him. He began his experimentation and lectures on nerves, especially the cranial nerves. Eventually he discovered that the VIIth nerve, if damaged, would lead to facial paralysis, what we today know as Bell's palsy.

In 1812 he took over the Great Windmill Street School of Anatomy and in 1814 took a position as Surgeon at the Middlesex Hospital. During this time he continued to research and write profusely.

The Waterloo watercolour paintings

In the summer of 1815 the French and British armies met in Belgium culminating in the Battle of Waterloo on 18 June. By day's end there were well over 5,000 British wounded to add to the casualties from the previous engagement at Quatre Bras and also the sick on campaign. Eventually the environs of Brussels, Antwerp and Ghent would have to deal with over 30,000 wounded and sick Allied and French soldiers.

After their initial treatment on the battlefield and in the field hospital at Ferme Mont St Jean, the wounded made the agonising 11-mile journey to Brussels. Each of the six large hospitals in Brussels was filled to bursting and local houses were also crowded with sick and wounded. To help ease the burden canal barges took many of the wounded to Antwerp. Shortage of beds and equipment were not the only problems; there was a lack of experienced surgeons and once word filtered back to England many, both military and civilian travelled out to Brussels. Amongst them was Charles Bell, it is said his only passport, was his set of surgical instruments. He arrived in Brussels on 28 June and commenced operating for up to 12 hours a day.

Bell was a master surgeon, but not a military man. He was given plenty of wounded Frenchmen to treat, but many of them were much delayed in surgery and were ill with sepsis and fever. Inevitably, his results were not impressive (whilst we remain uncertain how many amputations he personally performed, the overall mortality for primary amputation was 27% and for secondary, 47%). He evocatively described his eight days solid toil in Brussels,

Sir Charles Bell,
Surgeon, author, artist, anatomist and pioneer neurological physiologist.
He painted remarkable series of images of casualties from the Retreat to
Corunna and the Battle of Waterloo.
(Courtesy Archives, the Middlesex Hospital)

'I found that the best, that is the most horrid wounds [i.e. the most challenging] left totally without assistance were found in the hospital of the French wounded [the Gens d'Armeries]. This hospital was only forming; they were even then bringing in these poor creatures from the woods [ten to eleven days after the action]. It is impossible to convey to you the picture of human misery continually before my eyes….. At six o'clock [am] I took the knife in my hand, and continued incessantly at work until seven in the evening; and so on the next day, and again on the third.

And all the decencies of performing surgical operations were soon neglected; while I amputated one man's thigh, there lay at one time thirteen, all beseeching to be taken next; one full of entreaty, one calling upon me to remember my promise to take him, another execrating. It was a strange thing to feel my clothes stiff with blood, and my arms powerless with the exertion of using the knife… [232]

Bell took his sketchbook with him and filled it with about 45 black lead sketches (tinted with a red crayon) and copious notes of each case. The watercolours themselves, life size and seventeen in number were completed in 1836 to supplement his own lectures on his return to Edinburgh as Professor of Surgery.

After Waterloo Bell went back to his medical duties and his work on cranial and somatic nerve function continued. In 1821, a paper on one particular subject that Bell had claimed as his discovery, was read to the Royal Society. A French physiologist named François Magendie, however would later claim that his was the pivotal publication on that pioneering work that Bell had initiated. This whole controversy upset Bell considerably.

Appointed as **Professor of Anatomy and Surgery** of the Royal College of Surgeons of London in 1824, this was followed in 1827 by his appointment as **Professor of Physiology** at the University of London but this latter appointment was short lived and he resigned from it in 1831, after disagreements with his colleagues.

Edinburgh finally beckoned him back and he returned as **Professor of Surgery** in 1836 but still continued to travel south to England and it was on such a trip to London in 1842 that he made a short stop at Hallow, near Worcester and whilst sketching remarked, *'here I would like to rest till they come to fetch me away.'* That night 28 April 1842, he died of a heart attack cradled in his wife's arms. He was buried in the local churchyard. Sir Charles Bell leaves the world two unique series of evocative, educational and poignant images of the casualties from the Napoleonic Wars.

Dr Richard Bright

Consulting Physician to Guy's Hospital.
A renowned physician, who was on the Continent around the time of the battle. It is said that he visited the field after the action and obtained a piece of the famous 'Wellington Elm'. This he had made into a snuff-box, now in the possession of the Gordon Museum of Guy's Hospital, London.

---

[232] Gordon-Taylor G. and Walls E.W. (1958), *Sir Charles Bell, His Life and Times*, p. 87.

Appendix VII:
Regimental Medical Staff of the Cavalry

1st Life Guards

Michael Lambton Este - Surgeon (late arrival)

Born 3 August 1779;

MD (Erfurt) 1798;

Assistant Surgeon 3rd Foot Guards 4 September 1800 to 24 October 1802; served in Egypt 1801;

accompanied special mission to Egypt and Levant as **Physician** and **Secretary** 1803-4; served with Nelson's squadron off Toulon in 1804;

re-appointed **Surgeon** to 1st Life Guards 3 October 1812; served in the Peninsula 1812-14.

John Haddy James - Assistant Surgeon

Assistant Surgeon 1st Life Guards 27 October 1812; retired on half pay (by exchange) 30 July 1816; commuted half pay 30 September 1830.

Haddy James wrote a charming journal and he commenced his career with the army at Quatre Bras and Waterloo. Separated from his instruments and equipment, he could do little for Quatre Bras victims. At Waterloo, he followed the 1st Life Guards a way down the slope, but was reprimanded for exposing himself to French ordnance. Still without his instruments, Haddy James, extracted some cavalry casualties to the rear. When his equipment came up, Haddy James was still on the field and treated a Captain White for a lance wound of the chest. Ordered to the rear with his regiment, Haddy James worked at Mont St Jean farm, where he left us little detail, but wrote,

> *'Our work behind the lines was grim in the extreme, and continued far into the night. It was all too horrible to commit to paper, but this I will say, that the silent heroism of the greater part of the sufferers was a thing I shall not forget. When one considers the hasty surgery performed on such an occasion, the awful sights the men are witness to, knowing that their turn on the blood soaked operating table is next, seeing the agony of an amputation, however swiftly performed, and the longer torture of a probing, then one realises fully of what our soldiers are made....... Those who regain their native shores indeed deserve the prayers and the ovation of the population.'* [233]

---

[233] Vansittart J. (1964), *Surgeon James's Journal 1815*, p. 36.

**Surgeon John Haddy James, later Mayor of Exeter and a
co-founder of the British Medical Association.**
(Courtesy the Exeter Hospital Postgraduate Medical Centre)

Richard Gough - Assistant Surgeon

Assistant Surgeon 1st Life Guards 22 December 1812; after the action at Quatre Bras, Gough dressed, treated and possibly amputated Captain Hardinge's left hand after it had been wounded by a missile- the operation was carried out in the attic of the Inn called, 'Le Roi d'Espagne'; retired on half pay 5 December 1818; **MD;** commuted half pay 24 July 1832.

2nd Life Guards

Samuel Broughton - Surgeon

Surgeon Dorsetshire Militia before September 1812;
Assistant Surgeon 2nd Life Guards 22 September 1812;
Temporary rank of **Surgeon** to 2nd Life Guards 22 September 1812; retired on half pay 25 July 1818; **Surgeon** 2nd Life Guards 1821. Died 20 August 1837.

Thomas Drinkwater - Assistant Surgeon

Assistant Surgeon 2nd Life Guards 22 September 1812; retired 25 December 1818.

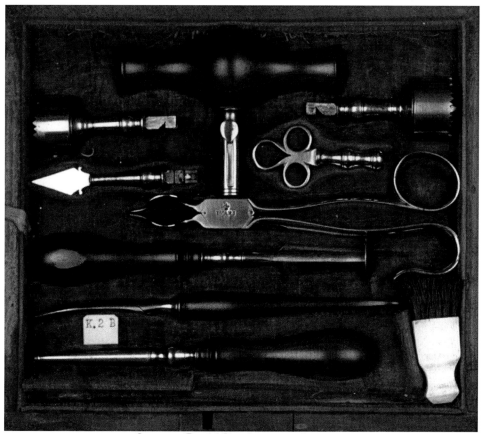

Surgeon David Slow's trepanning set.
(Courtesy of Mrs Margaret Humphries)

Royal Horse Guards

David Slow - Surgeon

Apprenticed to a surgeon and an apothecary in Cambridge 1785-90; pupil in Edinburgh and London 1790-4;

MRCS (London) 16 July 1795;

Hospital Mate 30 July 1795;

Assistant Surgeon Royal Horse Guards 4 July 1798;

Surgeon 52nd Foot 23 August 1799; served at Quiberon Bay and Ferrol; **Surgeon** Royal Horse Guards 18 July 1805; after Waterloo he intermittently attended lecture sessions and demonstrations in 1815/16, 1817 and 1822-4, so continuing and updating his education; retired on half pay 12 January 1826. Died 6 November 1820.

William Maurice - Assistant Surgeon[234]

Hospital Mate (general service), afterwards

Hospital Assistant, 1811; served in the Peninsula 1812-14; on half pay 1814; on full pay 25 March 1815; attached to Royal Horse Guards - in the Netherlands after Waterloo and then in Paris (with rank of **Hospital Assistant**);

Assistant Surgeon 7th Light Dragoons 9 November 1815; retired on half pay 25 December 1818; commuted half pay 26 October 1830.

---

[234] Not with the regiment at Waterloo - see above.

1st (King's) Dragoon Guards

John Going - Surgeon[235]

Regimental Mate Royal Garrison Battalion 6 October 1782; **Regimental Mate** 66th Foot; **Regimental Mate** 54th Foot;
at the time of his first commission, he was a **Hospital Mate** in Grenada;
MD (Edinburgh) 1789;
Surgeon 11th Foot 25 April 1793; **Surgeon** 16th Light Dragoons 13 October 1796;
Surgeon 5th Dragoons 15 March 1798; on half pay in 1799;
on full pay as **Staff Surgeon** 4 April 1800;
Surgeon 1st Dragoon Guards (by exchange) 17 December 1801; retired on half pay 25 February 1817. Died on 7 April 1838.

James William MacAuley (or M'Auley) - Assistant Surgeon[236]

Born 26 April 1790;
Hospital Mate (general service) 1 February 1810;
Assistant Surgeon 63rd Foot 8 February 1810; **Assistant Surgeon** 1st Dragoon Guards 16 August 1810; on half pay 22 August 1816; **Assistant Surgeon** Royal Hibernian School 1817;
Surgeon Royal Hibernian School 1825;
MD (Edinburgh) 1825;
on full pay as **Physician** and **Surgeon** Royal Kilmainham Hospital 12 February 1829; Local rank of **Surgeon** (2nd Class) 2 March 1849; retired on half pay (pension was £333 6s 8d per annum) 1 April 1858.

Richard Arthur (or Robert) Pearson - Assistant surgeon

Hospital Mate Irish Establishment 30 April 1811 to 12 May 1813;
Assistant Surgeon 1st Dragoon Guards 13 May 1813;
MD (Glasgow) 1828;
Surgeon 87th Foot 19 November 1830; retired on half pay 2 March 1847.

---

[235] In *London Gazette* (March 1798) and *Army List* (1799), he is erroneously named 'Goring'.
[236] His name is wrongly spelt 'M'Auley' in the *Army Lists* previous to 1849. His name was shown on the *Army List* (1858) for the last time.

1st (Royal) Dragoons

George Steed - Surgeon

Born 10 December 1781;

Hospital Mate 4 March 1805;

Assistant Surgeon 52nd Foot 14 March 1805; **Assistant Surgeon** 1st Royal Dragoons 15 August 1805;

Surgeon 1st Royal Dragoons 15 august 1811; retired on half pay 22 September 1825;

MD (Edinburgh) 1825. Died 25 February 1853.

Thomas Prosser - Assistant Surgeon

Temporary Hospital Mate January 1809; served at Walcheren 1809;

Hospital Mate (general service) 28 September 1809; served in the Peninsula;

Assistant Surgeon 1st Foot 29 August 1811; **Assistant Surgeon** (by exchange) 1st Royal Dragoons 9 December 1813; on half pay 18 January 1816;

on full pay as **Staff Surgeon** 22 July 1824;

Surgeon 2nd West India Regiment 1 December 1825; **Surgeon** 35th Foot 5 January 1826. Died at St Lucia 27 March 1827.

Christopher Richard Alderson - Assistant Surgeon

Hospital Mate 7 December 1807; served at Copenhagen 1807; served in the Peninsula 1808; served at Walcheren 1809;

Assistant Surgeon 3rd Dragoons 4 October 1810; **Assistant Surgeon** 1st Royal Dragoons 28 October 1813;

MD (Marischal College Aberdeen) 1814;

Surgeon York Rangers 30 November 1815; on half pay 28 March 1816; on full pay as **Surgeon** 62nd Foot 25 February 1821; retired on half pay (by exchange) 14 October 1824. Died 7 February 1829.

2nd (North British) Dragoons

Robert Daun (or Dann) - Surgeon[237]
Born 10 April 1785;
Hospital Mate 14 October 1803;
MA (Marischal College, Aberdeen) 1803;
Assistant Surgeon 59th Foot 17 December 1803; served at the Cape of Good Hope 1806; **Assistant Surgeon** 25th Dragoons 10 August 1807;
MD (King's College Aberdeen) 1813;
Surgeon 2nd (North British) Dragoons 4 August 1814; **Surgeon** 89th Foot 16 January 1817 (by exchange); on half pay 21 April 1826;
on full pay as **Staff Surgeon** 19 January 1832;
DIG 20 January 1832; retired on half pay 15 May 1832. Died 14 June 1871.

James Alexander - Assistant Surgeon
Hospital Mate January 1811;
Assistant Surgeon 2nd (North British) Dragoons 9 January 1812; on half pay (by exchange) 1 March 1821; resigned 1825.

William Henry Young - Assistant Surgeon
Hospital Mate (general service) 19 December 1811;
Assistant Surgeon 91st Foot 4 February 1813; served at Bergen-op-Zoom 1814;
Assistant Surgeon 2nd (North British) Dragoons, but not appointed until 22 June 1815 - transferred from 91st Foot - serving in which, he had received his Waterloo Medal; on half pay 25 December 1818;
MD (Erlangen);
on full pay **Staff Surgeon** 23 May 1822;
Surgeon Ceylon Rifle Regiment 4 September 1828; **Surgeon** 44th Foot 30 September 1836; **Surgeon** 2nd Foot 13 July 1838; **Surgeon** 28th Foot 30 July 1844; retired on half pay 3 November 1854. Died 12 August 1879.

---

[237] Munk's *Roll,* iii, p. 119.

6th (Inniskilling) Dragoons

John Bolton - Surgeon
Born 5 April 1765;
Surgeon 6th Dragoons (by purchase) 14 September 1791; retired on half pay as **Surgeon** 7th West India Regiment 19 February 1824. Died 14 October 1851.

William Henry Ricketts - Assistant Surgeon
Medical Cadet 22 December 1807; served in the Peninsula 1808;
Assistant Surgeon 6th Dragoons 16 March 1809;
Surgeon 35th Foot 7 September 1815; retired on half pay 25 September 1817; on full pay as **Surgeon** 51st Foot 14 May 1829; retired receiving a commuted allowance for his commission 20 November 1829.

7th Hussars

David Irwin - Surgeon
Regimental Mate 24 December 1793;
Surgeon 7th Light Dragoons (by purchase) 22 July 1795. Died before 31 May 1816.

Robert Alexander Chermside - Assistant Surgeon[238]
Assistant Surgeon 7th Light Dragoons 16 August 1810; he served in the Peninsula;
Surgeon 10th Hussars 29 June 1815;
MD (Edinburgh) 1817;
on half pay 30 October 1823; commuted half pay 7 June 1831;
KB 1835;
KCH 1840;
Knight St John of Jerusalem; Knight Red Eagle of Prussia; Chevalier Legion of Honour;
FRCP (London) 1843;
Physician to the British Embassy in Paris;
Physician Extraordinary to HRH Duchess of Kent. Died at Oxford 18 September 1860.

James Moffat (or Moffit) - Assistant Surgeon
Born 10 December 1790;
Assistant Surgeon 7th Hussars 24 October 1811; after the action was over, Moffat rode out to gather in his wounded comrades. Rounding up some peasants, he had them carry the casualties back to the 1st Corps dressing station at Mont St Jean;[239]
MD, CM (Glasgow) 1820;
Surgeon 70th Foot 17 January 1828; **Surgeon** 12th Light Dragoons 1 April 1836;
Staff Surgeon 1st Class 20 January 1843; retired on half pay 13 July 1849.

---

[238] Monk's *Roll*, iii, p. 231.
[239] Adkin M, (2001) *The Waterloo Companion*, p. 314.

10th Hussars

Robert Grant - Staff Surgeon[240]

He was a **Staff Surgeon** at the time of the battle (see above) but may have stood in for Charles Morison who was absent from the battle.

Born 29 May 1777;

Assistant Surgeon 10th Light Dragoons 15 June 1797; on half pay 25 December 1797; on full pay as **Assistant Surgeon** 60th Foot 31 May 1798; **Assistant Surgeon** 69th Foot 19 April 1799; **Assistant Surgeon** 10th Hussars 30 August 1799;

Surgeon 28th Foot 9 July 1803; served in the Peninsula;

Staff Surgeon 1811; retired on half pay 1814; on full pay 25 March 1815; retired on half pay 1818. Died 13 May 1847.

Charles Morison (or Morrison) - Surgeon[241]

Hospital Mate 11 November 1800;

MD (Edinburgh) 1800;

Hospital Mate 10 August 1803;

Assistant Surgeon 10th Hussars 10 September 1803; served in the Peninsula;

Surgeon 10th Hussars 20 June 1811;

Physician afterwards

AIH 29 June 1815; retired on half pay 25 January 1816. Died in Paris 4 May 1849.

George Samuel Jenks - Assistant Surgeon

Hospital Mate (general service) 14 August 1812;

Assistant Surgeon 10th Hussars 22 October 1812; retired on half pay 25 December 1818; half pay commuted 22 June 1830.

---

[240] His Christian name first appeared in the *Army List* (1812).

[241] His name is spelled 'Morrison' in *London Gazettes* and some *Army Lists*. He was absent from the battle.

11th Light Dragoons

Assistant Surgeon Henry Steel
(Courtesy of Mr Peter Steel)

James O'Malley - Surgeon

Assistant Surgeon 16th Light Dragoons 31 December 1803; **Surgeon** 50th Foot 11 July 1811; served in the Peninsula; **Surgeon** 11th Light Dragoons 11 March 1813. Died at Cawnpore 27 July 1820.

Henry Steel (or Steele) - Assistant Surgeon

Hospital Mate (general service) 3 May 1810; served in the Peninsula; **Assistant Surgeon** 5th Foot 25 June 1812; **Assistant Surgeon** 11th Light Dragoons 28 April 1814. Died at Meerut, Bengal 17 January 1825.

12th Light Dragoons

Benjamin Robinson - Surgeon[242]

Born 26 October 1769;

Ensign and Surgeon East Riding Militia 24 March 1793;

Hospital Mate 22 October 1794; served in Holland 1794;

Surgeon 95th Foot 2 February 1795; served at the Cape of Good Hope 1795; retired on half pay 25 December 1796; **Surgeon** 46th Foot 29 June 1797; **Surgeon** 12th Light Dragoons 15 October 1803; served in the Walcheren campaign 1809; served in the Peninsula 1811-14; retired 30 June 1825. Died in Jersey 14 June 1856, aged 87 years.

John Gordon Smith - Assistant Surgeon

Matriculated **MA** (Marischal College, Aberdeen) 1807;

MD (Edinburgh) 1810;

Hospital Mate (general service) 25 April 1811; served in the Peninsula 1811-14;

Assistant Surgeon 11th Light Dragoons 11 March 1813; **Assistant Surgeon** 12th Light Dragoons 28 October 1813; retired on half pay 25 December 1818. Died in London September 1833.

Author of (1830) *The English Army at Waterloo and in France*, by An Officer, 2 volumes, London.

13th Light Dragoons

Thomas Galbraith Logan - Surgeon

Assistant Surgeon 48th Foot 31 January 1805; **Assistant Surgeon** 7th Dragoon Guards 18 September 1806;

Surgeon 71st Foot 24 December 1812; **Surgeon** 13th Light Dragoons 9 September 1813; **Surgeon** 5th Dragoon Guards (by exchange) 25 November 1818;

MD (Glasgow) 1823. Died in Edinburgh 6 March 1823.

He was the father of Sir Thomas Galbraith, who became DG of the Army Medical Department in 1867 and who served in the Crimea.

Abraham Armstrong - Assistant Surgeon

Born 18 June 1779;

Hospital Mate 25 April - 17 May 1809;

Assistant Surgeon 13th Light Dragoons 18 May 1809;

Surgeon 76th Foot 7 March 1816; on half pay as **Surgeon** 44th Foot 28 November 1816; on full pay as **Surgeon** 1st Ceylon Regiment (by exchange) 22 May 1817;

Surgeon 87th Foot 24 April 1826;

Staff Surgeon 19 November 1830; retired on half pay 14 July 1843. Died at Southsea 13 October 1849.

---

[242] In the notification in the *London Gazette*, dated 20 October 1803 and in the *Army Lists* 1804-1810 inclusive, he is wrongly named 'Robertson'. He was the grandfather of S.C.B. Robinson.

15th Hussars

Thomas Cartan - Surgeon

Assistant Staff Surgeon 6 April 1807;

Assistant Surgeon 7th Garrison Battalion 6 August 1807; **Assistant Surgeon** 40th Foot 16 June 1808; served in the Peninsula 1810-14;

Surgeon 15th Hussars 9 September 1813; retired on half pay 15 May 1817;

MD (Glasgow) 1818;

on full pay as **Surgeon** 8th Foot 25 September 1818;

Physician 2 February 1826. Died on his passage home from Sierra Leone September 1826.

Samuel Jeyes - Assistant Surgeon

Born 24 May 1791;

Hospital Mate (general service) 14 May 1811;

Assistant Surgeon 15th Hussars 28 November 1811;

MD (Edinburgh) 1821;

Surgeon 15th Hussars 2 May 1822;

Staff Surgeon 7 December 1838; retired on half pay 17 December 1841. Died at Leamington 15 August 1872.

William Gibney - Assistant Surgeon

Hospital Assistant 19 July 1813;

MD (Edinburgh) 1813;

Assistant Surgeon 15th Hussars 28 October 1813; arriving too late for the action of the 16 June, at Quatre Bras, he noted the dwellings around the village crammed with casualties. Retiring to Mont St Jean, he was ravaged by thirst. The next day, after some time the regiment moved off and Gibney not allowed to go with them. He was ordered to the Mont St Jean field hospital. Here he helped for a while, before being ordered off to find his regiment, which proved difficult. Having found his comrades, Gibney found them rather indifferent to their casualties and a flask of gin was passed round. He had to remain in a lane until ordered back to the farm. He assisted with the amputation of his colonel's leg and stayed on behind in Brussels. He joined Assistant Surgeon Moffat of the 7th Hussars on the 26 June and then they both set out for Paris. He retired on half pay 25 December 1818; commuted half pay 27 July 1830.[243] Gibney wrote a charming and fascinating account of his training and details of his service and experience at Waterloo - *Eighty Years Ago or the Recollections of an Old Army Doctor* 1896.

---

[243] Gibney J., (1896) *Eighty Years Ago or the Recollections of an Old Army Doctor*, pp. 179-216 [The Late Dr Gibney - accounts edited by his son, Major RD Gibney].

16th Light Dragoons

Isaac Robinson - Surgeon
Born 25 April 1770;
Hospital Mate 22 October 1794;
Surgeon 17th Light Dragoons 16 September 1795; **Surgeon** 62nd Foot 3 February 1803; on half pay 1803; on full pay as **Surgeon** 83rd Foot 21 December 1803; **Surgeon** 16th Light Dragoons 21 April 1804; served in Mahratta Wars; served in the Peninsula 1809-14;
DIG 22 July 1830; retired on half pay 22 July 1830. Died 22 September 1848.

John MacGregor Mallock - Assistant Surgeon
Hospital Mate (general service) 28 September 1809; served at Walcheren 1809; served in the Peninsula 1810-1814;
Assistant Surgeon 16th Light Dragoons 16 April 1812;
Surgeon 46th Foot 2 February 1826. Died at Secunderabad 2 June 1832.

Denis Murray - Assistant Surgeon[244]
Born January 1793;
Hospital Mate (general service), afterwards **Hospital Assistant** 9 November 1812; retired on half pay 25 August 1814; on full pay 25 March 1815;
Assistant Surgeon 16th Light Dragoons 22 June 1815 - i.e. he was not officially appointed from hospital assistant until 22 June but was probably serving at the battle; on half pay 25 December 1818;
MD (Edinburgh) 1820; on full pay 25 May 1822;
Assistant Surgeon 31st Foot 1831;
Surgeon 46th Foot 1832; **Surgeon** 13th Foot (by exchange) 2 June 1833; **Surgeon** 10th Hussars 14 December 1841; **Surgeon** 44th Foot 20 March 1846;
Staff Surgeon (1st Class) 18 September 1846; retired on half pay 10 September 1847.

---

[244] Although his forename is spelt with one 'n' in the *Army Lists*, it was invariably spelt with two.

18th Hussars

William Chambers - Surgeon
Regimental Mate 18th Light Dragoons 1 December 1793;
Assistant Surgeon 18th Light Dragoons 26 December 1796; served in Holland 1799;
Surgeon 8th Battalion of Reserve 9 July 1803; **Surgeon** 18th Light Dragoons 25 February 1804; served in the Peninsula; on half pay 1821 (regiment reduced);
on full pay as **Surgeon** 22nd Foot 13 December 1821; retired on half pay 3 September 1825; served in France after Waterloo. Died 23 February 1833.

John Quincey - Assistant Surgeon
Hospital Mate (general service) 16 January 1812;
Assistant Surgeon 18th Light Dragoons 5 March 1812; served in the Peninsula 1813-14; on half pay 25 December 1818; on full pay 13 May 1819; retired on half pay 1821;
on full pay as **Surgeon** 15th Light Dragoons 6 June 1822;
Staff Surgeon 21 December 1826. Died in London 3 October 1827.

Lucas Pulsford. - Assistant Surgeon
Hospital Mate (general service) 12 April 1810;
Assistant Surgeon 8th Foot 17 August 1810; **Assistant Surgeon** 18th Light Dragoons 14 March 1811; served in the Peninsula. Died at Manchester 20 April 1819.

23ⁿᵈ Light Dragoons

Samuel L. Steel (or Steele) - Surgeon

Hospital Mate 11 September 1799;

Assistant Surgeon 89th Foot 7 January 1801;

Surgeon 1st Division of Light Infantry in Ireland 12 November 1801; retired on half pay 25 August; 1806; on full pay as **Surgeon** 6th Garrison Battalion 18 December 1806; **Surgeon** 23rd Light Dragoons (by exchange) 20 April 1809. Died at Weymouth 11 July 1816.

Samuel Steel, Surgeon to the 23rd Light Dragoons.
(Courtesy of Mr Peter Steele)

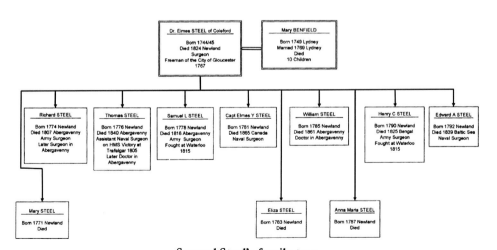

Samuel Steel's family tree.
(Courtesy of Mr Peter Steel)

Henry Cowen - Assistant Surgeon

Hospital Mate 12 June 1808;

Assistant Surgeon 23rd Light Dragoons 4 August 1808; served in the Peninsula 1809-10, during which he had been taken prisoner-of-war, probably after Talavera, when he might have been left as a junior surgeon in charge of casualties of the 23rd Light Dragoons and others, after Marshal Victor had entered the city;

Surgeon 73rd Foot 7 September 1815; on half pay 25 July 1817; on full pay as **Surgeon** 97th Foot 30 July 1818; retired on half pay 1818 or 1819;

MD (Trinity College, Dublin) 1818;

on full pay as **Surgeon** 10th Royal Veteran Battalion 1 November 1819; **Surgeon** 41st Foot 8 June 1820. Died on passage from Rangoon to Calcutta 9 August 1824.

Appendix VIII:
Medical Staff of the Infantry

2-3/1st (Grenadier) Regiment of Foot Guards

Samuel William Watson - Surgeon[245]
Born 12 December 1776;
Assistant Surgeon 1st Foot Guards 20 March 1799;
Surgeon Grenadier Battalion of the Brigade of Foot Guards 14 July 1809; served in the Peninsula;
Battalion Surgeon 1st Foot Guards 25 December 1813;
Surgeon Major 1st Foot Guards 11 November 1824; retired on half pay 17 March 1837. Died 3 November 1849.

William Curtis - Surgeon
Assistant Surgeon 1st Foot Guards 25 December 1796;
Surgeon Flank (Light) Battalion of Brigade of Foot Guards 2 October 1806;
Surgeon Grenadier Battalion of Brigade of Foot Guards 21 August 1809;
Battalion Surgeon 1st Foot Guards (afterwards the Grenadier Guards) 5 October 1809; served at Bergen-op-Zoom 1814;
DIH (local rank) for continental service, in the Netherlands 11 May 1815. Died in London 25 April 1824.

John Harrison - Assistant Surgeon
Born 7 July 1787;
Hospital Mate 30 December 1808 to 28 June 1809;
Assistant Surgeon 1st Foot Guards 29 June 1809; served at Walcheren 1809; served at Cadiz and in the Peninsula 1811-13; served in Holland 1814; served in the Netherlands and in France 1814-18;
Battalion Surgeon Grenadier Guards 29 April 1824;
Surgeon Major Grenadier Guards 17 March 1837; retired on half pay 17 April 1840. Died in London 21 March 1873.
He was father of Brigade Surgeon Lieutenant Colonel CE Harrison Grenadier Guards.

Andrew Armstrong - Assistant Surgeon
Hospital Mate (general service) 12 July 1810;
Assistant Surgeon 1st Foot Guards 18 July 1811;
Battalion Surgeon 1st Foot Guards 11 November 1824. Died 23 February 1828.

---

[245] In the *London Gazettes* and the *Army Lists*, prior to 1813, he was named as Samuel Watson.

John Gardner - *Assistant Surgeon*

Assistant Surgeon 1st Foot Guards 25 December 1813; retired on half pay (by exchange) as **Assistant Surgeon** 52nd Foot 10 October 1816; half pay commuted 12 November 1830;
Surgeon Wiltshire Yeomanry 1840.

Frederic Gilder - *Assistant Surgeon*

Born 16 October 1794;
Assistant Surgeon 1st Foot Guards 9 June 1814; apparently had trouble amputating Captain Robert Adair's thigh in square at Waterloo (see above); on half pay 25 December 1818; on full pay as **Assistant Surgeon** Coldstream Guards (by exchange) 20 June 1822;
Surgeon Coldstream Guards 16 March 1838; retired on half pay 14 April 1843.

2/Coldstream Regiment of Foot Guards

William Whymper - *Surgeon*[246,247]

Born 9 December 1786;
Assistant Surgeon Coldstream Guards 14 November 1805; served in the Peninsula, where he was taken prisoner twice and presumably released or exchanged;
Battalion Surgeon Coldstream Guards 25 December 1813; during the day of Waterloo he was kept busy, possibly working in Hougoumont Farm;
MD (Marischal College Aberdeen) 1817; **MD** (Edinburgh) 1822;
KB 1822;
Surgeon Major Coldstream Guards 24 February 1825; retired on half pay 29 April or 4 September 1836. Died at Dover 26 November 1850.

George Smith - *Assistant Surgeon*

Born 7 January 1793;
Assistant Surgeon Coldstream Guards 17 December 1812; served in Holland and was present at the bombardment of Antwerp;
Battalion Surgeon Coldstream Guards 24 February 1825;
Surgeon Major Coldstream Guards 4 September 1836; in 1836, he took the new surname of 'Chenevix' in lieu of Smith; retired on half pay 16 March 1838. Died in London April 1852.

William Hunter - *Assistant Surgeon*

Born 21 March 1794;
Assistant Surgeon Coldstream Guards 10 February 1814; on half pay 25 February 1819; on full pay 24 February 1825;
Surgeon Coldstream Guards 4 September 1836;
Surgeon Major Coldstream Guards 16 March 1838; retired on half pay 2 September 1845.

---

[246] In the *London Gazette* (1805) named 'Whimper' and in the *Army Lists* of 1806-13 and the *London Gazette* (1 February 1814), he is named 'Wimper'.
[247] Munk's *Roll*, iii, p. 301.

What remains of William Hunter's private diary (much detail of the cases and care of the wounded was removed and destroyed, as it was deemed too sensitive for family reading!) reveals how he spent time before the action at Quatre Bras on June 16 1815.

Assistant Surgeon William Hunter, Coldstream Guards,
later President of the Royal College of Surgeons of London
(Courtesy Mr D Hunter FRCS)

Consultant Surgeon David Hunter, wearing the cloak and cocked hat worn by his ancestor at Waterloo.
(Courtesy Mr D Hunter FRCS)

With his fellow officers he,

> 'slept [sic] with his fellow officers, in a clover field - made a fire with some sticks - champagne from our suttler [sic] and also a little gin - very little to eat. While sitting round the fire - a trooper of the Scots Greys - not knowing us to be officers came and asked that he might be allowed to light his pipe - this request we very readily granted - and in turn we had all round a whiff of his pipe'.[248]

Hunter carried his flute into battle with him.

---

[248] Hunter D (2012), *Personal Communication* re his ancestor's role, diaries and artefacts.

2/3rd (Scots) Regiment of Foot Guards

Samuel Good - Surgeon

Assistant Surgeon 3rd Foot Guards 20 February 1806;

Battalion Surgeon 3rd Foot Guards 25 December 1813; his services to his regiment over 39 years and the work he carried out during the Waterloo Campaigns was regarded as highly commendable. A native of Worcester, he worked inside the farm at Mont St Jean all day. His overall efforts were much praised by his regiment - so much so that Samuel was presented with a later King's Colour of the battalion. This trophy has been since removed (and destroyed) from Worcester Cathedral.

Surgeon Major Scots Fusilier Guards 24 February 1837; retired on half pay 22 July 1845. Died before 1850. A memorial to this surgeon is found in Worcester Cathedral.

An engraved tin container, used for pocket surgical instruments or personal toiletries.
(Courtesy of Mr Gary Barnshaw)

John Richard Warde - Assistant Surgeon

Born 27 January 1780, the only son of John James Warde of Bloomsbury, Middlesex;

Hospital Mate 4 November 1805;

Assistant Surgeon 1st Foot 10 July 1806; **Assistant Surgeon** 1st Foot Guards 2 October 1806; on half pay 25 March 1808; on full pay as **Assistant Surgeon** 3rd Foot Guards (exchanged by purchase) 27 April 1809; served in the Peninsula 1810-11; he was posted to Brussels during the actions at Quatre Bras and Waterloo with a sergeant and four privates to guard the heavy baggage and battalion hospital

equipment. He was engaged in caring for the incoming casualties; on half pay 24 February 1819;
Battalion Surgeon 3rd Foot Guards 4 December 1823; retired on half pay 12 July either in 1823 or 1824. Died at Exmouth 22 May 1867.

Francis Gashry Hanrott - Assistant Surgeon
Assistant Surgeon 1st Foot Guards 28 March 1811; resigned the same year;
Rejoined as **Assistant Surgeon** 3rd Foot Guards 10 December 1812; Francis Hanrott was sickened at a decision after the battle was over. Eighteen men of the light company of the 3rd Foot Guards were disciplined as a result of retiring into the North Gate of Hougoumont, instead of continuing to fight against a severe assault by the French on the west face of the farm complex. The two NCOs of the section were reduced to the ranks, refused further hope of promotion and given 300 lashes each. This and the horrors of the day caused Hanrott to resign his commission in 1815.

3/1st Foot
William Galliers - Surgeon
Born 28 July 1775;
Hospital Mate 2 May 1803;
Assistant Surgeon 1st Foot 25 March 1804;
Surgeon 8th West India Regiment 10 September 1807; **Surgeon** 1st Foot 20 April 1809; served in the Peninsula;
Staff Surgeon 7 September 1815; retired on half pay 25 July 1816. Died 15 December 1861.

William Finnie - Assistant Surgeon
Hospital Mate (general service) 25 June 1812;
Assistant Surgeon 1st Foot 12 November 1812;
Surgeon 19th Foot 26 October 1826; **Surgeon** 1st Foot 13 August 1829; **Surgeon** to the Hibernian School 25 March 1836; retired on half pay 5 March 1841. Died in Glasgow January 1863.

Thomas Bolton - Assistant Surgeon
He was the nephew of Inspector of Hospitals Abraham Bolton, who had served in the Peninsula as a Deputy Inspector of Hospitals.
Hospital Mate 20 April 1810; **Hospital Mate** (general service) 21 February 1811; served in the Peninsula;
Assistant Surgeon 1st Dragoons 5 March 1812; **Assistant Surgeon** 1st Foot (by exchange) 9 December 1813. Died at Trichinopoly 29 March 1821.

**Right; Surgeon Francis Burton of the 4th Regt.
Foot about to perform a field amputation.**
(Painting by Jason Askew)

4th Foot
Francis Burton - Surgeon[249]
He was one of the five Army Medical Officers present at the autopsy of Bonaparte.
Assistant Surgeon North Devon Militia; **Assistant Surgeon** 5th Garrison Battalion 5 March 1807; **Assistant Surgeon** 36th Foot 10 March 1808; served in the Peninsula 1808-9; served in Walcheren 1809; served again in the Peninsula 1811-14;
Surgeon 4th Foot 9 September 1813; retired on half pay 10 December 1818; on full pay as **Surgeon** 66th Foot 16 December 1819;
MD (Edinburgh) 1820;
Surgeon 12th Regiment of Lancers 30 June 1825. Died in London 24 October 1828.

William Morrah - Assistant Surgeon
Assistant Surgeon 4th Foot 25 January 1810; served in the Peninsula 1812-14; served in North America 1814. Died at Barbados 26 December 1821.

3/14th Foot
Henry Terry - Assistant Surgeon
Assistant Surgeon Wiltshire Militia 6 May 1812; **Assistant Surgeon** 14th Foot 21 March 1814; retired on half pay 25 March 1816; commuted half pay 7 December 1830;
FRCS (London) 1843 (one of the first batches of Fellowships to be awarded by the College). Died at Northampton 26 December 1873.
He was grandfather of Professor Sandford Terry, a noted historian and musician.

Alexander Shannon - Assistant Surgeon[250]
Hospital Assistant 4 October 1813;
MD (Edinburgh) 1813;
Assistant Surgeon 14th Foot 27 January 1814. Died at Cawnpore 19 June 1817.

---

[249] Wrongly named 'Barton' in the *London Gazette* (1808) and *Army Lists* (1809 and 1810). Named in the Arnold Chaplin, *Illnesses and Death of Napoleon*, p. 48.
[250] Referred to in the *Gentleman's Magazine* (April 1818), Vol II.

23rd Foot

John Dunn - Surgeon

Regimental Mate 7th Light Dragoons 25 December 1795;
Assistant Surgeon 7th Light Dragoons 9 March 1797; served in Holland in the Helder expedition 1799;
Surgeon 30th Foot 9 July 1803; **Surgeon** 23rd Foot 10 September 1803; served in Germany 1805-6; served at Walcheren 1809; served in the Peninsula; retired on half pay as **Surgeon** to 67th Foot 10 December 1823;
MD (Marischal College Aberdeen) 1824. Died at Plymouth 5 December 1827.

Thomas Smith - Assistant Surgeon[251]

Born at Rathin, Aberdeenshire 26 May 1789; graduated alumnus Marischal College, Aberdeen 1805-8;
Hospital Mate (general service) 6 February 1812;
Hospital Assistant 29 March 1812;
Assistant Surgeon 23rd Foot 2 July 1812; served in the Peninsula, particularly at Vitoria, the Pyrenees, Nivelle, Orthez and finally at Toulouse;
MD (Edinburgh) 1825;
Surgeon 23rd Foot 13 July 1826;
Staff Surgeon then later, **Staff Surgeon** (1st Class) 4 January 1839, at which time he served as **Surgeon Major** to the Forces at Kingston, Canada; retired on half pay 25 September 1846. Died in Aberdeen 29 April 1875, aged 85 years.

John Munro - Assistant Surgeon

Born 3 July 1793;
Hospital Mate 10 December 1812 to 25 May 1814; served in the Peninsula;
Assistant Surgeon 23rd Foot 26 May 1814; after the battle, Munro assisted his commanding officer, Sir Henry Walton Ellis out of a burning byre, after Ellis had been mortally wounded (see above); retired on half pay 25 December 1818;
on full pay as **Staff Surgeon** 23 May 1822;
Surgeon 58th Foot 8 February 1839. Died in Glasgow 10 April 1841.

---

[251] A silver oval regimental medal awarded to this officer is held by the Royal Welch Fusiliers Museum in Caernarvon.

27th Foot

Henry West, John McRobert and Henry Franklin were all gazetted **surgeons** to this regiment at this time, but none of them was present at the Battle.

Gerald Fitzgerald - Assistant Surgeon
Hospital Mate 1808; served in the Peninsula;
Assistant Surgeon 27th Foot 25 April 1811; he was wounded in 1812, possibly at the Battle of Salamanca;
Surgeon 69th Foot 7 September 1815; retired on half pay 25 November 1816; on full pay as **Surgeon** 33rd Foot (by exchange) 9 October 1823; **Surgeon** 1st Foot 23 October 1828; retired receiving a commuted allowance for his commission 16 October 1829.

Thomas Mostyn - Assistant Surgeon
Hospital Mate 7 November 1810 to 18 December 1811;
Assistant Surgeon 27th Foot 19 December 1811;
Surgeon 27th Foot 6 October 1825;
Staff Surgeon (2nd Class) 12 May 1857;
Surgeon Major 1 October 1858; retired on half pay with honorary rank of **DIG** on 7 December 1858. Died in Dublin 6 July 1871.

28th Foot

Patrick Henry Lavens - Assistant Surgeon
Hospital Mate (general service) 28 June 1810;
Assistant Surgeon 28th Foot 24 October 1811;
Surgeon 51st Foot 3 August 1826; **Surgeon** 14th Light Dragoons 13 November 1818. Died at Kirkee, India 16 January 1842.

Alexander Stewart - Assistant Surgeon
BA (Trinity College Dublin) 1812;
Assistant Surgeon 6th Garrison Battalion 25 November 1813; retired on half pay 5 February 1815; on full pay as **Assistant Surgeon** 28th Foot (by exchange) 9 February 1815; retired on half pay 5 August 1819; **Assistant Surgeon** 2nd Dragoons (by exchange) 1 March 1821;
Staff Surgeon 15 May 1835. Died at Falmouth, Jamaica 20 October 1837.

2/30ᵗʰ Foot

James Goodall Elkington - Surgeon

Born 2 October 1784; He was apprenticed to Mr Sloper of Bath for five years and attended St Bartholomew's Hospital as a pupil from 1805-7. During the last of these years, he received his diploma from the London College of Surgeons; present at the capture of Madeira in 1807,

Hospital Mate between 8 August 1807 and 6 July 1808;

Assistant Surgeon 24ᵗʰ Foot 7 July 1808; served in the Peninsula 1809, also between 1810-12; after Talavera, he became a prisoner of war, having been left with around 1,500 wounded in the city. He was sent to Verdun and released in June 1810 and rejoined the army in Portugal and was, yet again, left behind with the wounded after the siege of Burgos had been raised by Wellington in the autumn of 1812. He requested some

Surgeon James Goodall Elkington of the 2/30th Foot.
(Courtesy of the Journal of the Royal Army Medical Corps)

possibility of advancement as a condition of his capture for a second time! Before he was thus made prisoner of war for a second time, a French surgeon took away Elkington's capital surgical instruments, leaving him with an inferior set!

Surgeon 30ᵗʰ Foot 11 March 1813; served in Holland 1814; he noted that the men of the 30ᵗʰ were pretty much ready for combat on the 18 June by 1000hrs. He remained working at Mont St Jean for three days. He was clearly busy at the action of Quatre Bras and at Waterloo. Three days after the battle, he rode out to collect any neglected French wounded. He found many missing casualties, who either from being hidden in dwellings (e.g. La Haye Sainte) or lying too badly hurt to move, under shrubbery etc., escaped notice. These men would not have done well. He noted that the local peasantry was employed in burying the bodies of men and their mounts. Interestingly, he attended the Hotel Dieu Hospital in Paris for three months in 1818.[252]; retired on half pay 25 June 1817; on full pay as **Surgeon** 1ˢᵗ Foot 12 July 1821; **Surgeon** 17ᵗʰ Lancers 11 September 1828; **Surgeon** to the Hibernian School 5 March 1841. Died 3 October 1853.

A biography with portrait and extracts from his journal appear in the Journal of the Royal Army Medical Corps, January 1911, vol. xvi p.78 onwards. He was father of **DSG** A.G. Elkington and grandfather to Lieutenant Colonel, Elkington, RAMC.

---

[252] Elkington HP, "Some Episodes in the Life of James Goodall Elkington, an army surgeon in the Peninsula days, together with extracts from his journal," *Journal of the Royal Army Medical Corps*, Vol XVI, pp. 98-99.

John Evans - *Assistant Surgeon*

Evans was apprenticed to a Carmarthen surgeon for three years. He attended courses of lectures in London. Served at Colchester, then on the expedition to Walcheren (suffered the 'Walcheren Fever') in 1809 (by warrant possibly in anticipation of his commission);

MRCS (London) 16 February 1810;

Hospital Mate (general service, which he carried out at Lisbon, Elvas and Badajoz) 1 March 1810;

Examined for promotion, then **Assistant Surgeon** 30th Foot 22 August 1811; served in the Peninsula, and in the Low Countries under Sir Thomas Graham. In 1816, he served in India, sometimes taking charge of the regiment's sick and wounded, on account of his surgeon's indisposition. Died at Secunderabad 16 July 1821.

Patrick Clarke - *Assistant Surgeon*

Hospital Mate (general service) 12 July 1810;

Assistant Surgeon 30th Foot 25 June 1812; retired on half pay 18 January 1816. Name shown on the Army list of 1823 for the last time.

32nd Foot

William Buchanan - *Surgeon*

Hospital Mate prior to his being commissioned;

Assistant Surgeon 28th Light Dragoons 5 November 1800; on half pay 25 May 1802; on full pay as **Assistant Surgeon** 21st Light Dragoons 23 September 1802;

Surgeon 13th Battalion of Reserve 9 July 1803; **Surgeon** 32nd Foot 17 March 1804; retired on half pay 1 August 1816. Died at Glasgow 14 August 1824.

Rhynd (or Rynd) Lawder - *Assistant Surgeon*

Assistant Surgeon 32nd Foot 25 May 1809; on half pay 23 May 1817;

MD (Edinburgh) 1821;

on full pay as **Staff Surgeon** 20 February 1823;

Surgeon 2nd Royal Veteran Battalion 25 October 1823; **Surgeon** 98th Foot 25 May 1826; **Surgeon** 59th Foot 21 November 1828; **Surgeon** 7th Hussars (by exchange) 12 August 1834. Died at Hounslow 1836.

Hugh McClintock (or M'Clintock) - *Assistant Surgeon*

Hospital Mate (general service) 19 March 1812;

Assistant Surgeon 32nd Foot 5 November 1812; served in the Peninsula 1812-14; on half pay 25 April 1819; on full pay as **Assistant Surgeon** (by exchange) 1st Dragoons 20 April 1820; retired on half pay 6 November 1823;

on full pay as **Staff Surgeon** 16 January 1832; retired on half pay 30 May 1834. Died in Jersey on 15 March 1841.

33rd Foot

Robert Leaver - Surgeon
Assistant Surgeon 33rd Foot 26 November 1805;
Surgeon 53rd Foot 12 October 1813; **Surgeon** 33rd Foot 31 March 1814; retired on half pay 15 December 1817; commuted half pay 8 July 1831.

William Dowell Fry - Assistant Surgeon
Hospital Mate prior to his first commission;
Assistant Surgeon 30th Foot 25 October 1803; superseded, being absent without leave, 19 December 1805;
re-appointed **Hospital Mate** (general service) 29 October 1812;
Assistant Surgeon 33rd Foot 12 November 1812; served in Holland 1814; on half pay (by exchange) 24 July 1817; on full pay as **Assistant Surgeon** 41st Foot 19 July 1831; retired on half pay 28 September 1832. Died 21 August 1837.

Donald Finlayson - Assistant Surgeon
Hospital Assistant 4 October 1813;
Assistant Surgeon 33rd Foot 31 March 1814.
He wrote letters to Dr Somerville of Edinburgh on the 25 and 26 June 1815, from Brussels and Bruges respectively. The following being the extracts from the young surgeon's experiences at Quatre Bras and then at Waterloo. At the former action,

> 'The 300 yards of a road [i.e. he had moved 300 yards in front of the Nivelle/Namur road up front to join his battalion] I had mentioned, was scoured by shot as thick as hail. As I was beginning to enter in on it, the Colonel of the 42nd was killed behind me. Men & horses were lying on it. As I came back I was afraid one ball had broken my horse's leg. I lost one of my spurs here.'

This passage shows he had taken a risk in moving out in front of his battalion and, interestingly, he was mounted and may not have been the assistant surgeon appointed to be up in line that day.

> 'I think more of my escape from this danger than I do of all the dangers I have been saved from, because I had no right to be there'. Later, he recalled, 'As we formed in the solid square on the 16th - Captain Haigh was killed with a cannon ball, as he was most coolly & gallantly encouraging his men & directing them how to act. His brother Lieutenant Haigh was close by and saw him fall & his bowls [sic] gush out. He exclaimed, "Oh kill me with him!" I endeavoured to console him & said it might soon be our own fate. He has since had his wish fulfilled, being shot through the neck on the 18th and dying soon after.'

Young Donald was up with the 33rd on the 18th and commented after the action,

> 'I had myself the charge of about 70 of their [Prussian] wounded & knew of a good many more. They were on our left. There may be about 6,000 wounded French prisoners. One of the Purveyor's Department drew rations for about 4,000 of them. There are said to be about 22,000 prisoners, not wounded..... Of the total loss, one in 7 or 8 may be killed [actually one in three], the rest are wounded. A great number of wounds are from cannon balls. Officers have the discharges of the cannon, to discharges of musketry. Most wounds of the limbs are in the lower extremities. There are perhaps 15 or 16 legs taken off for one arm,

there are not many bayonet wounds. There are sabre and lance wounds. The French cavalry have lances, we have none. Brussels is full of wounded, they have also been sent to Antwerp and Ostend. The Prussians are sent to Louvain. Poor Larrey the French surgeon is there, a prisoner and wounded [see above], having two sabre cuts in his head.'

Donald was out on the field, collecting, dressing and moving the casualties from the 18 to the 23 and on that day was ordered to the hospitals, then on the night of the 25 June, was ordered away to rejoin the battalion.

He had died before 9 November 1815. The tragic story of the demise of this young man will always be clouded in mystery. His brother George, a hospital assistant had met up with another Hospital Assistant, John Davy. After Waterloo, both had purchased horses and rode to Paris together. They were joined by an officer of the Buffs (3rd Foot), who drove a cart for Donald and his baggage. Davy recounted the tragedy,

> *'My friend had an only brother, who was in the same service, but attached as assistant surgeon to a regiment [i.e. the 33rd Foot]. Near Peronne he lost his life and, there was reason to believe was assassinated. He left his detachment on the march to Paris for the purpose of seeing a tunnel in the neighbourhood of the town and was never more heard of. He, like his brother was a young man of great ability. An account of him is given by Sir Stamford Raffles in a short memoir prefixed by him to a work of George Finlayson's, which the former edited. (The mission to Siam and Hué in 1821, published by John Murray, London, 1826).*

We can only speculate that an aggrieved Frenchman, greedy Prussian or an accident terminated young Finlayson's life.[253]

---

[253] Glover (2010), *The Waterloo Archive*, Volume I: British Sources, pp. 221-222.

2/35th Foot (in reserve near Hal)

Charles Simon Doyle - Surgeon
Hospital Mate 7 February 1801 to 11 October 1802;
Assistant Surgeon 55th Foot 12 October 1802; **Assistant Surgeon** 85th Foot 8 January 1807;
Surgeon 35th Foot 31 March 1808; served at Walcheren 1809; served in Holland 1814;
Staff Surgeon 7 September 1815;
MD (St Andrew's) 1816; retired on half pay 25 February 1816;
MD (Louvain) 1818;
on full pay as **Staff Surgeon** (by exchange) 9 October 1823. Died at Demerara 30 October 1836.

William Keoghoe - Assistant Surgeon
Hospital Mate (general service) 3 August 1809; served at Walcheren 1809;
Assistant Surgeon 35th Foot 22 February 1810; on half pay 5 July 1821; on full pay as **Assistant Surgeon** 1st Royal Veteran Battalion 25 October 1823; retired on half pay (the regiment disbanded) 1825. Died before October 1828.

John Purcell - Assistant Surgeon
Hospital Assistant 10 May 1813; served in Holland 1813-14;
Assistant Surgeon 35th Foot 28 July 1814; on half pay 17 December 1817; on full pay as **Assistant Surgeon** 78th Foot (by exchange) 9 April 1818; retired on half pay 24 October 1818; half pay commuted 6 September 1831.

40th Foot

William Jones (not James) - Surgeon
Born 21 October 1782;
Hospital Mate 12 November 1805;
Assistant Surgeon 95th Foot 21 November 1805; taken prisoner of war at the Rio Plata expedition in Buenos Ayres 1807; served in the Peninsula 1808-14;
Surgeon 40th Foot 3 Sept 1812; served in the United States of America 1814-15;
MD (Glasgow) 1818; retired on half pay 10 May 1831. Died at Burton-on-Trent 8 August 1862.

William Barry - Assistant Surgeon
Born 23 February 1785;
Hospital Mate prior to being commissioned;
Assistant Surgeon 40th Foot 4 January 1810; served in the Peninsula;
MD (Glasgow) 1818;
Staff Surgeon 19 November 1821;
DIH 10 November 1825; retired on half pay 25 June 1828. Died at Bath 2 June 1863.

George Scott - Assistant Surgeon
Hospital Mate (general service);
Afterwards, **Hospital Assistant** 24 July 1812; served in the Peninsula 1812-14;
Assistant Surgeon 40th Foot 9 September 1813; served at New Orleans 1814; retired on half pay 25 December 1818;
MD (Edinburgh) 1818;
on full pay as **Assistant Surgeon** 5th Royal Veteran Battalion 1 November 1819; retired on half pay 5 August 1821; on full pay as **Assistant Surgeon** 8th Foot (by exchange) 4 April 1822; resigned 27 July 1825.

42nd Foot

Swinton Macleod - Surgeon[254]
Born 12 June 1777;
Assistant Staff Surgeon 8 September 1797; served in Egypt 1801;
Surgeon 42nd Foot 9 July 1803; served in the Peninsula 1809-12, also in 1813-14;
DIH, afterwards
DIG 5 November 1829; retired on half pay 5 Nov 1829. Died 27 December 1847.

Donald MacPherson - Assistant Surgeon
Assistant Surgeon 42nd Foot 1 June 1809;
Surgeon 62nd Foot 17 February 1825; **Surgeon** 64th Foot 21 Sept 1830; retired on half pay 24 July 1835. Died 25 June 1839.

John Stewart - Assistant Surgeon
Assistant Surgeon to the Perthshire Militia; **Assistant Surgeon** 38th Foot 4 May 1809; served at Walcheren; **Assistant Surgeon** 42nd Foot 20 July 1809; served in the Peninsula 1812-14; retired on half pay 25 December 1818; half pay commuted 1 January 1832. Died at Perth 2 January 1837.

2/44th Foot

Oliver Halpin - Surgeon
MD (Edinburgh) 1802;
Assistant Surgeon 44th Foot 25 September 1803;
Surgeon Royal Corsican Rangers 11 April 1811; **Surgeon** 44th Foot 29 April 1813; on half pay 25 March 1816; on full pay (by exchange) 28 Nov 1816; retired on half pay 12 April 1821. Died at Ostend June 1838.

John Collins - Assistant Surgeon
Born 26 July 1782;
BA (Trinity College, Dublin) 1799;
MB 1803 (possibly Trinity College, Dublin);
MD (possibly Trinity College, Dublin);
Hospital Mate prior to being commissioned;
Assistant Surgeon 44th Foot 1 December 1808; served in the Peninsula from 1808 until 1814, but was taken prisoner of war and was held between January and November 1814;
Surgeon Royal Corsican Rangers 28 March 1816; **Surgeon** 38th Foot (by exchange) 8 July 1816; retired on half pay 13 May 1818. Died 17 February 1841.

---

[254] Named 'Maccloud' in the *London Gazette* (1798).

William Newton - Assistant Surgeon
Hospital Mate (general service) 20 July 1809;
Assistant Surgeon 44th Foot 27 December 1810; on half pay as **Assistant Surgeon** 8th Royal Veteran Battalion 29 November 1821; on full pay as **Assistant Surgeon** 17th Foot 15 June 1830;
Surgeon 17th Foot 8 June 1832; allowed to retire, having received a commuted commission 19 February 1836.

51st Foot

Richard Webster - Surgeon
Hospital Mate 25 November 1800; served in Egypt in 1801;
Assistant Surgeon 90th Foot 26 January 1802; **Assistant Surgeon** 4th Battalion of Line, Ireland 26 October 1804; on half pay (regiment disbanded) 25 October 1806; on full pay as **Assistant Surgeon** 9th Garrison Battalion 18 December 1806;
Surgeon 51st Foot 14 July 1808; served in the Peninsula 1808 and also between 1810 and 1814; served at Walcheren 1809; **Surgeon** 4th Dragoon Guards 3 August 1826; gazetted **DIG** 22 July 1830, but he declined this promotion, which was accordingly cancelled. Died at Piershill Barracks, Edinburgh 14 February 1831.

John Frederick Clarke - Assistant Surgeon
Born 25 August 1873;
Hospital Mate (general service) 27 June 1811;
Assistant Surgeon 51st Foot 25 June 1812;
MD (Trinity College, Dublin) 1815;
Staff Surgeon 21 December 1826;
Physician, afterwards
AIH 4 September 1828; on half pay 11 May 1830; on full pay 22 May 1835;
DIG 9 August 1839;
IG 5 September 1843; retired on half pay 25 June 1847. Died 29 October 1848.

Percy Fitzpatrick - Assistant Surgeon
Hospital Mate (general service) 23 August 1810; served in the Peninsula 1811-14;
Assistant Surgeon 51st Foot 11 March 1813; retired on half pay 25 December 1818; half pay commuted 23 March 1830.

52nd Foot

John Bushby Gibson - Surgeon
Born 11 February 1782;
Hospital Assistant 8 August 1803;
Assistant Surgeon 20th Dragoons 17 September 1803; served in Egypt 1807, he was taken prisoner at El Hamet in April, after which he was transported by a Nile boat to Cairo, the preserved heads of his fallen comrades in the hold below his feet. Heads and prisoners were triumphantly paraded round the city. Gibson was released in September; present at the capture of Ischia and Procida, in 1809;
Surgeon to the Sicilian Rangers 7 December 1809; **Surgeon** 52nd Foot 20 December 1810; retired on half pay 27 September 1833. Died 3 August 1849.

Pryce Jones - Assistant Surgeon
Hospital Mate prior to being commissioned;
Assistant Surgeon 52nd Foot 20 April 1809;
Surgeon 1st Foot 7 September 1815; retired on half pay 25 March 1816; on full pay as **Surgeon** 50th Foot 17 February 1820. Died in Jamaica 9 December 1821.

William MacArtney - Assistant Surgeon
MD (Edinburgh) 1808;
Hospital Mate (general service) 26 October 1809; served in the Peninsula;
Assistant Surgeon 52nd Foot 3 September 1812;
Surgeon 81st Foot 18 October 1827. Died in Ireland 25 May 1833.

54th Foot (in reserve near Hal)

George Redmond - Surgeon
Hospital Mate 5 July 1800;
Assistant Surgeon 54th Foot 8 January 1801;
Surgeon 54th Foot 11 September 1806. Died at the Cape of Good Hope 24 January 1820.

Moore Francis Finan[255] - Assistant Surgeon
Hospital Mate (general service) 7 June 1810;
Assistant Surgeon 54th Foot 28 February 1811. Died at Madras 23 August 1824.

George Leich (or Leech, Leach) - Assistant Surgeon
Born 1797;
Hospital Assistant 10 May 1813;
Assistant Surgeon 54th Foot 25 November 1813; on half pay 25 December 1818; on full pay as **Assistant Surgeon** 6th Royal Veteran Battalion 1 November 1819; retired on half pay 25 May 1821; on full pay as **Assistant Surgeon** 54th Foot 20 December 1821. Died in India, in camp with Brigadier General Morrison's division 12 March 1825, aged 28 years.

---

[255] Name incorrectly spelt as 'Fynan' in all Army Lists.

2/59th Foot (in reserve near Hal)

James Hagan - Surgeon

Hospital Mate previous to his being commissioned;
Assistant Surgeon 59th Foot 26 November 1807;
Surgeon 53rd Foot 9 September 1813; **Surgeon** 59th Foot (by exchange) 25 November 1813. Died after being lost at sea. He was drowned when the transport *Sea Horse* foundered in Tranmore Bay, Waterford 30 January 1816, along with 200 officers and men of the 59th Foot.

Peter K Lambe - Assistant Surgeon

Hospital Mate (general service) 1 February 1810;
Assistant Surgeon 59th Foot 8 February 1810. Died after being lost at sea, on 30 January 1816, following the wreck of the *Sea Horse*. (see above).

Andrew Colvin - Assistant Surgeon

Hospital Mate (general service);
afterwards, **Hospital Assistant** 25 June 1812; served in the Peninsula;
Assistant Surgeon 59th Foot 9 September 1813; retired on half pay 14 June 1816;
on full pay as **Assistant Surgeon** 21st Foot (by exchange) 22 May 1817. Died at Tobago 22 October 1820.

2/69th Foot

Clement Bancks (or Banks) - Surgeon

Hospital Mate 13 June 1800; taken prisoner of war and was held in France;
Assistant Surgeon Royal Regiment of Malta 16 April 1805;
Surgeon Royal Regiment of Malta 5 June 1806; on half pay 25 May 1814; on full pay as **Surgeon** 69th Foot (by exchange) 19 January 1815;
Staff Surgeon 7 September 1815; was employed in the Army Medical Board office in Berkeley Street. Died in London 16 October 1816.

James Bartlet[256] - Assistant Surgeon

Born 28 February 1794;
Hospital Mate (general service) 4 May 1812;
Assistant Surgeon 69th Foot 16 July 1812; **Assistant Surgeon** 88th Foot 3 October 1816; on half pay 25 December 1818;
MD (Edinburgh) 1818; on full pay 8 July 1819; retired on half pay (by exchange) 8 November 1821. Died 1 March 1848.

---

[256] In *London Gazette* (1812) and *Army Lists* of 1813-15, his name was incorrectly spelt 'Bartlett'.

71st Foot

Arthur Stewart - Surgeon
Born 26 July 1785;
Hospital Mate 5 November 1805 to 9 April 1806;
Assistant Surgeon 88th Foot 10 April 1806;
Surgeon 71st Foot 3 September 1812;
MD (Glasgow) 1820;
on half pay as **Surgeon** 62nd Foot 20 November 1823; on full pay as **Surgeon** Royal Staff Corps 25 August 1825;
Staff Surgeon 9 November 1826;
Physician, afterwards **AIH** 27 September 1827; on half pay 11 February 1833; on full pay 5 July 1833;
DIG 9 December 1836; retired on half pay 20 October 1843;
IG 16 December 1845, remaining on half pay. Died in Aberdeen 28 December 1854.

John Winterscale - Assistant Surgeon
Hospital Mate (general service) 28 September 1809;
Assistant Surgeon 71st Foot 8 February 1810;
Surgeon 71st Foot 12 June 1828; **Surgeon** 2nd Dragoons 28 June 1836; retired on half pay 1 October 1847.

Samuel Hill - Assistant Surgeon
Born 1784;
Hospital Mate (general service) 22 March 1810;
Assistant Surgeon 71st Foot 22 March 1810; served in the Peninsula 1811-12 and 1812-14; retired on half pay 25 December 1818;
on full pay as **Assistant Staff Surgeon** 25 March 1819;
MD (Edinburgh 1822);
Staff Surgeon 19 February 1824;
FRS and **FLS**. Died at Portsmouth 31 October 1830, aged 46 years.

2/73rd Foot

Duncan McDiarmid (or McDermid, McDearmid or M'Dearmid) - Surgeon

Hospital Mate 15 October 1803;

Assistant Surgeon 42nd Foot 24 November 1803; **Assistant Surgeon** 6th Garrison Battalion 18 December 1806; **Assistant Surgeon** 6th Royal Veteran Battalion 2 July 1807; **Assistant Surgeon** 85th Foot 1 June 1809; served at Walcheren 1809;

Surgeon 60th Foot 24 January 1811; served in the Peninsula 1811; **Surgeon** 73rd Foot 5 September 1811; after Quatre Bras he is recorded as pronouncing a young lieutenant dead, killed by a tragic accident (see above);

Staff Surgeon 7 September 1815; retired on half pay 25 February 1816; on full pay (exchanged) 25 April 1821. Died in October 1830.

John Riach - Assistant Surgeon

Born at Perth 26 December 1790, son of John Riach, English teacher and Helen Riach (maiden surname Watt);

MD (Edinburgh) 1811;

Hospital Mate (general service) 18 May 1812;

Assistant Surgeon 73rd Foot 2 July 1812 (vice Elmore appointed to 5th Dragoon Guards) served at Ghorde, Hanover, 16 September 1813, where he received the thanks of General Count Walmoden, communicated through Major General Sir Samuel Gibbs, for his conduct on that occasion; served during the campaign of 1814 in the Netherlands, under Sir Thomas Graham (Lord Lynedoch), including the affair near Antwerp, January 1814, the attack on the village of Merxem on the 2 February 1814 and subsequent operations against the French fleet at Antwerp. He served through the Battles of Quatre Bras and Waterloo, losing the sight of an eye from ophthalmia, contracted at Courtrai in the Netherlands, in the discharge of his duties in the hospital of the 2/73·; retired on half pay 25 June 1817, with a temporary pension of £50 per annum, later made permanent to £70; on full pay as **Assistant Surgeon** 19th Lancers (by exchange) 25 September 1817; retired on half pay 11 November 1821 by reduction and bad health contracted in the service; on full pay as **Assistant Surgeon** 63rd Foot 19 January 1826 (by exchange); **Assistant Surgeon** 10th Hussars 24 August 1826;

Surgeon 67th Foot 19 November 1830; retired on half pay 19 November 1841.

He was first married to Margaret McFarlane at St Paul's church, Perth 22 February 1826. He had issue by her and they lived at Allan Bank, Perth. At the time of his death he was married to Jane Clink (maiden name Mondel). Died of an apoplexy 14 May 1864, at 57, King Street, Perth.

Frederick Blundstone White - Assistant Surgeon

Hospital Assistant 26 November 1813;

Assistant Surgeon 73rd Foot 23 March 1815; retired on half pay 25 June 1817; commuted half pay 27 July 1830.

79th Foot

George Ridsdale[257] - Surgeon

Hospital Mate 12 November 1806;

Assistant Surgeon 10 December 1807; served at Walcheren 1809; served in the Peninsula 1811-13;

Surgeon 79th Foot 9 September 1813; retired on half pay 17 March 1816; on full pay as **Surgeon** 15th Dragoons 15 May 1817; **Surgeon** 47th Foot (by exchange) 5 November 1818. Died in Bombay 8 October 1820.

William George Burrell - Assistant Surgeon

Medical Cadet 17 May 1808; served at Walcheren;

Assistant Surgeon 63rd Foot 13 July 1809; **Assistant Surgeon** 79th Foot 14 December 1809;

MD (Glasgow) 1813; served in the Peninsula;

Surgeon 5th Foot 11 January 1816; **Surgeon** 65th Foot 20 June 1816; served in Pindaree War of 1817-9, where the battalion took a leading role at Kirkee and Poona. Died on passage from India to Britain 19 May 1820.

David Perston - Assistant Surgeon

Hospital Mate 19 October 1808 to 31 January 1810;

Assistant Surgeon 79th Foot 18 October 1810;

MD (Glasgow) 1821;

Surgeon 26th Foot 17 February 1825; **Surgeon** 4th Dragoons 15 March 1831; **Surgeon** 13th Foot 28 February 1840; retired on half pay 30 May 1843.

---

[257] Name incorrectly spelt 'Ridesdale' and 'Reedsdell' in various *Army Lists*.

2/81st Foot (in Brussels)[258]
Probably, either;
Peter Schoole - Surgeon
Assistant Surgeon 4th Dragoon Guards 1 May 1797;
Surgeon 2nd Battalion Light Infantry 25 August 1803; on half pay; on full pay as **Surgeon** 81st Foot 17 April 1806. Being the senior of the two candidates for serving with the 81st Foot, he might well have been the man to go out with the 2nd Battalion to the Low Countries.

Or

William Bampfield - Surgeon
Hospital Mate 26 December 1804 to 27 January 1808;
Assistant Surgeon 58th Foot 28 January 1810; served in the Peninsula;
Regimental Surgeon for a particular service in the Mediterranean 21 January 1813;
Surgeon 81st Foot 13 May 1813; on half pay 25 March 1816; on full pay as **Surgeon** 31st Foot (by exchange) 9 May 1816; on half pay De Meuron's Regiment 1 April 1824; on full pay as **Surgeon** 32nd Foot 22 July 1824. Died at Armagh 16 April 1845.

Probably both Assistant Surgeons served in hospitals at Brussels;

Joseph Stockdale - Assistant Surgeon
Hospital Mate prior to being commissioned;
Assistant Surgeon 81st Foot 7 May 1812; retired on half pay 3 April 1817. Died at Downpatrick 17 January 1823.

Walter Richardson Gibb - Assistant Surgeon
Born 19 September 1787;
Hospital Mate, General service, 8 July 1811;
MD (Glasgow) 1811;
Assistant Surgeon 81st Foot 25 July 1812; on half pay 25 March 1816; on full pay as **Assistant Surgeon** 88th Foot (by exchange) 25 May 1816; retired on half pay (by exchange) 8 July 1819. Died 25 February 1855.

---

[258] The 2nd battalion was part of Lambert's Brigade but the battalion remained in Brussels, its surgeons no doubt working on the casualties following the actions at Quatre Bras and Waterloo.

91st Foot (in reserve near Hal)

Robert Douglas - Surgeon
Born 2 September 1782;
Hospital Mate 13 August 1801;
Assistant Surgeon 91st Foot 25 June 1802;
Surgeon 91st Foot 5 June 1805; served at Walcheren 1809; served in the Peninsula; retired on half pay 25 October 1821. Died at Harwich 25 November 1845.

George Murray McLachlan - Assistant Surgeon
Hospital mate (general service) 6 February 1812; served in the Peninsula;
Assistant Surgeon 91st Foot 26 March 1812; retired on half pay (by exchange) 7 June 1821;
MD (Edinburgh) 1822;
Surgeon to the Royal Infirmary Glasgow 1827. Died at Demerara 16 April 1832.

William Henry Young - Assistant Surgeon
Hospital Mate (general service) 19 December 1811;
Assistant Surgeon 91st Foot 4 February 1813; served at Bergen-op-Zoom 1814;
Assistant Surgeon 2nd Dragoons 22 June 1815; retired on half pay 25 December 1818;
on full pay as **Assistant Staff Surgeon** 23 May 1822;
MD (Erlangen);
Surgeon Ceylon Rifle Regiment 4 September 1828; **Surgeon** 44th Foot 30 September 1836; **Surgeon** 2nd Foot 13 July 1838; **Surgeon** 28th Foot 30 July 1844; retired on half pay 3 November 1854. Died 12 August 1879.

92nd Foot

George Hicks - Surgeon
Assistant Surgeon York Rangers 28 April 1804; **Assistant Surgeon** 44th Foot 25 March 1805; **Assistant Surgeon** 2nd Foot 21 April 1808;
Surgeon 92nd Foot 22 August 1811. Died in Ireland November 1817.

John Stewart - Assistant Surgeon
Hospital Mate (general service) 21 November 1811;
Assistant Surgeon 92nd Foot 5 November 1812; he was one of the few medical men wounded during the Waterloo campaigns - during the action at Quatre Bras. After a strong volley from the muskets of the 92nd, a group of French cavalry charged on past a dressing station (possibly the farm of Quatre Bras), where all stragglers were cut down and Stewart, who was dressing a casualty behind the farm had his bonnet cut in two and a lance thrust through his side. His name was seen for the last time on the *Army List* of 1817.

1/95th Foot (Rifles)

Joseph Burke - Surgeon
Hospital Mate prior to his being commissioned;
Assistant Surgeon The Queen's German Regiment, afterwards the 97th Foot 20 November 1802;
Surgeon 95th Foot, (afterwards the Rifle Brigade) 29 June 1809; served in the Peninsula;
MD (probably Trinity College Dublin); retired on half pay 25 September 1828. Died in Dublin 16 September 1838.

James Robson - Assistant Surgeon
Hospital Mate (general service) 1 February 1810;
Assistant Surgeon 43rd Foot 22 February 1810; **Assistant Surgeon** 95th Foot, (afterwards the Rifle Brigade) 21 November 1811; granted a pension of £50 per annum from 25 December 1817; retired on half pay 11 February 1819. Died in Ireland July 1821.

Robert Hobart Hett (or Heyt) - Assistant Surgeon
Hospital Mate (general service) 26 March 1812;
Assistant Surgeon 1st Battalion 95th Foot, (afterwards the Rifle Brigade) 3 September 1812; served in the Peninsula 1812-14; retired on half pay 9 August 1820. Died at Chatham on 27 August 1827.

2/95th Foot (Rifles)

Francis Scott - Surgeon
Born 15 February 1784;
Assistant Surgeon 93rd Foot 14 May 1803;
Surgeon 95th Foot, afterwards the Rifle Brigade, 25 January 1810;
MD (Edinburgh) 1825; retired on half pay 30 September 1836. Died before May 1849.

John Armstrong - Assistant Surgeon
Hospital Mate (general service) 23 May 1811; served in the peninsula;
Assistant Surgeon 95th Foot, afterwards the Rifle Brigade, 11 March 1813; retired on half pay 25 December 1818;
MD (Edinburgh) 1820; on full pay (by exchange) 17 June 1824. Died 3 September 1827.

Robert Scott - Assistant Surgeon[259]
Received his commission on 15 September 1814.

---

[259] The author has found no detailed record of this surgeon. He is listed in the *Army List* of 1815 and in the (1984) *Waterloo Medal Roll*, published by the London Stamp Exchange.

3/95th Foot (Rifles) - two companies

Thomas Putman MacAbe - Assistant Surgeon
MD (Edinburgh) 1812;
Hospital Assistant 19 July 1813;
Assistant Surgeon 95th Foot, afterwards the Rifle Brigade 19 August 1813; retired on half pay 25 December 1818;
on full pay as **Staff Surgeon** 20 or 25 November 1823; resigned 18 February 1824.

Appendix IX:
Medical Staff of the Ordnance

Assistant Surgeon General and DIH

William Wittman

Assistant Surgeon Royal Artillery June 1787;

Surgeon Royal Artillery 9 September 1794; **Surgeon** Ordnance Medical Department 1 January 1804; **Resident Surgeon** (Woolwich) 13 March 1812;

Assistant Surgeon General and **DIH** Ordnance Medical Department 26 Sept 1814; **MD**. He was attached to Headquarters Staff in Belgium and was in charge of the local administration of battery hospitals. Died in Paris a year after Waterloo on 22 July 1816.

Surgeons

Edward Simpson

Supernumerary Assistant Surgeon 25 April 1805;

Assistant Surgeon Ordnance Medical Department 1 August 1806; served in Martinique 1809; served in Guadeloupe 1810;

Surgeon Ordnance Medical Department 5 August 1813; on half pay 1822; on full pay 15 March 1823;

Senior Surgeon Ordnance Medical Department 16 January 1841; retired on full pay 24 January 1844. Died at Jessfield, Scotland 23 September 1854.

John Morgan

Supernumerary Assistant Surgeon Ordnance Medical Department 11 Dec 1805;

Assistant Surgeon Ordnance Medical Department 2 October 1806;

Surgeon Ordnance Medical Department 16 February 1814; retired on half pay 1 September 1817. Died at Dover 4 September 1849.

James Powell

Supernumerary Assistant Surgeon 11 December 1805;

Assistant Surgeon Ordnance Medical Department 4 June 1807;

Surgeon Ordnance Medical Department 28 May 1814; a possible attendant on Sir William Howe De Lancey, at the hamlet of Mont St Jean, a few days before the latter's demise (but see above, p.185 with regard to the apothecary of the same name). He may also have assisted Dr Hume and Mr Fogo in amputating Lord Uxbridge's leg (see page 87); retired on half pay 1 October 1817. Died before January 1842.

Thomas MacMillan Fogo

Supernumerary Assistant Surgeon Ordnance Medical Department 22 January 1806; **Assistant Surgeon** Ordnance Medical Department 1 February 1808; served in the Peninsula;

Surgeon Ordnance Medical Department 26 September 1814; probably assisted with the assessment and surgery performed on Lord Uxbridge (see p87); retired on half pay 1 September 1816;

MD; on full pay 19 March 1825;

Senior Surgeon 1 January 1843; retired on full pay 25 July 1849. Died at Tiverton, Devon 28 September 1850.

Assistant Surgeons

Richard Hitchins

Second Assistant Surgeon Ordnance Medical Department 1 September 1806;

First Assistant Surgeon Ordnance Medical Department 11 November 1811;

Surgeon Ordnance Medical Department 22 July 1815; retired on half pay 1 April 1816. Died at St Ives 17 January 1866.

Mercer's well-known reminiscences of Waterloo include an amusing account of young Hitchin's first nervous impressions of intense combat,

> 'Hitchins was darting his head around in an alarmed fashion as the hail of shot, heat and noise intensified. Mercer was amused and observed the surgeon's comments, "My God. Mercer, what is that? What is all this noise? How curious! - How very curious!" And then, when a cannon shot rushed hissing past, "There! - there! What is it all?" It was all that Mercer could do to persuade the surgeon to retire.'[260]

James Ambrose

Second Assistant Surgeon Ordnance Medical Department 4 September 1806;

First Assistant Surgeon Ordnance Medical Department 11 November 1811;

Ambrose was a rather volatile character, as seen in a passage from Mercer's Journal. Ambrose was troop surgeon to Mercer's battery. Mercer recalls,

> 'After leaving Sir G. Woods, I find no notice of further transactions until the evening, when, accompanied by Ambrose (our troop surgeon), I set off to ride home by the Rue de St Denis and La Chapelle. Returning through La Chapelle accompanied by Ambrose, a fellow sitting on his cart drove against him. Ambrose's temper is rather peppery, and he repaid the affront by a cut across the shoulders with a horsewhip.

> The carter, standing up in his cart, fell furiously on Ambrose in return with his whip, and a regular battle ensued, Ambrose trying to mount the cart, the other keeping him down and flogging him. In a twinkling a crowd assembled, and from reviling soon came to active operations; but I rode round the cart and prevented interference. At last they began to throw stones. This was too much. I drew my sword and charged in all directions, everywhere scattering the wretches like chaff, and thus kept the cowardly herd at bay until Ambrose succeeded in mounting the cart and breaking the fellow's whip over his own back, when, the crowd becoming very serious, he jumped on his horse, and we made our retreat, not, however,

---

[260] Mercer C. (1985), *Journal of the Waterloo Campaign*, pp. 169-70.

without a shower of stones, none of which touched us, and being obliged two or three times to turn on our persecutors, who followed us some distance. At last we effected our retreat.[261]

Ambrose retired on half pay in October 1816;
Surgeon South Mayo Militia. Died at Westport, Ireland, on 17 April 1824.

Alexander MacDonald
MA (Marischal College, Aberdeen) 1799;
MD (Edinburgh) 1806;
Second Assistant Surgeon Ordnance Medical Department 2 September 1807;
First Assistant Surgeon Ordnance Medical Department 5 August 1813;
Surgeon Ordnance Medical Department 20 September 1826; retired on half pay 11 September 1838. Died at Aberdeen 8 March 1860.

Second Assistant Surgeons
Matthias Kenny
Second Assistant Surgeon Ordnance Medical Department 1 December 1810; served in the Peninsula;
First Assistant Surgeon Ordnance Medical Department 5 January 1816; retired on half pay 1 February 1819;
MD. Died in Dublin 24 September 1874.

Edward Rudge
Temporary Assistant Surgeon Ordnance Medical Department 20 May 1812; served in the Peninsula;
Second Assistant Surgeon Ordnance Medical Department 3 December 1812; retired on half pay 1 June 1816. Died at Fakenham 29 November 1854.

Thomas Beard
Temporary Assistant Surgeon Ordnance Medical Department 12 November 1812;
Second Assistant Surgeon Ordnance Medical Department 5 August 1813; retired on half pay 1 November 1822. Died at some spa town on 29 August 1848.

Henry Gatty
Temporary Assistant Surgeon Ordnance Medical Department 26 April 1813;
Second Assistant Surgeon Ordnance Medical Department 20 November 1813; retired on half pay 31 December 1824. Died 6 April 1858.

Edward Donovan Verner
Temporary Assistant Surgeon Ordnance Medical Department 9 June 1813;
Second Assistant Surgeon Ordnance Medical Department 29 November 1813; retired on half pay 30 March 1825. Died in London 9 July 1861.

---

[261] Mercer C. (1985), *Journal of the Waterloo Campaign*, p. 355.

Henry Peter Lædel
Temporary Assistant Surgeon Ordnance Medical Department 9 September 1813; **Second Assistant Surgeon** Ordnance Medical Department 16 February 1814. Died at Montreal 24 March 1825.

William Barker Daniel
Temporary Assistant Surgeon Ordnance Medical Department 8 October 1813; **Second Assistant Surgeon** Ordnance Medical Department 16 April 1814. Died 28 January 1824.

John Bingham
Temporary Assistant Surgeon Ordnance Medical Department 30 November 1813; **Second Assistant Surgeon** Ordnance Medical Department 26 September 1814; retired on half pay 1 May 1816. Died in Ireland 20 January 1825.

Walter Raleigh
Temporary Assistant Surgeon Ordnance Medical Department 30 November 1813; **Second Assistant Surgeon** Ordnance Medical Department 12 October 1814; was three times on temporary half pay but finally retired on half pay 8 November 1832. Died before 1840.

Stewart Chisholm
Born 25 October 1793;
Temporary Assistant Surgeon Ordnance Medical Department 30 November 1813 to 19 October 1814;
Second Assistant Surgeon Ordnance Medical Department 20 October 1814; on half pay 1 March 1817; on full pay 6 July 1825;
First Assistant Surgeon Ordnance Medical Department 17 April 1827;
Surgeon Ordnance Medical Department 11 September 1838;
Senior Surgeon Ordnance Medical Department 1 June 1846; on half pay 8 November 1852; on full pay as **Senior Surgeon** (1st Class) 20 July 1855;
retired on half pay with honorary rank of **DIG** 7 December 1858. Died at Inverness 30 September 1862.

Appendix X:
Medical Staff of the Royal Wagon Train

Surgeon

Thomas Wynne

Hospital Mate 12 March 1794;

Surgeon 2nd Regiment of the Irish Brigade 18 January 1797; served in the West Indies 1798; retired on half pay (regiment disbanded) 1798; on full pay as **Surgeon** 69th Foot 20 June 1799; **Surgeon** Royal Wagon Train (by exchange) 6 October 1808; retired on half pay 12 March 1818. Died before 1825.

Appendix XI:
Medical Staff of the King's German Legion

The Legion was formed in November 1803 and disbanded on 24 February 1816 (thus a frequent resignation date for medical staff of the Legion). The dispersal and fate of some of the Legion's medical staff by this time was; one surgeon and two assistant surgeons had died of illness or accident, one surgeon and one assistant surgeon were placed on 'Reduced Allowance' for infirmity, two surgeons and two assistants were placed on half pay for wounds received or other infirmities, six assistant surgeons had resigned or retired without any allowance, none was dismissed the service by court martial and 12 surgeons and four assistants left the Legion by promotion or transfer to British regiments or the staff of the army.[262]

Staff Surgeons

Christian William Bach
Assistant Surgeon 2nd Battalion Light Infantry King's German legion 25 May 1805;
Assistant Surgeon to the Cape Regiment 25 September 1808;
Surgeon Duke of Brunswick Oel's Corps 25 September 1809;
Staff Surgeon (Continent only) 19 April 1813; retired on half pay 1816. Died at Würtemberg before December 1824.
It was to the house where 'Dr' Bach worked in Brussels that a Sergeant Tuittmeyer of the King's German Legion struggled, after being wounded at Waterloo. Tuittmeyer's arm had been avulsed by a round shot and he had the stump covered, purloined a horse and rode the steed, faint from the loss of blood, until he arrived at Bach's hospital, the St Elizabeth, where he passed out for half an hour, yet survived, as far as we know. [263]

Charles Groskopf
Assistant Staff Surgeon King's German Legion 20 March 1804;
Assistant Surgeon 1st Dragoons King's German Legion 30 June 1804;
Surgeon 3rd Light Dragoons King's German Legion (noted in the London Gazette as being 25 September 1806);
Staff Surgeon, for services of the King's German Legion 4 February 1813; served in the Peninsula 1813-4;
local rank of **DIH** on the Continent 22 May 1816;
MD. Died on half pay at Hanover 1 May 1847.

Victor Christopher Sergel (late arrival)
Surgeon 2nd Dragoons King's German Legion 30 December 1805;
Staff Surgeon 6 July 1809; served in the Peninsula 1810-14; retired on half pay sometime before 1815;
MD; on full pay 25 April 1815;
Physician (local rank on the Continent only) 22 February 1816. Died on half pay early in 1839.

---

[262] Beamish N (1832), *History of the King's German Legion,* Vol 1, Return A.
[263] Crumplin MKH and Starling PH (2005), *A Surgical Artist at War*, p. 82.

KGL Artillery
Henry Kels - Surgeon
Assistant Surgeon King's German Legion Artillery 18 December 1805; served in the Peninsula 1810-13;

most likely promoted **Surgeon**, retired on half pay 24 February 1816. Serving in the Netherlands 1814-15 - Beamish does not seem to credit him for being present at the Battle.[264] Died at Liebenan, Hanover 26 August 1840.

Christopher Frederick Gottlieb Edward Schmersahl - Assistant Surgeon (horse artillery)
Assistant Surgeon 2nd Light Dragoons, King's German Legion 30 December 1805; **Assistant Surgeon** Horse Artillery, King's German Legion 15 November 1809; **MD**; retired on half pay 24 February 1816. Died at Hanover 12 October 1829.

George Crone (or Kroner) - Assistant Surgeon (horse artillery)
Hospital mate (general service) 8 February 1810; **Assistant Surgeon** Horse Artillery, King's German Legion 10 February 1810; retired on half pay 24 February 1816. Later promoted brevet surgeon. Living at Wunstorf, Hanover on half pay. Died 28 April 1845.

Christian Adolphus Rentzhauzen - Assistant Surgeon (foot artillery)
Hospital Mate (general service) 14 August 1812; **Assistant Surgeon** Artillery, King's German Legion 15 April 1813; retired on half pay 24 February 1816. Died at Hameln in Hanover 15 December 1826.

Joseph Christopher William Beyer - Assistant Surgeon (foot artillery)
Assistant Surgeon Artillery, King's German Legion16 January 1814; retired on half pay 24 February 1816. Died at Bergedorff, in Hanover 1819.

---

[264] Beamish N, *History of the King's German Legion*, Vol. 2, p. 538.

1st KGL Dragoons

Frederick Groskopf - Surgeon
Surgeon 1st Dragoons, King's German Legion 30 June 1804;
Staff Surgeon 9 September 1813;
Surgeon 1st Dragoons, afterwards Light Dragoons King's German Legion 27 December 1813; **Staff Surgeon** (continent only) 22 February 1816; retired on half pay 24 February 1816. Died 21 April 1823.

Nicholaus Daniel Meyer - Assistant Surgeon
Hospital Mate previous to being commissioned;
Assistant Surgeon 1st Dragoons, afterwards Light Dragoons, King's German Legion 31 March 1810; retired on half pay 24 February 1816. Died at Hamburg 1 October 1838.

John Henry Christoph Friderici - Assistant Surgeon
Hospital Mate previous to being commissioned;
Assistant Surgeon 1st Dragoons, afterwards Light Dragoons, King's German Legion 2 March 1812; served in the Peninsula 1812-13;
MD; retired on half pay 24 February 1816. Died at Merseburg, Prussia 6 June 1826.

2nd KGL Dragoons

William Frederick Detmer - Surgeon
Assistant Surgeon 2nd Dragoons, King's German Legion 25 December 1805; served in the Peninsula 1812-13;
Surgeon 1st Light Dragoons, King's German Legion 13 July 1813; **Surgeon** 2nd Light Dragoons afterwards Hussars (by exchange), King's German Legion 28 October 1813; retired on half pay 24 February 1816; later became **Surgeon** Hanoverian Garde du Corps. Died at Hanover 9 April 1860.

John Diedrick Lange - Assistant Surgeon
Hospital Mate (general service) 8 February 1810;
Assistant Surgeon 2nd Light Infantry Battalion, King's German Legion 6 October 1812; served in the Peninsula 1813; **Assistant Surgeon** 2nd Dragoons, afterwards Light Dragoons, King's German Legion 16 March 1813; retired on half pay 24 February 1816; later became an **Assistant Surgeon** 1st Hanoverian Cuirassiers. Died at Papenburg, Hanover 27 January 1826.

Charles Thalacker - Assistant Surgeon
Hospital Mate previous to being commissioned; served in the Peninsula 1813; **Assistant Surgeon** 2nd Light Dragoons, King's German Legion 28 October 1813; retired on half pay 24 February 1816. Died at Rudolstadt 3 April 1821.

1ˢᵗ KGL Hussars

Frederick Fiorillo - Surgeon

Assistant Surgeon 1ˢᵗ Light Dragoons, afterwards Hussars, King's German Legion 12 December 1807; served in the Peninsula 1809-13;

Surgeon 1ˢᵗ Light Dragoons, 9 September 1813; retired on half pay 24 February 1816; later **Surgeon** to Hanoverian Guard Hussars.

Fiorillo described (between 1807-13) a case of tetanus (Lockjaw). The patient had a lacerated wound of the foot. Opium and probably potassium bicarbonate were administered half, then quarter hourly. After 24 hours, the patient sweated profusely and his wound was fomented and recovered - a rare event and one of a few cases with this infection that recovered in the Peninsula - described by Sir James McGrigor in his *Sketch of the British Armies in the Peninsula of Spain and Portugal*.[265] Died at Hanover 31 March 1817.

Frederick Deppe (or Deppee) - Assistant Surgeon

Assistant Surgeon 5ᵗʰ Line Battalion, King's German Legion 6 December 1805; served in the Peninsula 1809-13; **Assistant Surgeon** 1ˢᵗ Light Dragoons, afterwards Hussars, King's German Legion 11 April 1811; retired on half pay 24 February 1816; later, **Surgeon** by brevet on half pay at Gersdorff, in Hanover. Died at Gersdorff 19 May 1840.

George Charles Meyer - Assistant Surgeon

Assistant Surgeon 1ˢᵗ Hussars, King's German Legion 15 December 1813; **Assistant Surgeon** Foreign Veterans Battalion 6 October 1815; retired on half pay 24 February 1816. Died 5 November 1823.

---

[265] McGrigor J. (20 June 1815), *Sketch of the British Armies in the Peninsula of Spain and Portugal*, read to the Medical and Chirurgical Society.

2nd KGL Hussars

Frederick William Wollring (or Woolring) - Surgeon

Assistant Surgeon 2nd Light Dragoons, afterwards Hussars, King's German Legion (in London Gazette as 3 December 1805);

Surgeon 2nd Light Dragoons, King's German Legion 19 April 1806 - in the Netherlands, at one stage, the regiment was deployed near Courtrai;

Staff Surgeon (continent only) 22 February 1816; retired on half pay 24 February 1816. Died before February 1839.

Achatz William Holscher - Assistant Surgeon

Assistant Surgeon 2nd Light Dragoons, afterwards Hussars, King's German legion 19 April 1806; served in the Peninsula 1810-13; retired on half pay 24 February 1816; **MD**;

later, **Surgeon** to Hanoverian 11th Line Battalion. Died at Lingen, Hanover 13 November 1847.

Joseph Ader - Assistant Surgeon (late arrival)

Hospital Mate previous to being commissioned;

Assistant Surgeon 1st Line Battalion, King's German Legion 8 June 1809; served in the Peninsula 1809-14; **Assistant Surgeon** 2nd Light Dragoons, afterwards Hussars, King's German Legion 31 January 1811; retired on half pay 24 February 1816; was later appointed, **Assistant Surgeon** to the Hanoverian Rifle Guards. Died at Hanover 30 December 1819.

3rd KGL Hussars

George Ripking - Surgeon

Assistant Surgeon 3rd Light Dragoons, King's German Legion 25 December 1805; served in the Peninsula 1808-9;

Surgeon 3rd Light Dragoons, afterwards Hussars, King's German Legion 4 February 1813; retired on half pay 24 February 1816. Died at Celle 21 October 1824.

Gerhard Lewis Wahl - Assistant Surgeon

Assistant Surgeon 3rd Light Dragoons, afterwards Hussars, King's German Legion 16 December 1805; served in the Peninsula 1808-9; retired on half pay 24 February 1816. Died at Bovenden near Göttingen 6 December 1827.

George Lewis Bauermeister - Assistant Surgeon

Assistant Surgeon 3rd Hussars, King's German Legion 7 September 1813; retired on half pay 24 February 1816. Died at Hamburg 7 October 1848.

1st KGL Light Infantry Battalion

John Grupe - Surgeon

Surgeon 1st Light Infantry Battalion, King's German Legion 25 December 1805; served in the Peninsula 1808-13; retired on half pay 24 February 1816. Died in Hanover 21 October 1833.

Daniel Fehlandt - Assistant Surgeon

Assistant Surgeon 1st Light Infantry Battalion, King's German Legion 9 December 1805; he served in the Peninsular 1808-13; retired on half pay 24 February 1816; **Surgeon** to the Hanoverian Hussar Guards. Died at Hanover 6 March 1829.

George Henry Düvel - Assistant Surgeon

Assistant Surgeon 1st Light Infantry Battalion, King's German Legion 12 December 1807; served in the Peninsula 1808-13; retired on half pay 24 February 1816; was on the Hanoverian retired list. Died at Uslar in Hanover 1 October 1822.

2nd KGL Light Infantry Battalion

Two Surgeons were credited present at the battle.

George Henry Christian Heisse - Surgeon

Christian Heisse was probably the surgeon who drew up and tabulated the list of dead and wounded officers, NCOs and rankers in the Legion from inception to dissolution, namely; 66 officers killed, 39 died of wounds, 153 severely wounded and 154 slightly wounded - 412 in total. Total NCOs, trumpeters, buglers, drummers and rank and file of the Legion 1803-16, deaths from disease, killed in action accident, drowning - 5,300.[266]

Assistant Surgeon King's German Legion 23 July 1805; **Assistant Surgeon** 1st Dragoons, King's German Legion 19 April 1806;

Surgeon 2nd Light Infantry Battalion, King's German Legion 5 October 1812; retired on half pay 24 February 1816. Died 31 July 1839.

Ernst Nieter - Surgeon

Assistant Surgeon Horse Artillery King's German Legion 5 May 1804;

Surgeon 2nd Light Infantry Battalion King's German Legion 22 July 1809; served in the Peninsula 1811; retired on half pay 24 February 1816. Died at Celle 3 March 1825.

Henry Gehse - Assistant Surgeon

Hospital Mate prior to being commissioned;

Assistant Surgeon 2nd Light Infantry Battalion, King's German Legion 3 March 1812; served in the Peninsula 1813; **Assistant Surgeon** 1st Hussars, King's German Legion 6 October 1815 - thus replacing George Charles Meyer on that date; retired on half pay 24 February 1816;

MD. Died 23 February 1847.

H. Frederick A. Müller - Assistant Surgeon

Assistant Surgeon 2nd Light Infantry Battalion, King's German Legion 9 December 1805; served in the Peninsula 1808-11; retired on half pay 24 February 1816. Died at Lüneberg 5 June 1815.

---

[266] Beamish N, *History of the King's German Legion*, Vol. 2, numerical return, B2.

1ˢᵗ KGL Line Battalion

Gottlieb Jacob Hieronimus Wetzig - Surgeon
Hospital Mate previous to being commissioned;
Assistant Surgeon Artillery, King's German Legion 19 April 1806;
Staff Surgeon 25 December 1812;
Surgeon 1ˢᵗ Line Battalion, King's German Legion 12 February 1813; served in the Peninsula 1813; retired on half pay 24 February 1816;
MD. Died at Hildesheim, Prussia 6 February 1830.

Frederick Harzig - Assistant Surgeon
Assistant Surgeon 7 December 1805; served in the Peninsula 1808-13; later on half pay as a surgeon in Hanover;
MD.

Philip Langeheineken - Assistant Surgeon
Hospital Mate (general service) 25 January 1810;
Assistant Surgeon 1ˢᵗ Line Battalion, King's German Legion 31 January 1811; served in the Peninsula 1812-13; retired on half pay 24 February 1816,
MD. Died at Rethem on the Aller, in Hanover 25 March 1851.

2ⁿᵈ KGL Line Battalion

Charles Thompson - Surgeon
Assistant Surgeon 1ˢᵗ Battalion Light Infantry, King's German Legion 1 November 1804;
Surgeon 2ⁿᵈ Line Battalion, King's German Legion 3 September 1805; served in the Peninsula 1808-13;
Later, **Staff Surgeon** of the Hanoverian Rifles; retired on half pay 24 February 1816;
MD; commuted 3 May 1833.

Henry Rathje - Assistant Surgeon
Assistant Surgeon 2ⁿᵈ Line Battalion, King's German Legion 7 December 1805; retired on half pay 24 February 1816;
MD;
remained as a **Surgeon** on half pay at Celle.
Died 6 March 1838.

3rd KGL Line Battalion

Haman Deppen - Surgeon

Surgeon 3rd Line Battalion, King's German Legion 1 December 1804;
Staff Surgeon (continent only) 22 February 1816; retired on half pay 24 February 1816.[267]

Charles Schuntermann (or Suntermann) - Assistant Surgeon

Assistant Surgeon 3rd Line Battalion, King's German Legion 25 October 1805; served in the Peninsula 1812-13; retired on half pay 24 February 1816. Died at Manheim, Grand Duchy of Baden September 1837.

Francis Dagenhart - Assistant Surgeon

Hospital Mate previous to being commissioned;
Assistant Surgeon 3rd Line Battalion, King's German Legion 7 October 1813; retired on half pay 24 February 1816. Resided and died in Vienna.

4th KGL Line Battalion

George Gunther - Surgeon

Assistant Surgeon 1st Line Battalion, King's German Legion 21 April 1804;
Surgeon 4th Line Battalion, King's German Legion 24 May 1805; served in the Peninsula 1812-14; retired on half pay 24 February 1816;
MD. Died at Nienburg 10 January 1830.

John Daniel Matthaei (or Matthias) - Assistant Surgeon

Assistant Surgeon 4th Line Battalion, King's German Legion 12 December 1805; served in the Peninsula 1812-14; retired on half pay 24 February 1816. Died at Lüneburg 15 March 1836.

John Henry Wicke - Assistant Surgeon

Assistant Surgeon 4th Line Battalion, King's German Legion 28 February 1812; served in the Peninsula 1812-14; retired on half pay 24 February 1816,
MD.
Served as **Assistant Surgeon** in Wustrow, in Hanover. Died at Wustrow 5 October 1858.

---

[267] Shown on the *Army List* for the last time in 1831.

5th KGL Line Battalion
Lewis Stuntz - Surgeon
Surgeon 5th Line Battalion, King's German Legion 14 August 1805; served in the Peninsula 1808-14; retired on half pay 24 February 1816;
MD. Died at Hanover 24 November 1841.

Dr. George Hartog Gerson
(Courtesy Dr Anne-Marie Liethen)

George Hartog Gerson - Assistant Surgeon
Hospital Mate (general service) 25 July 1811;
Assistant Surgeon 5th Line Battalion 9 August 1811; served in the Peninsula 1811-13; retired on half pay 24 February 1816;
MD; later served in Hamburg. Died 3 December 1844.

Julius Balthasar Kohrs
Assistant Surgeon 5th Line Battalion, King's German Legion 6 December 1805; retired on half pay 1815. Died at Bergon, Hanover 1 May 1826.

7th KGL Battalion Line Detachment
The **Surgeon** of this battalion was serving with the main part of the battalion and the light company in the Mediterranean (Malta and Sicily and Catalonia)

Casper Henry Brüggemann - Assistant Surgeon[268]
Assistant Surgeon 7th Line Battalion, King's German Legion 30 December 1805; served in the Peninsula 1808-9. Died at Nordheim, in Hanover 3 March 1816.

Henry Schuchardt (or Schuchart) - Assistant Surgeon
Assistant Surgeon 7th Line Battalion, King's German Legion 16 January 1814; possibly assisted with the work of the 1st Line Battalion at or after Waterloo; retired on half pay 24 May 1816;
MD; lived in Cassel, Electorate of Hesse. Died 15 August 1852.

---

[268] Whilst Johnston (1917) has him dying in 1810, Beamish has a specific and later date of death.

8th KGL Line Battalion

John Augustus Frederick Ziermann - Surgeon

Surgeon 8th Line Battalion, King's German Legion 17 July 1806; retired on half pay 24 February 1816. Died at Celle 13 January 1831.

Ernest Sander - Assistant Surgeon

Assistant Surgeon 8th Line Battalion, King's German Legion 4 July 1806; retired on half pay 25 February 1816. Died at Döhren, near Hanover 23 January 1853.

John Christian Lewis Ziermann - Assistant Surgeon

Assistant Surgeon 8th Line Battalion, King's German Legion 5 July 1806; retired on half pay 24 February 1816; remained on the Hanoverian retired list. Died at Celle, 8 April 1825.

Glossary of Abbreviations

AIH	Assistant Inspector of Hospitals
AMS	Army Medical Services
AQMG	Assistant Quartermaster General
BA	Bachelor of Arts
CB	Commander of the Bath
DCL	Doctor of Civil Law
DG	Director General
DIG	Deputy Inspector General
DIH	Deputy Inspector of Hospitals
DSG	Deputy Superintendent General
FLS	Fellow of the Literary Society
FRCOG	Fellow of the Royal College of Obstetricians and Gynaecologists
FRCP	Fellow of the Royal College of Physicians
FRCS	Fellow of the Royal College of Surgeons
FRS	Fellow of the Royal Society
HEIC	Honourable East India Company
IG	Inspector General
IH	Inspector of Hospitals
KB	Knight of the Bath
KCB	Knight Commander of the Bath
KCH	Knight Commander of Hanover
KH	Knight of Hanover
LLD	Doctor of Laws
MA	Master of Arts
MB	Bachelor of Medicine
MD	Doctor of Medicine
MRCS	Member of the Royal College of Surgeons
PMO	Principle Medical Officer
RMC	Royal Military College

Bibliography

Papers and Manuscripts

Anon., (1813) *Instructions for the Regulation of Military Hospitals and the Sick with Divisions of the Army in the Peninsula*, Lisbon.

Anon (1864) *Calendar of State Papers, Domestic series*, 1665-6, July 1666 (Charles II), synopses of original documents, Longman, Green, Longman, Roberts and Green, London.

Anon., (1868) *Calendar of Treasury Papers*, 1556-1696, Vol. XXVII, Longman, Green, Reader and Dryer, London.

Becke AF, (1910), *The Waterloo Campaign,*[269]

Colonel J Muter of the 6th Inniskilling Dragoons (1815). Letter written to his brother [Crumplin MKH, *private collection*].

Crumplin MKH, (1988) "Surgery at Waterloo," *Journal of the Royal Society of Medicine*, Vol. 81, 38-42.

Crumplin MKH and Leaper J, (2012) "The Angels of Waterloo," *The Waterloo Journal*, Spring Edition.

Haythornthwaite PJ, (1989) "The Waterloo Uniform of Lieutenant Colonel Sir Thomas Noel Harris, KH," *Journal of the Society for Army Historical Research*, Vol LXVII, 272, 206-10.

Howard M, (1988) "British Medical Services at the Battle of Waterloo," *British Medical Journal*, Vol. 297, 1653-6.

Hunter D (2010), *Personal Communication* re his ancestor's role at Waterloo - diaries and artefacts.

McGrigor J, (20 June 1815), "Sketch of the British Armies in the Peninsula of Spain and Portugal," *Read to the Medical and Chirurgical Society*.

Personal data from Sir Robert Grant - *a nominal roll of senior medical officers*, found in a despatch case owned by Deputy Purveyor George Robinson. The case also contained Robinson's Waterloo medal and other letters.

Mr Hannington FRCOG (a consultant gynaecologist) c1960 *List of Waterloo Medical Officers*.

Sir Alexander Drummond (April 1965) *List of Medical Officers*.

Two personal (1970s and 1990s) *Surveys of the Medical Staff at Waterloo* .

Major General Alistair MacLennan[270] (1983) *Aldershot personal surveys*.

Captain Peter Starling[271] (1990s) *List of Medical Officers at Waterloo,*

---

[269] An original typewritten account written for and accepted by the XI Edition of the Encyclopedia Britanica
[270] Director of Army Medical Services Museum, Keogh Barracks, Aldershot.

Various donated or lent personal letters and diaries of surgeons, combatants and recorded lectures. Generous personal communications from David Milner, Gareth Glover and Mr John Cruickshank.

Primary Military Sources

Beamish NL, (1832), *History of the King's German Legion*, London.

Booth J, (1815), *A Near Observer, The Battle of Waterloo etc. 1815*, Whitehall, London.

Bowyer R (1816), *The Campaign of Waterloo*, Pall Mall, London

Boyce E, (1816) *The second Usurpation of Buonaparte, or a history of the causes, progress and termination of the revolution in France in 1815, particularly comprising a minute and circumstantial account of the ever memorable Victory of Waterloo*, Volumes I-II, Samuel Leigh, London.

Broughton-Mainwaring R, (1889) *Historical Record of the Royal Welch Fusiliers*, Hatchards, London.

Clode CM, (1869) *The Military Forces of the Crown, their administration and government*, Vol. II, John Murray, London.

Costello, (1997) *The True Story of a Peninsular War Rifleman (including the Adventures of a Soldier)*, written and edited by Hathaway E, Shinglepicker Publications.

Craan JUD, (1817) *An Historical Account of the Battle of Waterloo etc*, Samuel Leigh, London.

Dalton (1890 and 1978), *Waterloo Medal Roll*.

De Lancey, Lady, (1906) *A Week at Waterloo in 1815, Lady de Lancey's Narrative* (Ed. Ward BR), John Murray, London.

Gronow HR, (1877) *Recollections and Anecdotes of the Camp, the Court and the Clubs*, Smith, Elder & Co., London.

Gurwood J, (1867) *Despatches, Correspondence, and Memoranda of Field Marshal Arthur, Duke of Wellington, KG*, John Murray, London, Vol. VII, p. 643.

Jones G, (1852) *The Battle of Waterloo*, Booth L, London.

Mercer C, (Introduction by Sir J Fortescue) (1985), *Journal of the Waterloo Campaign*, Greenhill Books.

Mudford W, (1817) *An Historical Account of the Campaign in the Netherlands in 1815, under His Grace the Duke of Wellington etc.* Henry Colburn, London.

Robinson HB, (1835) *Memoirs of Lieutenant General Sir Thomas Picton*, Vol. II, Richard Bentley, London.

Siborne HT, (1983), *Waterloo Letters*, re-published, Arms and Armour Press.

Siborne W, (1815), *The Waterloo Campaign*, Archibald Constable and Co. Ltd., London.

---

[271] Director of AMS Museum, Aldershot, 1990s.

Walton C, (1894) *History of the British Standing Army*, 1660-1700, Harrison and Sons, London.

War Office, (13th March 1815) *A list of all the Officers of the Army and Royal Marines on Full and Half Pay.*

Secondary Military Sources

Adkin M, (2001) *The Waterloo Companion*, Aurum Press.

Anglesey, the Marquis of, (1961) *One leg, the Life and Letters of Henry William Paget, the First Marquis of Anglesey*, Jonathan Cape, London.

Bowen HV, (1998) *War and British Society 1688-1815*, Cambridge University Press

Brett-James A, (1972) *Life in Wellington's Army*, Tom Donovan Publishing Co.

Divall C, (2009) *Redcoats against Napoleon*, Pen and Sword Military.

Divall C, (2011) *Inside the Regiment*, Pen and Sword Military.

Fletcher I, Editor (2007), *The Waterloo Campaign 1815*, the Folio Society, London.

Fletcher I, (2001), *A Desperate Business, Wellington, the British Army and the Waterloo Campaign*, Spellmount Publishing.

Glover G, (2010) *The Waterloo Archive*, Volume I: British Sources, Frontline Books.

Grant C, Youens M, (1971) *The Black Watch*, Osprey Publishing, Reading.

Hamilton-Williams D, (1993) *Waterloo, New Perspectives*, Brochampton and Arms and Armour Presses, London.

Hope Pattison F, (Ed. Monick S), (2001) *Horror recollected in Tranquillity (Memoirs of the Waterloo Campaign)*, Naval and Military Press.

Hope Pattison F, (1997) *Personal Recollections of the Waterloo Campaign*, (Edited by Elmer R), WG Blackie & Co., Glasgow.

Howarth H, (1997) *Waterloo, a Near Run Thing*, The Windrush Press.

Judd D, (1975) *The Crimean War*, William Clowes and Sons Ltd.

Laudy L, (1921) *Les Lendermains de Waterloo*, Braine-L'Alleud.

Lawrence W, (edited by Bankes NG), (1886) *The Autobiography of Sergeant William Lawrence, a Hero of the Peninsular and Waterloo Campaigns*, Sampson Low, Marston, Searle and Rivington, London.

Morris T, (Edited by Selby J), (1967) *The Recollections of Sergeant Morris*, The Windrush Press, Gloucestershire.

Roberts A, (2005) *Waterloo, Napoleon's Last Gamble*, Harper Collins.

Robinson M, (2009) *The Battle of Quatre Bras 1815*, the History Press.

Snow P, (2010) *To War with Wellington*. John Murray.

Sweetman J, (1993) *Raglan, from the Peninsula to the Crimea*, Arms and Armour Press.

Walton C, (1894) *History of the British Standing Army*, 1660-1700, Harrison and Sons, London.

Weller J, (1967) *Wellington at Waterloo*, Longmans, Green and Co. Ltd.

Primary Medical Sources

Anon, (26 January 1808) *The Fifth Report of the Commissioners of Military Enquiry, appointed by an Act of the Forty-fifth Year of the Reign of His Present Majesty*, cap. 47., Volume 2.

Bell B, (1796) *A System of Surgery*, printed for Bell and Bradfute; and GG & J Robinson, and Murray and Highley, Edinburgh and London.

Bell C, (1814) *A Dissertation on Gunshot Wounds*, Longman, Hurst, Rees, Orme and Brown, London.

Bell C, (1814) *A System of Operative Surgery, Founded on the Basis of Anatomy* (two Vols.), Longman, Hurst, Rees, Orme and Brown.

Bell C, (1821) *Illustrations of the Great Operations of Surgery, Trepan, Hernia, Amputation, Aneurism and Lithotomy*, Longman, Hurst, Rees, Orme and Brown, London.

Bell J, (1800) *Discourses on the Nature and Cure of Wounds* (Vols I & II), printed in Edinburgh for Cadell T, Jnr. and Davies W, London.

Bell J, (1810) *The Principles of Surgery*, Collins and Perkins, New York.

Cooper S, (1822) *A Dictionary of Practical Surgery*, Fourth Edition, printed for Longman, Hurst, Rees, Orme and Brown, London.

Elkington HP, (January 1911) "Some Episodes in the Life of James Goodall Elkington, an army surgeon in the Peninsula days, together with extracts from his Journal," *Journal of the Royal Army Medical Corps*, Vol. XVI, p. 78 onwards.

Gibney J (1896) *Eighty Years Ago or the Recollections of an Old Army Doctor*, Bellairs & Company London. [The Late Dr Gibney - accounts edited by his son, Major RD Gibney]

Guthrie GJ, (1815) *A Treatise on Gunshot Wounds of the Extremities*, Burgess and Hill, London.

Guthrie GJ, (1838) *Clinical Lectures on Compound Fractures of the Extremities*, John Churchill, London.

Guthrie GJ, (1846) *Wounds and Injuries of the Arteries of the Human Body*, 1846, John Churchill, London.

Guthrie GJ, (1847) *Wounds and Injuries of the Abdomen and Pelvis*, John Churchill, London.

Guthrie GJ, (1847) *Injuries of the Head affecting the Brain [also with data on the anatomy and surgery of hernia*, John Churchill, London.

Guthrie GJ, (1848) *Wounds and Injuries of the Chest*, 1848, John Churchill, London.

Guthrie GJ, (1855) *Commentaries on the Surgery of the War in Portugal, Spain, France and the Netherlands,* sixth edition, Henry Renshaw, London.

Hennen J, (1830) *Principles of Military Surgery,* third London and first American edition, Carey and Lea, Philadelphia.

Johnston W, (1917) *Roll of Commissioned Officers in the Medical Service of the British Army who served on full pay within the period between the accession of George II and the formation of the Royal Army Medical Corps, 20 June 1727 to June 1898,* Aberdeen University Press.

Longmore T, (1866) *Description of a series of Watercolour Drawings executed by the Late Sir Charles Bell, illustrative of the Wounds Received at the Battle of Waterloo,* Army Medical School Museum.

Munk W, (not dated) *the Roll of the Royal College of Physicians of London,* Vols II-IV.

Thomson J., (1816) *Report of Observations made in the British Military Hospitals in Belgium after the Battle of Waterloo with some remarks on amputations,* William Blackwood, Edinburgh and T. Cadell and W. Davies of London.

Secondary Medical Sources

Ackroyd M, Brockliss L, Moss M, Retford K, and Stevenson J, (2006) *Advancing with the Army, Medicine, the Professions, and social Mobility in the British Isles, 1790-1850,* Oxford University Press.

Blanco RL, (1974) *Wellington's Surgeon general: Sir James McGrigor,* Duke University Press.

Cantlie N, (1974) *A History of the Army Medical Department,* Vol. 1., Churchill Livingstone.

Chaplin A, (1919) *Medicine in England during the reign of George III,* London.

Crawford DG, (1914) *A History of the Indian Medical Service, 1600-1913,* W. Thacker & Son, London.

Crumplin MKH and Starling PH, (2005) *A Surgical Artist at War, the paintings and sketches of Sir Charles Bell 1809-1815,* the Royal College of Surgeons of Edinburgh.

Crumplin MKH, (2007) *Men of Steel,* Quiller Publishing.

Crumplin MKH, (2010) *Guthrie's War,* Pen and Sword Publishing.

Dible JH, (1970) *Napoleon's Surgeon,* William Heinemann Medical Books, London.

Evrard E, (not dated) *Chirurgiens Militaire Britannique à la Bataille de Waterloo et dans les Hôpitaux de Bruxelles en Juin 1815,* Waterloo Committee, Brussels,

Gordon-Taylor G and Walls EW, (1958) *Sir Charles Bell, His Life and Times,* E & S Livingstone Ltd., Edinburgh and London.

Howard M, (2002) *Wellington's Doctors: the British Army Medical Services in the Napoleonic Wars,* Spellmount Publishing, Staplehurst.

Howard M. (2006) *Napoleon's Doctors,* Spellmount Publishing Ltd.

Hurt R, (2008) *George Guthrie, Soldier and Pioneer Surgeon*, The Royal Society of Medicine Press.

Kaufman MH, (2001) *Surgeons at War: Medical Arrangements for the Treatment of the Sick and Wounded in the British Army during the late 18th and early 19th Centuries*, Greenwood Publishing Group.

Kaufman MH (2003) *The Regius Chair of Military Surgery in the University of Edinburgh, 1806-55*. Clio Medica.

Kaufman MH, (2003) *Musket-Ball and Sabre Injuries from the first half of the Nineteenth Century*, the Royal College of Surgeons of Edinburgh.

Keegan J, (1976) *The Face of Battle*, Jonathan Cape, London.

McGrigor M, Ed. (2000) *Sir James McGrigor, The Scalpel and the Sword*, Scottish Cultural Press.

Richardson R, (1974) *Larrey: Surgeon to Napoleon's Imperial Guard*, John Murray, London.

Shepherd J (1991) *The Crimean Doctors, A History of the British Medical Services in the Crimean War*, Volume I, Liverpool University Press.

Stanley P, (2003) *For Fear of Pain, British Surgery, 1790-1815*, Clio Medical, Amsterdam.

Vansittart J., Ed., (1964) *Surgeon James's Journal 1815*, Cassell & Co. Ltd., London

Index

To assist the reader, six indexes have been created [*Casualties at Waterloo, Waterloo Medical Staff, Index of Names, Index of Medical Terms, Place Index* and *Military Unit Index*]. Page numbers in **bold** refer to sections.

Casualties at Waterloo

Waterloo Medical Staff

Apothecaries:
Garnier, George, Apothecary General; 52
Lyons, William; **185**
Mathews, Richard; **185**
Powell, James; 98, **185**
Shower, John; **185**
Simpson, James Wooley; **185**
Taylor, James; **186**

Assistant Staff Surgeons and Hospital Assistant Surgeons to the Forces:
Blackadder, Henry Home; **179**
Cahill, Thomas William; **175**
Cannan, William; **175**
Caverhill, Robert; **175**
Davy, John; **177-178**
Dease, James; **173**
Donaldson, David; **179**
Evers, George; **175**
Finlayson, George; **179**
Freer, John; **175**
Gibson, Andrew; **176**
Gilmour, Ninian; **179**
Grier, William; **179**
Hall, John; 175, **179-180**
Huggins, John; **176**
James, Henry; **181**
James, Isaac; **181**
Knox, Robert; **181-182**
Lloyd, William; **182**
Lough, Thomas; **176**
Maurice, William; **183**
McChristie, William; **176**
McDermott, Michael; **182**
McWhirter, Thomas; **174**
Mitchell, James; **182**
Morgan, James Rowland; **182**
Murray, Denis; **176**
Silver, Daniel; **177**
Thin, Robert; **183**
Thompson, Charles; **183**
Twining, William; **173**
Voysey, Henry William; **183**
Walsh, John Hutchinson; **177**
Walshe, Richard; **177**
Williams, William; **177**
Wilmore, Frederick; **183**

Civilian Medical Staff at Waterloo,
Bell, Sir Charles, **189-192**
Bright, Dr. Richard; **192**

Director General of the Army Medical Department:
McGrigor, Sir James; 7, 9, 11, **149-151**, 190, 244

Hospital Mates (warranted):
Clarke, WD; **184**
Nivison, John Finlayson; **184**
Watson, William Daniel; **184**

Inspector of Hospitals / Principal Medical Officer:
Grant, Inspector Sir James Robert; 12, 13, 43, **151**

Inspectors, Deputy:
Albert, George Frederick; **154**
Curtis, William; **153**
Gunning, John; **152**
Guthrie, George James; 10, 41, 60, 62, 64, 66, 70, 73, 81-82, 144, **155-156**, 160, 167,
Higgins, Summers; 63, **154**
Hume, John Robert (personal physician to the Duke of Wellington); 118, **153**, 235
McNeil, Donald; **155**
Sommerville, William; **156**, 179
Taylor, William; **152**
Thomson, Thomas; **155**
Wittman, William (Assistant Surgeon General); **236**
Woolriche, Stephen; 96, **152-153**

Physicians,
Denecke, George; 148, **157**
Dwyer, John; **158**
Eyre, John; **158**
Forbes, James; **159**
Home, Francis; **158**
MacDougle, James; **159**
MacKenzie, John; **158**
Somers, Edmund Sigismund; **157**
Tice, Charles Graham; **159**
Walsh, Edward; **157**
Wray, William Galbraith; **158**

Purveyors:
Usher, William; **187**

Purveyors, Deputy:
Croft, Jonathon; **187**
Pratt, George; **188**
Robinson, George; **187**

Index of Names

Index of Medical Terms

Place Index

Military Unit Index

28th Light Dragoons; 220
29th Light Dragoons; 119

British Cavalry Brigades
1st (Household) Brigade; 17-18, 88, 94, 102, 107
2nd (Union) Brigade; 17-18, 94, 110, 112-114

British Garrison Battalions
2nd Garrison Battalion; 138
5th Garrison Battalion; 218
6th Garrison Battalion; 207, 230
7th Garrison Battalion; 169, 171, 204
8th Garrison Battalion; 161
9th Garrison Battalion; 226
Royal Garrison Battalion; 192

British Infantry Regiments
1st (Grenadier) Foot Guards; 22; 36, 54, 56, 84, 97, **124**, 154, **209-210**, 213, 214
2nd (Coldstream) Foot Guards; 36, 54, 56, 84, **125, 210-212**
3rd Foot Guards; 12, 14, 36, 54, 56, 61, 84, 154, 158, 193, **213-214**
1st (Royal Scots) Foot; 36, 177, 198, 213, 218, 219, 227; 3/; **214**
2nd Regiment; 199, 233
3rd Regiment; 154, 167, 176, 222
4th Regiment; 152, 165, 177, 216; 1/; **214-215**
5th Regiment; 167, 184, 202, 231
6th Regiment; 158, 167, 170
7th Regiment; 177, 181
8th Regiment; 171, 204, 206, 224
10th Regiment; 167
11th Regiment; 151, 197
13th Regiment; 168, 170, 176, 205, 231
14th Regiment; 161, 175; 3/; **125, 216**
15th Regiment; 178
17th Regiment; 225
19th Regiment; 214
21st Regiment; 175, 228
22nd Regiment; 206
23rd Regiment; 114, **126, 217**
24th Regiment; 219
25th Regiment; 184
26th Regiment; 231
27th Regiment; **128**, 158, 177, **218**
28th Regiment; **129**, 161, 167, 199, 201, **218**, 233
29th Regiment; 155, 157

30th Regiment; 159, 169, 176, 217; 2/; **129-130, 219-220**, 221
31st Regiment; 163, 176, 205, 232
32nd Regiment; 160, **220**, 232
33rd Regiment; **131**, 135, 179, 218, **221**
34th Regiment; 185
35th Regiment; 198, 200; 2/; **223**
36th Regiment; 182, 216
37th Regiment; 171
38th Regiment; 168, 170, 225
39th Regiment; 158, 159, 171
40th Regiment; 169, 204; 1/; **132, 224**
41st Regiment; 208, 221
42nd Regiment; 31, **133, 225**, 230
43rd Regiment; 170, 234
44th Regiment; 177, 199, 203, 205; 2/; **134, 225**, 233
45th Regiment; 167, 170
46th Regiment; 177, 203, 205
47th Regiment; 231
48th Regiment; 182, 203
49th Regiment; 157, 170
50th Regiment; 202, 227
51st Regiment; 200, 218, **226**
52nd Regiment; 137, 162, 167, 196, 198, 210, **227**
53rd Regiment; 160, 161, 171, **221**, 223
54th Regiment; 197; 2/; **227**
55th Regiment; 223
57th Regiment; 124
58th Regiment; 158, 165, 176, 217, 232
59th Regiment 154, 199, 220; 2/; **135, 228**
60th Regiment; 161, 164, 168, 170, 201, 230
61st Regiment; 182
62nd Regiment; 157, 170, 198, 205, 225, 229
63rd Regiment; 157, 170, 197, 230, 231
64th Regiment; 225
65th Regiment; 157, 231
66th Regiment; 161, 197, 216
67th Regiment; 171, 217, 230
68th Regiment; 168
69th Regiment; 160, 161, 176, 201, 218, 240; 2/; **228**
70th Regiment; 168, 200
71st Regiment; **135**, 170, 203, **229**
72nd Regiment; 173, 181
73rd Regiment; 208; 2/; **136, 230**
74th Regiment; 173
76th Regiment; 175, 203
78th Regiment; 161, 223
79th Regiment; **136**, 153, 164, **231**
80th Regiment; 96

10th Veteran Battalion; 208

French Cavalry
Carabinières; 20
Cuirassiers; 18, 20, 21, 24, 94, 107, 114, 122,
126, 134, 135, 142

French Infantry Regiments
45e Regiment de Ligne; 18, 111, **144**
123e Regiment de Ligne; 108

French Divisions and Corps
I Corps (d'Erlon); 18, 93-94, 110, 114
II Corps; 12
III Corps; 12
IV Corps; 12
6e Division; 14
9e Division; 14
Armée du Nord; 28
French artillery; 18, 114, 142, 155

French Imperial Guard
Middle Guard; 25
Old Guard; 25, 103
Young Guard; 25, 26

German Units,
Brunswick contingent; 91, 133
Field Jaeger Corps; 12
Grübenhagen Battalion; 13
Lüneburg Battalion; 12
2nd Nassau Regiment; 12, 24

King's German Legion Cavalry,
1st KGL Dragoons; 241, **243**, 247
2nd KGL Dragoons; 241; **243**
1st KGL Hussars; **244**, 247
2nd KGL Hussars; **245**
3rd KGL Hussars; **245**
1st KGL Light Dragoons (became 1st KGL
Hussars); 243, **244**
2nd KGL Light Dragoons (became 1st KGL
Hussars); 242, 243, **245**
3rd KGL Light Dragoons (became 3rd KGL
Hussars); 241

King's German Legion Infantry,
1st Light Infantry Battalion; **246**
2nd Light Infantry Battalion; 24, **247**
1st Line Battalion; 245, **248**, 249, 250

2nd Line Battalion; 157, **248**
3rd Line Battalion; **249**
4th Line Battalion; **249**
5th Line Battalion; 24, 142, 244, **250**
7th Line Battalion (detachment); **250**
8th Line Battalion; **251**

Other British Offices and Services
Commission of Military Enquiry, 5th; 42,
151
Master General of Ordnance; **57-58**
Royal Navy; 26, 57, 174
Royal Staff Corps; **157**

Prussian
1st Corps (Ziethen); 23
4th Corps (Bulow); 23

Royal Artillery
Bull's Troop, RHA; 141
Mercer's Troop, RHA; **140-141**, 237
Ramsay's Troop, RHA; **141**
Whinyate's Rocket Troop, RHA; **141**